# Solution Manual
# Engineering
# Economic
# Analysis

### Seventh Edition

## Donald G. Newnan
## Jerome P. Lavelle

**Engineering Press**                    Austin, Texas

ISBN 0-910554-80-3

Cover Illustration courtesy of Monex International Ltd.
Printed in the United States of America

Engineering Press    P.O. Box 200129    Austin, TX 78720-0129

# Introduction

Note please that there may be no absolute answers to these
questions. The goal is to make students think, rather than
to grade them on a Right-Wrong basis.

## 1-1

A survey of students answering this question indicated that they
thought about 40% of their decisions were conscious decisions.

## 1-2

(a) Yes.   The choice of an engine has important money consequences
           so would be suitable for engineering economic analysis.

(b) Yes.   Important economic - and social - consequences.
           Some might argue the social consequences are more
           important than the economics.

(c)  ?     Probably there are a variety of considerations much more
           important than the economics.

(d) No.    Picking a career on an economic basis sounds terrible.

(e) No.    Picking a wife on an economic basis sounds even worse.

## 1-3

Of the three alternatives, (b) the $150,000 investment problem
is <u>most</u> suitable for economic analysis.  There is not enough data
to figure out how to proceed, but if the "desirable interest rate"
were 9%, then foregoing it for one week would mean a loss of
$\frac{1}{52}(0.09) = 0.0017 = 0.17\%$ immediately.

It would take over a year at 0.15% more to equal the 0.17% foregone
now.

(a) The candy bar problem is suitable for economic analysis.
    Compared to (a), of course, it is trivial.

(c) A real problem with serious economic consequences.  The
    difficulty may be in figuring out what one gains if they pay
    for the fender damage, instead of having the insurance company
    pay for it.

# 1-4

Gambling, the stock market, drilling for oil, hunting for buried treasure --- there are sure to be a lot of interesting answers. Note that if you could double your money every day, then

$$2^X(\$300) = \$1,000,000 \quad \text{and} \quad x \text{ is less than 12 days.}$$

# 1-5

Maybe their stock market "systems" don't work!

# 1-6

It may look simple to the owner because <u>he</u> is not the one losing a job. For the three machinists it represents a major event with major consequences.

# 1-7

For most high school seniors there probably are only a limited number of colleges and universities that are feasible alternatives. Nevertheless, it still is a complex problem.

# 1-8

It really is not an economic problem - it is a complex problem.

# 1-9

Since it takes time and effort to go to the bookstore, the minimum number of pads might be related to the smallest saving worth bothering about. The maximum number of pads might be the quantity needed over a reasonable period of time, like the rest of the academic year.

# 1-10

While there might be a lot of disagreement on the "correct" answer, only 'd' [automobile insurance] represents a <u>substantial amount of money</u> and a situation where money might be the <u>primary</u> basis for choosing between alternatives.

# 1-11

The overall problems are all complex. The student will have a hard time coming up with examples that are truly <u>simple</u> or <u>intermediate</u> until he/she breaks them into smaller and smaller subproblems.

**1-12**

Let $X$ = annual production (units)

Total Cost to Company A = Total Cost to Company B

$$15000 + 0.002X = 5000 + 0.05X$$

$$X = \frac{10000}{0.048} = 208,330 \text{ units}$$

# The Decision Making Process

## 2-1

Feasible alternatives might include:

1. Live at home.
2. A room in a private home in return for work in the garden, etc.
3. Become a Resident Assistant in a University dormatory.
4. Live in a camper - or a tent - in a nearby rural area.
5. Live in a trailer on a construction site in return for "keeping an eye on the place."

## 2-2

The situation is an example of the failure of a low cost item that may have major consequences in a production situation. While there are alternatives available, one appears so obvious that the foreman discarded the rest and asks to proceed with the replacement.

One could argue that the foreman, or the plant manager, or both are making decisions. There is no single "right" answer to this problem.

## 2-3

While everyone might not agree, the key decision seems to be in providing Bill's Dad an opportunity to judge between purposely limited alternatives. Although suggested by the clerk, it was Bill's decision.

[One of my students observed that his Father would not fall for such a simple deception, and surely would insist on the weird shirt as a subtle form of punishment.]

## 2-4

This is an example of a "sunk cost." The $4000 is a past cost and should not be allowed to alter a subsequent decision unless there is some real - or perceived - affect. Since either home is really an individual plan selected by the homeowner, each should be judged in terms of value to the homeowner vs. the cost. On this basis the stock plan house appears to be the preferred alternative.

5

# 2-5

Itemized Expenses:   $0.123 x 18,000 miles + $2000 = $4214
Based on Standard Mileage Rate:   $0.22 x 18,000  =  3960

Itemizing produces a larger reimbursement.

Breakeven:   Let x = mileage at which both methods yield the
            same amount

$$x = \frac{\$2000}{\$0.22 - \$0.123} = 20,619 \text{ miles}$$

# 2-6

The fundamental concept here is that we will trade a hour of study in one subject for an hour of study in another subject so long as we are improving the total results. The stated criterion is to "get as high an average grade as possible in the combined classes." [This is the same as saying "get the highest combined total score."]

Since the data in the problem indicate that additional study always increases the grade, the question is how to apportion the available 15 hours of study among the courses. One might begin, for example, assuming five hours of study on each course. The combined total score would be 190.

Decreasing the study of mathematics one hour would reduce the math grade by 8 points (from 52 to 44). This hour could be used to increase the physics grade by 9 points (from 59 to 68). The result would be:

| | | |
|---|---|---|
| Math | 4 hours | 44 |
| Physics | 6 hours | 68 |
| Engr Econ | 5 hours | 79 |
| | | 191 |

Further study would show that the best use of the time is:

| | | |
|---|---|---|
| Math | 4 hours | 44 |
| Physics | 7 hours | 77 |
| Engr Econ | 4 hours | 71 |
| | | 192 |

# 2-7

Let t = time from the present (in weeks)
Volume of apples at any time = (1000 + 120t - 20t)
        Price at any time = 3.00 - 0.15t

Total Cash Return (TCR) = (1000 + 120t - 20t)(3.00 - 0.15t)
                        = 3000 + 150t - 15t$^2$

This is a minima-maxima problem.
Set the first derivative equal to zero and solve for t.

$$\frac{dTCR}{dt} = 150 - 30t = 0 \qquad t = \frac{-150}{-30} = 5 \text{ weeks}$$

$$\frac{d^2TCR}{dt^2} = -10 \quad \text{(The negative sign indicates the function is a maximum for the critical value.)}$$

At  t = 5 weeks:

Total Cash Return (TCR) = $3000 + 150(5) - 15(5)^2 = \$3375$

## 2-8

The remaining costs for the year are:

Alternative:

1.  To stay in the dormitory the rest of the year
    Food: 8 months at \$120/month                              = \$960

2.  To stay in the dormitory the balance of the
    first semester; apartment for second semester
    Housing:   4½ months x \$80 apartment – \$190 dorm  =   170
    Food:      3½ months x \$120 + 4½ x \$100            =   870
                                                          $\overline{\$1040}$

3   Move into an apartment now
    Housing:  8 mo x \$80 apartment – 8 x \$30 dorm   =   400
    Food:     8 mo x \$100                             =   800
                                                          $\overline{\$1200}$

Ironically, Jay had sufficient money to live in an apartment all year. He originally had \$1770(\$1050 + 1 mo dorm food of \$120 plus \$600 dorm contract cost). His cost for an apartment for the year would have been 9 mo x (\$80 + \$100) = \$1620.

Alternative 3 is not possible for the cost exceeds Jay's \$1050. Jay appears to prefer Alt. 2, and he has sufficient money to adopt it.

## 2-9

Some possible answers are:

1.  There are benefits to those who gain from the decision, but no one is harmed. (Pareto Optimum)
2.  Benefits flow to those who need them most. (Welfare criterion)
3.  Minimize air pollution or other specific item.
4.  Maximize total employment on the project.
5.  Maximize pay and benefits for some group. (e.g., union members)
6.  Most aesthetically pleasing result.
7.  Fit into normal workweek to avoid overtime.
8.  Maximize the use of the people already within the company.

and so on.

# 2-10

The garbage company sends out bills only six times a year.  Each
time they collect one month's bills one month early.

100,000 customers x $6.00 x 1% per month x 6 times/yr = $36,000.

# 2-11

These questions will create disagreement.  None of the situations
represents rational decision-making.
  (a)  Choosing the same career as a friend might be OK, but it
       doesn't seem too rational.
  (b)  Jill didn't consider all the alternatives.
  (c)  Don thought he was minimizing cost, but it didn't work.
       Maybe rational decision-making says one should buy better
       tools that will last.

# 2-12

This is a challenging question.  One approach might be:
  (a)  Find out what percentage of the population is left-handed.
  (b)  What is the population of the selected home-town?
  (c)  Next, market research might be required.  With some specific
       scissors (quality and price) in mind, ask a random sample of
       people if they would purchase the scissors.  Study the
       responses of both left-handed and right-handed people.
  (d)  With only two hours available, this is probably all the
       information one could collect.  From the data, make an
       estimate.

A different approach might be to assume that the people interested
in left-handed scissors in the future will be about the same as
the number who bought them in the past.
  (a)  Telephone several sewing and department stores in the area.
       Ask two questions:
           1.  How many pairs of scissors have you sold in one
               year (or six months or ?).
           2.  What is the ratio of sales of left-handed scissors
               to regular scissors?
  (b)  From the data in (a) estimate the future demand for left-
       handed scissors.

Two items might be worth noting.
    1.  Lots of scissors are universal, and equally useful for left
        and right-handed people.
    2.  Many left-handed people probably never have heard of left-
        handed scissors.

## 2-13

Surely planners would like to use criterion (a).  Unfortunately, people who are relocated often feel harmed, no matter how much money, etc., they are given.  Thus planners consider criterion (a) unworkable and use criterion (b) instead.

## 2-14

"choose the better of the undesirable alternatives."

## 2-15

"in decision-making the model is mathematical."

## 2-16

Since the firm requires a 20% profit on each increment of investment, one should examine the B-A increment of $200,000

| Alt | Initial Cost | Annual Profit | Incremental Cost | Incremental Profit | Incremental Profit Rate |
|-----|-----|-----|-----|-----|-----|
| A | $100,000 | $30,000 | | | |
| | | | $200,000 | $36,000 | 18% |
| B | 300,000 | 66,000 | | | |
| C | 500,000 | 80,000 | (with only 16% profit rate, C is unacceptable.) | | |

Alternative A produces a 30% profit rate.  The $200,000 increment of investment of B rather than A, that is, B-A, has an 18% profit rate and is not acceptable.  Looked at this way, Alt B with an overall 22% profit rate, may be considered as made up of Alt A plus the B-A increment.  Since the B-A increment is not acceptable, Alt B should not be adopted.

Thus the best investment of $300,000, for example, would be Alt A (annual profit = $30,000) plus $200,000 elsewhere (yielding 20% or $40,000 annually).  This combination yields a $70,000 profit, which is better than the Alt B profit of $66,000.  Select A.

## 2-17

Plan A   Profit = Income - Cost = $800 - 600 = $200/acre
     B   Profit = $1900 - $1500 = $400/acre
     C   Profit =  2250 -  1800 = $450/acre
     C   Profit =  2500 -  2100 = $400/acre
                To maximize profit per acre, select Plan C.

# 2-18

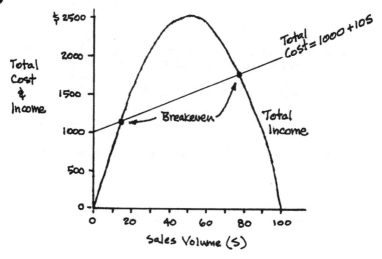

Profit $= S(100-S) -1000 - 10S = -S^2 + 90S - 1000$

b. For breakeven, set Profit $=0$

$-S^2 + 90S - 1000 = 0$   $S = \dfrac{-b \pm \sqrt{b^2 - 4ac}}{2a} = \dfrac{-90 \pm \sqrt{90^2 - 4(-1)(-1000)}}{2(-1)}$

$S = \dfrac{-90 \pm 64.03}{-2} = 12.98, 77.02$

c. For maximum profit

$\dfrac{dP}{dS} = -2S + 90 = 0$   $S = 45$ units

answers: Breakeven at 13 & 77 units
max Profit at 45 units

Alternate Solution: Trial & Error

| Price | Sales Volume | Total Income | Total Cost | Profit |
|---|---|---|---|---|
| 20 | 80 | 1600 | 1800 | -200 |
| 23 | 77 | 1771 | 1770 | ~0 Breakeven = 77 |
| 30 | 70 | 2100 | 1700 | 400 |
| 50 | 50 | 2500 | 1500 | 1000 |
| 55 | 45 | 2475 | 1450 | 1025 max Profit = 45 |
| 60 | 40 | 2400 | 1400 | 1000 |
| 80 | 20 | 1600 | 1200 | 400 |
| 87 | 13 | 1131 | 1130 | ~0 Breakeven = 13 |
| 90 | 10 | 900 | 1100 | -200 |

**2-19**

$$\text{Saving} = 2\left[185.00 + (2\times90\text{ miles})(0.60\text{ }\$/\text{mi.})\right] = \underline{586.\overset{00}{\phantom{.}}/\text{week}}$$

**2-20**

$x = \text{units/year}$

By hand = Painting machine

$$1.40x = \frac{15000}{3} + 0.20 \qquad x = \frac{5000}{1.20} = \underline{4167 \text{ units}}$$

**2-21**

Unit manufacturing Cost

(a) daytime shift $= \dfrac{2\,000\,000 + 9{,}109{,}000}{23000} = \underline{\$483 \text{/unit}}$

(b) two shifts $\quad = \dfrac{2\,400\,000 + (1+1.25)(9{,}109{,}000)}{46{,}000} = \underline{\$497.72 \text{/unit}}$

<u>Second shift increases unit cost.</u>

# 2-22

A tabulation of the decline in resale value plus the maintenance is needed to solve the problem.

| Age | Value of Car | Decline in Value for the year | Maintenance for the year | Sum of Decline in Value + Maintenance |
|-----|-----|-----|-----|-----|
| New | $11,200 | | | |
| | | 2800 | 50 | 2850 |
| 1 yr | 8400 | | | |
| | | 2100 | 150 | 2250 |
| 2 | 6300 | | | |
| | | 1575 | 180 | 1755 |
| 3 | 4725 | | | |
| | | 709 | 200 | 909 |
| 4 | 4016 | | | |
| | | 602 | 300 | 902 |
| 5 | 3414 | | | |
| | | 512 | 390 | 902 |
| 6 | 2902 | | | |
| | | 436 | 500 | 936 |
| 7 | 2466 | | | |

From the table it appears that minimum cost would result from buying a 3-year-old car and keeping it three years.

# 2-23

Area  A  preparation cost = 2 x $10^6$ x \$2.35 = \$4,700,000

Area  B  Difference in haul
   0.60 x 5 miles = 3.0 miles
   0.20 x -2 mi  = -0.4 miles
   0.20 x  0       0 miles
                  ‾‾‾‾‾‾‾‾‾
                  2.6 miles average addnl haul

   Cost of additional haul per load = $\frac{2.6 \text{ mi}}{15 \text{ mph}}$  x \$35/hr

                      = \$6.07

   Since truck capacity = 20 $m^3$

   Additional cost/cubic yard = \$6.07/20 $m^3$ = \$0.303/$m^3$

   For 14 million cubic meters:

   Total Cost = 14 x $10^6$ x \$0.303 = \$4,240,000

Area  B  with its lower total cost is preferred.

**9**

# 2-24

    A. Maximize the difference between output and input
    B. Minimize input
    C. Maximize the difference between output and input
    D. Minimize input

# 2-25

    A. Maximize the difference between output and input
    B. Maximize the difference between output and input
    C. Minimize input
    D. Minimize input

# 2-26

(a) Monthly bill:

$$50 \times 30 = 1500 \text{ Kw-hr at } 8.6¢ = \$129.00$$
$$\underline{1300} \quad \text{ at } 6.6¢ = \underline{\quad 85.80}$$
$$2800 \text{ Kw-hr} \qquad\qquad \$214.80$$

(b) Incremental cost of an additional 1200 Kw-hr/month:

$$200 \text{ Kw-hr at } 6.6¢ = \quad 13,20$$
$$\underline{1000} \quad \text{ at } 4.0¢ = \underline{\quad 40.00}$$
$$1200 \text{ Kw-hr} \qquad\qquad \$53.20$$

(c) New equipment:
Assuming the basic conditions are 30 HP and 2800 Kw-hr/month
Monthly bill with new equipment installed:

$$50 \times 40 = 2000 \text{ Kw-hr at } 8.6¢ = \$172.00$$
$$\underline{\quad 900} \qquad\quad 6.6¢ = \underline{\quad 59.40}$$
$$2900 \text{ Kw-hr} \qquad\qquad \$231.40$$

Incremental cost of energy = \$231.40 − 214.80 = \$16.60

Incremental unit cost = $\dfrac{\$16.60}{100}$ = 16.60¢/Kw-hr

# 2-27

(a) The suitable criterion is to maximize the difference between
output and input. Or simply, maximize net profit.
The data from the graphs may be tabulated as follows:

| Output Units/hour | Total Cost | Total Income | Net Profit | |
|---|---|---|---|---|
| 50 | \$300 | \$800 | \$500 | |
| 100 | 500 | 1000 | 500 | |
| 150 | 700 | 1350 | 650 | Best Production Rate |
| 200 | 1400 | 1600 | 200 | |
| 250 | 2000 | 1750 | -250 | |

The data are plotted on the next page.

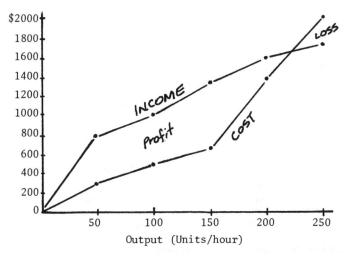

Output (Units/hour)

(b)  <u>Minimum input</u> is, of course, zero and <u>maximum output</u> is
     250 units/hr (based on the graph). Since one cannot achieve
     maximum output at minimum input, the statement makes no sense.

# 2-28

3000 gallon capacity = $\dfrac{3000 \text{ gal}}{7.48 \text{ gal/cf}}$ = 401 cubic feet capacity

Let L = tank length in feet
    d = tank diameter in feet

The volume of a cylindrical tank equals the end area x the length

$\quad$ Volume = $\dfrac{\pi}{4} d^2 L$ = 401 cf  or  L = $\dfrac{401 \times 4}{\pi d^2}$

The total surface area = two end areas + the cylinder surface area

$$S = 2\left(\frac{\pi}{4}d^2\right) + \pi d L$$

Substitute in the equation for L

$$S = \frac{\pi}{2}d^2 + \pi d \left[\frac{401 \times 4}{\pi d^2}\right] = \frac{\pi}{2}d^2 + 1604 d^{-1}$$

Take the first derivative and set it equal to zero

$$\frac{dS}{dd} = \pi d - 1604 d^{-2} = 0 \qquad \pi d = \frac{1604}{d^2}; \quad d^3 = \frac{1604}{\pi} = 510$$

$$\therefore d = 8'$$

Substitute back for L

$$L = \frac{401 \times 4}{\pi d^2} = \frac{1604}{\pi \, 8^2} = 8'$$

Tank diameter = 8'
Tank length = 8'

# 2-29

$$C = \$3,000,000 - \$18,000Q + \$75Q^2$$

where C = Total cost per year
Q = Number of units produced per year

Set the first derivative equal to zero and solve for Q

$$\frac{dC}{dQ} = -18,000 + 150Q = 0 \qquad Q = \frac{18,000}{150} = 120$$

Therefore total cost is a minimum at Q equal to 120. This indicates that production below 120 units per year is most undesirable, as it costs <u>more</u> to produce 110 units than to produce 120 units.

Check the sign of the second derivative:

$$\frac{d^2C}{dQ^2} = +150$$    The + indicates the curve is concave upward, ensuring that Q = 120 is the point of a minimum.

Average unit cost at Q = 120/year:

$$= \frac{3,000,000 - 18,000(120) + 75(120)^2}{120} = \$16,000$$

Average unit cost at Q = 110/year:

$$= \frac{3,000,000 - 18,000(110) + 75(120)^2}{110} = \$17,523$$

One must note, of course, that 120 units per year is <u>not</u> necessarily the optimal level of production. Economists would remind us that the optimum point is where Marginal Cost = Marginal Revenue, and Marginal Cost is increasing. Since we do not know the Selling Price, we cannot know Marginal Revenue, and hence we cannot compute the optimum level of output.

We can say, however, that if the firm is profitable at the 110 units/year level, then it will be much more profitable at levels <u>greater than</u> 120 units.

# 2-30

Profit = Income - Cost

$\qquad$ = PQ - C $\qquad$ where PQ = $35Q - 0.02Q^2$

$\qquad\qquad\qquad\qquad\qquad\qquad$ C = 4Q + 8000

Profit = $35Q - 0.02Q^2 - 4Q - 8000$

$\qquad$ = $31Q - 0.02Q^2 - 8000$

$\dfrac{d(\text{Profit})}{dQ}$ = 31 - 0.04Q = 0 $\qquad$ Solve for Q

$$Q = \frac{31}{0.04} = 775 \text{ units/year}$$

$\dfrac{d^2(\text{Profit})}{dQ^2}$ = -0.04 $\qquad$ The negative sign indicates that profit
$\qquad\qquad\qquad\qquad\qquad$ is a maximum at Q equals 775 units/year.

$\qquad\qquad\qquad\qquad\qquad\qquad$ Answer: Q = 775 units/year

# 2-31

Assume there is $30,000 available for investment. Compute the
amount of annual income for each alternative situation.

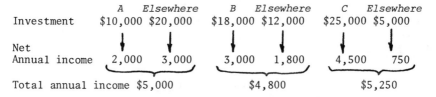

|  | A | Elsewhere | B | Elsewhere | C | Elsewhere |
|---|---|---|---|---|---|---|
| Investment | $10,000 | $20,000 | $18,000 | $12,000 | $25,000 | $5,000 |
| Net Annual income | 2,000 | 3,000 | 3,000 | 1,800 | 4,500 | 750 |
| Total annual income | $5,000 |  | $4,800 |  | $5,250 |  |

*Elsewhere* is the investment of money in other projects at a 15%
return. Thus if $10,000 is invested in *A*, then $20,000 is
available for other projects.

In addition to the three alternatives above, there is Alternative
*D* where the $30,000 investment yields a $5,000 annual income.

To maximize total annual income, choose *C*.

An alternate solution may be obtained by examining each separable
increment of investment. The computations are on the next page.

Incremental Analysis

|  | A | B | B-A | A | C | C-A |
|---|---|---|---|---|---|---|
| Investment | $10,000 | $18,000 | $8,000 | $10,000 | $25,000 | $15,000 |
| Net annual income | 2,000 | 3,000 | 1,000 | 2,000 | 4,500 | 2,500 |

Return on increment of investment 13%                                    17%
                                    no good                              OK
                                    reject B                        reject A


|  | C | D | D-C |
|---|---|---|---|
| Investment | $25,000 | $30,000 | $5,000 |
| Net annual income | 4,500 | 5,000 | 500 |

Return on increment of investment 10%
                                  no good
                                  reject D              choose C.

# 2-32

| Year | Cash flow |
|---|---|
| 0 | -$5000 |
| 1 | -7000 |
| 2 | -8000 |
| 3 | -8000 |
| 4 | +5000 |

# 2-33

| Year | Cash flow |
|---|---|
| 0 | -$2000 |
| 1 | -4000 |
| 2 | -3625 |
| 3 | -3250 |
| 4 | -2875 |

**2-34**

| Quantity sold per week | Selling price | Income | Cost | Profit |
|---|---|---|---|---|
| 300 packages | 60¢ | $180 | $105 | $ 75 |
| 600 | 45 | 270 | 210 | 60 |
| 1200 | 40 | 480 | 336 | 144 |
| 1700 | 33 | 561 | { 425* <br> 400** | 136 <br> 161 ◄── |
| 2300 | 26 | 598 | 460 | 138 |

*buy 1700 packages at 25¢ each
**buy 2000 packages at 20¢ each

Conclusion: Buy 2000 packages
Sell at 33¢ each

**2-35**

| Time period | Daily sales in time period | Cost of groceries | Hourly cost | Hourly profit |
|---|---|---|---|---|
| 0600-0700 | $ 20 | $ 14 | $ 10 | -$4 |
| 0700-0800 | 40 | 28 | 10 | +2 |
| 0800-0900 | 60 | 42 | 10 | +8 |
| 0900-1200 | 200 | 140 | 30 | +30 |
| 1200-1500 | 180 | 126 | 30 | +24 |
| 1500-1800 | 300 | 210 | 30 | +60 |
| 1800-2100 | 400 | 280 | 30 | +90 |
| 2100-2200 | 100 | 70 | 10 | +20 |
| 2200-2300 | 30 | 21 | 10 | -1 |
| 2300-2400 | 60 | 42 | 10 | +8 |
| 2400-0100 | 20 | 14 | 10 | -4 |

The first profitable operation is in the 0700-0800 time period.
In  the evening the 2200-2300 time period is unprofitable, but
next hour's profit more than makes up for it.

Conclusion:  Open at  0700
Close at 2400

# 2-36

| Alternative | Price | Net income per room | Occupancy Rate | No. rooms | Net Income |
|---|---|---|---|---|---|
| 1 | $36 | $24 | 100% | 50 | $1200 |
| 2 | 42 | 30 | 94 | 47 | 1410 |
| 3 | 48 | 36 | 80 | 40 | 1440 |
| 4 | 54 | 42 | 66 | 33 | 1386 |
| 5 | 48 | 36 | 70 | 35 | 1260 |
| 6 | 54 | 42 | 68 | 34 | 1428 |
| 7 | 62 | 50 | 66 | 33 | 1650 |
| 8 | 68 | 56 | 56 | 28 | 1568 |

To maximize net income, Jim should not advertise and charge $62 per night.

# 2-37

Examine increments of investment.

|  | Choosing Pear rather than the Pet | Choosing Pal rather than the Pet | Choosing Pearl rather than the Pal |
|---|---|---|---|
| Incremental cost | $2000 | $3000 | $1000 |
| Incremental benefit | 300 | 700 | 150 |
| Annual Percentage Rate | $\frac{300}{2000}$ x 100 = 15% | 23% | 15% |
|  | no good reject Pear | OK reject Pet | no good reject Pearl |

This is a very difficult problem at this point in the text. It is, however, an excellent problem for discussion purposes.

Answer: Choose Pal

# 2-38

Test marketing and pilot plant operation are situations where it is hoped that solving the subproblems gives a solution to the larger overall problem. On the other hand, Example 3-1 (shipping dept. buying printing) is a situation where the subproblem does not lead to a proper complex problem solution.

**2-39**

Basis: 1000 pieces

individual assembly: $\$22^{00} \times 2.6$ hrs $\times 1000 = 57,200$.   $\$57.20$/unit

team assembly: $(4 \times \$13.^{00}) \times 1.0$ hrs $\times 1000 = 52,000$   $\$52.00$/unit

<u>team assembly is less expensive.</u>

**2-40**

<u>Hand Solution</u>:     Cost of purchasing + Holding

Try 6 orders/yr    $\dfrac{8000 \times 15}{6 \times 2} \times 0.12 + 6(150)$        $= \$2100$/yr

(assuming average inventory = ½ the order)

7 orders/yr    $\dfrac{8000 \times 15}{7 \times 2} \times 0.12 + 7(150)$        $= \$2079$/yr

8 orders/yr    $\dfrac{8000 \times 15}{8 \times 2} \times 0.12 + 8(150)$        $= \$2100$/yr

∴ Place 7 orders/year

<u>Economic Order Quantity model</u>

$EOQ = \sqrt{\dfrac{2BD}{E}}$    where   B = Ordering Cost, \$/order
D = Demand per period, units
E = Inventory holding Cost \$/unit/period
EOQ = Economic Order Quantity, units

$= \sqrt{\dfrac{2 \times \$150 \times 8000}{0.12(15.00)}}$ = 1155 wheels.   Orders/yr $= \dfrac{8000}{1155} = 6.9$

Solutions to Spreadsheet supplement problems are after Chapter 19 .

# Interest And Equivalence

$$2000 + 2000(0.10 \times 3) = \$2600.$$

$$\frac{5350 - 5000}{0.08 \times 5000} = \frac{350}{400} = 0.875 \text{ years} = 10\tfrac{1}{2} \text{ months}$$

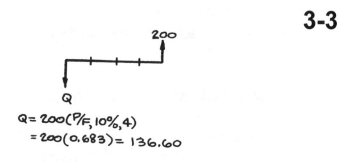

$$Q = 200(P/F, 10\%, 4)$$
$$= 200(0.683) = 136.60$$

$$P = 1400(P/A, 10\%, 5) - 80(P/G, 10\%, 5)$$
$$= 1400(3.791) - 80(6.862) = \underline{4758.44}$$

Using single payment factors:
$$P = 1400(P/F, 10\%, 1) + 1320(P/F, 10\%, 2) + 1240(P/F, 10\%, 3)$$
$$+ 1160(P/F, 10\%, 4) + 1080(P/F, 10\%, 5)$$
$$P = 1272.74 + 1090.85 + 931.61 + 792.28 + 670.57 = \underline{4758.05}$$

## 3-5

$P = \$750 \qquad n = 3 \, yrs \qquad i = 8\% \qquad F = ?$

$F = P(1+i)^n = 750(1.08)^3 = 750(1.26) = \$945.$

or using interest tables:

$F = 750 \, (F/P, 8\%, 3) = 750(1.260) = \$945.$

## 3-6

$F = \$8250 \qquad n = 4 \, \text{semiannual interest periods} \qquad i = 4\% \qquad P = ?$

$P = F(1+i)^{-n} = 8250(1.04)^{-4} = 8250(0.8548) = \$7052.10$

or using interest tables:

$P = 8250 \, (P/F, 4\%, 4) = 8250(0.8548) = \$7052.10$

## 3-7

Local Bank

$\qquad F = 3000 \, (F/P, 5\%, 2) = 3000(1.102) = \$3306$

Out of Town Bank

$\qquad F = 3000 \, (F/P, 1\frac{1}{4}\%, 8) = 3000(1.104) = \$3312$

$\qquad\qquad\qquad\qquad \text{additional Interest} = \quad \$6$

## 3-8

$P = 1 \qquad F = 2 \qquad i = 2\% \qquad n = \text{unknown no. of semiannual periods}$

$F = P(1+i)^n \qquad 2 = 1(1.02)^n \qquad 1.02^n = 2 \qquad n = 35$

$\qquad\qquad \text{Therefore, money will double in } 17\frac{1}{2} \text{ years}$

## 3-9

Lump Sum payment $= 350 \, (F/P, 1\frac{1}{2}\%, 8) = 350(1.126) = 394.10$

alternate Payment $= 350 \, (F/P, 10\%, 1) = 350(1.100) = 385.00$

$\qquad\qquad\qquad \text{choose the alternate payment plan.}$

# 3-10

$F = P(1+i)^n$ where $i$ = interest rate/interest period = $\frac{0.10}{365}$ = 0.000274

$\qquad\qquad$ n = no. of interest periods = 2.5 × 365 = 912

$F = 1500(1+0.000274)^{912} = \$1925.76$

# 3-11

write one equation with the interest rate as the only unknown.

$100 \overset{?}{=} 25(P/F, i\%, 1) + 45(P/F, i\%, 2) + 45(P/F, i\%, 3) + 30(P/F, i\%, 4)$

Trial & Error solution. Try i = 15%

$100 \overset{?}{=} 25(0.8696) + 45(0.7561) + 45(0.6575) + 30(0.5718) = 102.51$

i = 15% is too low.  Try i = 18%

$100 \overset{?}{=} 25(0.8475) + 45(0.7182) + 45(0.6086) + 30(0.5158) = 96.37$

15% < i < 18%.

Linear interpolation: $i = 15\% + 3\% \left( \frac{102.51 - 100}{102.51 - 96.37} \right) = 16.23\%$

# 3-12

Repayment at 4½% = \$1 Billion (F/P, 4½%, 30) = \$3.745 Billion

$\qquad\qquad\qquad\qquad\qquad\qquad$ 3.745

Repayment at 5¼% = \$1 Billion $(1+0.0525)^{30}$ = $\underline{4.642 \text{ Billion}}$

$\qquad\qquad$ Saving to foreign country = \$897 Million

# 3-13

<u>Calculator Solution</u>

$\qquad$ 1% per month $\qquad F = 1000(1+0.01)^{12} = 1126.83$

$\qquad$ 12% per year $\qquad F = 1000(1+0.12)^{1} = \underline{1120.00}$

$\qquad\qquad\qquad\qquad$ Saving in interest: \$6.83

<u>Compound interest table solution</u>

$\qquad$ 1% per month $\qquad F = 1000(1.127) \quad = 1127.00$

$\qquad$ 12% per year $\qquad F = 1000(1.120) \quad = \underline{1120.00}$

$\qquad\qquad\qquad\qquad$ Saving in interest: \$7.00

# 3-14

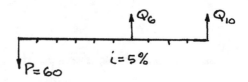

Either

$$Q_{10} = Q_6 \ (F/P, 5\%, 4) \qquad (1)$$

or

$$Q_{10} = P \ (F/P, 5\%, 10) \qquad (2)$$

Since P is known and $Q_6$ is not, solve Eqn (2).

$$Q_{10} = 60 (1.629) = \$97.74$$

# 3-15

$P=600$.   $F=29{,}152{,}000$   $n=92$years
$$F=P(1+i)^n$$

$$\frac{29{,}152{,}000}{600} = (1+i)^{92} = 48{,}587.$$

$$(1+i) = (48{,}587)^{1/92} = 1.124$$

$$i^* = 0.124 = 12.4\% \qquad \square$$

# 3-16

*a.*

   i. Interest rate for the past year = $\underline{\dfrac{100 - 90}{90}}$ = 10/90

                                        = 0.111  or 11.1%

  ii. Interest rate for the next year = $\dfrac{110 - 100}{100}$

                               = $\dfrac{10}{100}$ = 0.10 or 10%

*b.*     $90(F/P, i, 2) = 110$

        $(F/P, i, 2) = 110/90 = 1.222$

        So     $(1 + i)^2 = 1.222$

            $i = 1.1054\text{-}1 = 0.1054$  or  $\underline{10.54}$%

# 3-17

$n = 63$ years;   $i = 7.9\%$;   $F = \$175,000$

$P = F(1 + i)^{-n}$

  $= \$175,000(1.079)^{-63}$

  $= \underline{\$1454}$

# 3-18

$$F = P\,(1 + i)^n$$

Solve for $P$:  $P = \dfrac{F}{(1+i)^n}$  or :  $P = F\,(1+i)^{-n}$

$P = 150,000\,(1 + 0.10)^{-5}$ $= 150,000\,(0.6209) = 93,135$

# More Interest Formulas

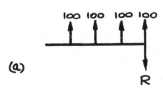

(a)

$$R = 100(F/A, 10\%, 4)$$
$$= 100(4.641) = 464.10$$

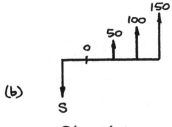

(b)

$$S = 50(P/G, 10\%, 4)$$
$$= 50(4.378) = 218.90$$

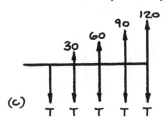

(c)

$$T = 30(A/G, 10\%, 5)$$
$$= 30(1.810) = 54.30$$

$$A = 500(A/P, 1\%, 16) = 500(0.0679) = \$33.95$$

$$A = P(A/P, i\%, 24)$$

$$\text{or } (A/P, i\%, 24) = \frac{A}{P} = \frac{499}{10,000} = 0.0499$$

From the compound interest tables we see that the interest rate per month is exactly 1-1/2%.

# 4-4

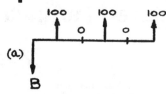

(a)

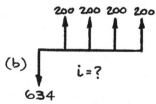

(b)    $i=?$

634

$$B = 100\left(\frac{P}{F}, 10\%, 1\right) + 100\left(\frac{P}{F}, 10\%, 3\right)$$
$$+ 100\left(\frac{P}{F}, 10\%, 5\right)$$
$$= 100\left(0.9091 + 0.7513 + 0.6209\right)$$
$$= 228.13$$

$$634 = 200\left(\frac{P}{A}, i\%, 4\right)$$
$$\left(\frac{P}{A}, i\%, 4\right) = \frac{634}{200} = 3.17$$
From compound interest
tables    $i = 10\%$

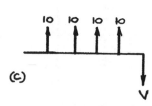

(c)

V

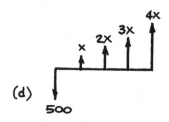

(d)

500

$$V = 10\left(\frac{F}{A}, 10\%, 5\right) - 10$$
$$= 10(6.105) - 10$$
$$= 51.05$$

$$500 = x\left(\frac{P}{A}, 10\%, 4\right) + x\left(\frac{P}{G}, 10\%, 4\right)$$
$$500 = x(3.170 + 4.378)$$
$$x = \frac{500}{7.548} = 66.24$$

# 4-5

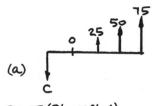

(a)

C

(b)    $i=?$

500

$$C = 25\left(\frac{P}{G}, 10\%, 4\right)$$
$$= 25(4.378)$$
$$= 109.45$$

$$500 = 140\left(\frac{P}{A}, i\%, 6\right)$$
$$\left(\frac{P}{A}, i\%, 6\right) = \frac{500}{140} = 3.571$$

| $\left(\frac{P}{A}, i\%, 6\right)$ | $i$ |
|---|---|
| 3.784 | 15% |
| 3.498 | 18% |

$$i = 15\% + 3\%\left(\frac{3.784 - 3.571}{3.784 - 3.498}\right)$$
$$i = 17.24\%$$

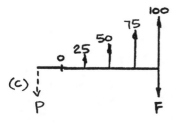

(c)

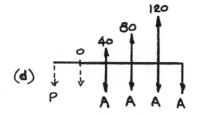

(d)

$F = 25(P/G, 10\%, 5)(F/P, 10\%, 5)$

$= 25(6.862)(1.611)$

$= 276.37$

$A = 40(P/G, 10\%, 4)(F/P, 10\%, 1)(A/P, 10\%, 4)$

$= 40(4.378)(1.10)(0.3155)$

$= 60.78$

## 4-6

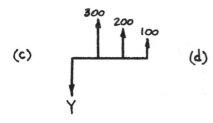

(a)

(b)

$W = 25(P/A, 10\%, 4) + 25(P/G, 10\%, 4)$

$= 25(3.170 + 4.378)$

$= 188.70$

$X = 100(P/G, 10\%, 4)(P/F, 10\%, 1)$

$= 100(4.378)(0.9091)$

$= 398.00$

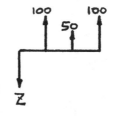

(c)

(d)

$Y = 300(P/A, 10\%, 3) - 100(P/G, 10\%, 3)$

$= 300(2.487) - 100(2.329)$

$= 513.20$

$Z = 100(P/A, 10\%, 3) - 50(P/F, 10\%, 2)$

$= 100(2.487) - 50(0.8264)$

$= 207.38$

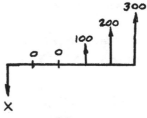

# 4-7

From compound interest tables:

$$(P/A,6\%,10) = 7.360$$
$$(P/A,7\%,10) = 7.024$$
$$\Delta = \overline{0.336} \qquad (P/A,6\text{-}1/2\%,10)$$
$$1/2\,\Delta + 7.024 = \overline{7.192}$$

Exact computed value:

$$(P/A,6\text{-}1/2\%,10) = 7.189$$

Why differ?  Since the compound interest factor is non-linear, linear interpolation will not produce an exact solution.

# 4-8

There are several ways the problem may be solved.  Here are two of them.

$$5000 = 1000\,(P/A,8\%,4) + X\,(P/F,8\%,5)$$
$$= 1000\,(3.312) + X\,(0.6806) \qquad X = \frac{1688}{0.6806} = \underline{2480.16}$$

alternate solution:

$$P = 1000\,(P/A,8\%,4) = 1000\,(3.312) = 3312$$
$$(5000-3312)\,(F/P,8\%,5) = \underline{2479.67}$$

# 4-9

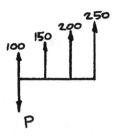

$$P = 100 + 150\,(P/A,10\%,3) + 50\,(P/G,10\%,3)$$
$$= 100 + 150\,(2.487) + 50\,(2.329)$$
$$= 589.50$$

**4-10**

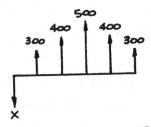

$X = 300 (P/A, 10\%, 5) + 100 (P/G, 10\%, 3) + 100 (P/F, 10\%, 4)$

$= 300 (3.791) + 100 (2.329) + 100 (0.6830) = \underline{1438.50}$

**4-11**

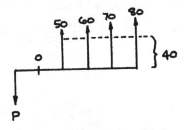

$P = 10 (P/G, 15\%, 5) + 40 (P/A, 15\%, 4)(P/F, 15\%, 1)$

$= 10 (5.775) + 40 (2.855)(0.8696) = \underline{157.06}$

**4-12**

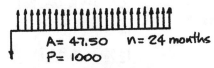

A= 47.50   n= 24 months
P= 1000

$P = A (P/A, i\%, n)$    $1000 = 47.50 (P/A, i\%, 24)$

$(P/A, i\%, 24) = 21.053$

From interest tables:

| $i$ | $(P/A, i\%, 24)$ |
|---|---|
| 1% | 21.243 |
| 1¼% | 20.624 |

interpolating:

$$i = 1\% + \tfrac{1}{4}\% \left[ \frac{21.243 - 21.053}{21.243 - 20.624} \right] = 1\% + \tfrac{1}{4}\% \left( \frac{0.190}{0.619} \right) = 1.077\%/mo.$$

Nominal Interest Rate $= 12(1.077\%) = 12.92\%$

# 4-13

$P = 2000$   $A = 51$   $n = 50$ months   $i =$ unknown

$A = P(A/P, i\%, n)$ ;   $51 = 2000(A/P, i\%, 50)$ ; $(A/P, i\%, 50) = 0.0255$

From interest tables   $i = 1\%$ (per month)

Nominal interest rate $= 12(1\%) = 12\%$

Effective interest rate $= (1+i)^m - 1 = (1+0.01)^{12} - 1 = 12.7\%$

# 4-14

$P = 1000$   Interest payment $= \$10.87/month$

Nominal interest rate $= \dfrac{10.87 \times 12}{1000} = 0.13 = 13\%$

# 4-15

$i = 1\%$ per month

Effective interest rate $= (1+i)^m - 1 = (1.01)^{12} - 1 = 0.127 = 12.7\%$

# 4-16

Common stock investment $P = 1000$   $F = 1307$   $n = 20$ quarter yrs

$F = P(F/P, i\%, n)$   $1307 = 1000(F/P, i\%, 20)$ ; $(F/P, i\%, 20) = 1.307$

From interest tables:

| $i$ | $(F/P, i\%, 20)$ |
|---|---|
| $1\tfrac{1}{4}\%$ | 1.282 |
| $1\tfrac{1}{2}\%$ | 1.347 |

Interpolating

$$i = 1.25\% + 0.25\% \left[ \frac{1.307 - 1.282}{1.347 - 1.282} \right] = 1.25 + 0.10 = 1.35\%$$

Nominal interest rate $= 4(1.35\%) = 5.40\%$

Effective interest rate $= (1+0.0135)^4 - 1 = 0.0551 = 5.51\%$

# 4-17

Nominal interest rate = $12(1.5\%) = 18\%$

Effective interest rate = $(1+0.015)^{12}-1 = 0.1956 = 19.56\%$

# 4-18

$P = 3000$   $i = 1\%$ per month   $n = 30$ months   $A = ?$

$A = P(A/P, i\%, n) = 3000(A/P, 1\%, 30) = 3000(0.0387) = \$116.10$

# 4-19

Note: there are 19 interest periods between P (40$^{th}$ birthday)
and P' (6 mo. prior to 50$^{th}$ birthday).

$P' = 1000 (P/A, 2\%, 30) = 1000 (22.396) = \$22,396$

$P = P'(P/F, 2\%, 19) = 22,396(0.6864) = \$15,373$   COST OF annuity

# 4-20

$A = \$20$   $i = \frac{1}{2}\%$ per month   $n = 12 \times 15 = 180$ months

$F = A(F/A, \frac{1}{2}\%, 180)$.   Since the $\frac{1}{2}\%$ interest table does not
contain $n = 180$, the problem must be split into workable
components. One way would be:

$F = 20(F/A, \frac{1}{2}\%, 90) + 20(F/A, \frac{1}{2}\%, 90)(F/P, \frac{1}{2}\%, 90) = \$5817$

<u>Alternate Solution</u>: Linear interpolation between $n=120$ & $n=240$

$F = 20\left[\dfrac{(F/A, \frac{1}{2}\%, 120) + (F/A, \frac{1}{2}\%, 240)}{2}\right] = \$6259$ (very inaccurate)

# 4-21

(a)   $A = P(A/P, 8\%, 6) = 3000(0.2163) = 648.90$

First 3 payments were 648.90 each.

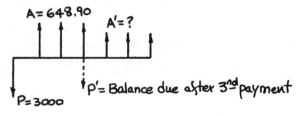

A = 648.90    A' = ?

P' = Balance due after 3$^{rd}$ payment

P = 3000

Balance due after 3$^{rd}$ payment = Present Worth of the originally planned last 3 payments of 648.90

$P' = 648.90 (P/A, 8\%, 3) = 648.90 (2.577) = 1672.22$

Last 3 Payments

$A' = 1672.22 (A/P, 7\%, 3) = 1672.22 (0.3811) = \$637.28$

## 4-22

$P = 40 (P/A, 5\%, 7) + 10 (P/G, 5\%, 7) = 40 (5.786) + 10 (16.232)$
$\quad = 231.44 + 162.32 = \$393.76$

## 4-23

The series of deposits are beginning-of-period deposits rather than end-of-period. The simplest solution is to draw a diagram of the situation and then proceed to solve the problem presented by the diagram.

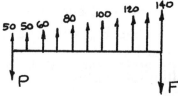

50 50 60    80    100    120    140

P        F

The diagram illustrates a problem that can be solved directly.

$P = 50 + 50 (P/A, 3\%, 10) + 10 (P/G, 3\%, 10)$
$\quad = 50 + 50 (8.530) + 10 (36.309) = 839.59$

$F = P (F/P, 3\%, 10) = 839.59 (1.344) = \$1128.41$

## 4-24

$i = 15\%$
$A = ?$

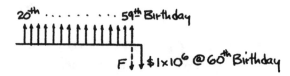

20$^{th}$ . . . . . . . . . . . 59$^{th}$ Birthday

F  $\$1 \times 10^6$ @ 60$^{th}$ Birthday

No. of yearly investments = 40    (59-20+1)= 40

The diagram indicates the problem is <u>not</u> in the form of the uniform series compound amount factor.

Find F that is equivalent to $1,000,000 one year hence.

$F = 1 \times 10^6 (P/F, 15\%, 1) = 1 \times 10^6 (0.8696) = \$869,600$

$A = F(A/F, 15\%, 40) = 869,600 (0.00056) = \$486.98$

[The result is very sensitive to the sinking fund factor.
(A/F, 15%,40) is actually 0.00056208 which makes
A = $488.78.]

**4-25**

This problem has a declining gradient

$P = 85000 (P/A, 4\%, 5) - 10,000 (P/G, 4\%, 5)$

$= 85,000 (4.452) - 10,000 (8.555)$

$= 378,420 - 85,550 = \$292,870.$

**4-26**

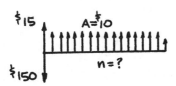

$(150-15) = \$10 \ (P/A, 1\frac{1}{2}\%, n)$    $(P/A, 1\frac{1}{2}\%, n) = \frac{135}{10} = 13.5$

From the 1-1/2% interest table we see that n is between 15 and 16.
This indicates there will be 15 payments of $10 plus a last payment
of a sum less than $10.

Compute how much of the purchase price will be paid by the fifteen $10 payments.

$$P = \$10\,(P/A, 1\tfrac{1}{2}\%, 15) = 10(13.343) = 133.43$$

Remaining unpaid portion of the purchase price
$$= \$150 - 15 - 133.43 = 1.57$$

$16^{th}$ payment $= 1.57\,(F/P, 1\tfrac{1}{2}\%, 16) = 1.57(1.269) = 1.99$

## 4-27

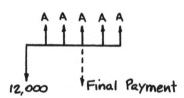

12,000        Final Payment

$$A = 12,000\,(A/P, 4\%, 5) = 12,000\,(0.2246) = 2695.20$$

The final payment is the present worth of the 3 unpaid payments.

Final payment $= 2695.20 + 2695.20(P/A, 4\%, 2)$
$$= 2695.20 + 2695.20(1.886) = 7778.35$$

## 4-28

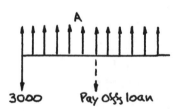

3000        Pay off loan

Compute monthly payment

$$3000 = A + A\,(P/A, 1\%, 11) = A + A(10.368) = 11.368\,A$$

$$A = \frac{3000}{11.368} = 263.90$$

Car will cost new buyer
$$= 1000 + 263.90 + 263.90(P/A, 1\%, 5)$$
$$= 1263.90 + 263.90(4.853) = 2544.61$$

**4-29**

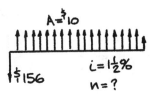

$\$156 = \$10 \, (P/A, 1\tfrac{1}{2}\%, n) \qquad (P/A, 1\tfrac{1}{2}\%, n) = \dfrac{156}{10} = 15.6$

From the $1\tfrac{1}{2}\%$ interest table n is between 17 and 18.

Therefore, it takes 18 months to repay the loan.

**4-30**

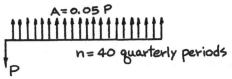

$F = P(1+i)^n = 0.98F(1+i)^1$

$i = \dfrac{1.00}{0.98} - 1 = 0.0204 = 2.04\%$

$i_{eff} = (1+i)^m = (1.0204)^{365/20} - 1 = 0.4456 = 44.6\%$

**4-31**

$$A = 0.05 \, P$$

$$n = 40 \text{ quarterly periods}$$

$$P$$

$P = 0.05P \, (P/A, i\%, 40) \qquad (P/A, i\%, 40) = \dfrac{P}{0.05P} = 20$

From interest tables:

| $i$ | $(P/A, i\%, 40)$ |
|---|---|
| $3\tfrac{1}{2}\%$ | $21.355$ |
| $4\%$ | $19.793$ |

Linear interpolation:

$i = 3\tfrac{1}{2}\% + \tfrac{1}{2}\% \left[ \dfrac{21.355 - 20.}{21.355 - 19.793} \right] = 3\tfrac{1}{2}\% + \tfrac{1}{2}\% \left( \dfrac{1.355}{1.562} \right)$

$= 3.93\%$ per quarter year.

Effective interest rate $= (1 + 0.0393)^4 - 1 = 0.1667 = 16.67\%$

# 4-32

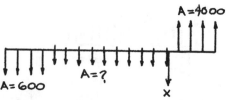

To have sufficient money to pay the four $4000 disbursements,

x= 4000 (P/A, 5%, 4) = 4000 (3.546) = $14,184

This $14,184 must be accumulated by the two series of deposits.
The four $600 deposits will accumulate by x (17th birthday)

   F= 600 (F/A, 5%, 4)(F/P, 5%, 10)

     = 600 (4.310)(1.629) = 4212.59

Thus the annual deposits between 8 and 17 must accumulate
a future sum = 14,184 - 4212.59 = 9971.41

The series of 10 deposits must be:

   A= 9971.41 (A/F, 5%, 10) = 9971.41(0.0745) = $792.73

# 4-33

   5% compounded annually

     F= 5000 (F/P, 5%, 3) = 5000 (1.158) = $5790.

   5% compounded continuously

     F= $Pe^{rn}$ = 5000 $e^{0.05(3)}$ = 5000(1.1618) = $5809

# 4-34

Compute effective interest rate for each alternative

   (a)   4.375%

   (b)   $\left(1 + \dfrac{0.0425}{4}\right)^4 - 1$ = $(1.0106)^4 - 1$ = 0.0431 = 4.31%

   (c)   $e^{rn} - 1$ = $e^{0.04125}$ - 1 = 0.0421 = 4.21%

The $4\frac{3}{8}$% interest has the highest effective interest rate.

**4-35**

$$F = Pe^{rn} = 100\,e^{0.04\,(5)} = 100(1.2214) = \$122.14$$

**4-36**

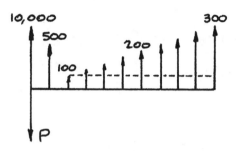

$P = 10,000 + 500(P/F, 6\%, 1) + 100(P/A, 6\%, 9)(P/F, 6\%, 1)$
$\quad + 25\,(P/G, 6\%, 9)(P/F, 6\%, 1)$

$= 10,000 + 500(0.9434) + 100(6.802)(0.9434)$
$\quad + 25(24.577)(0.9434)$

$= 11,693.05$

**4-37**

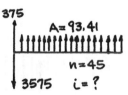

$3575 = 375 + 93.41\,(P/A, i\%, 45)$ ; $(P/A, i\%, 45) = \dfrac{3200}{93.41} = 34.258$

From compound interest tables $i = 1\tfrac{1}{4}\%$

For an $\$800$ downpayment, unpaid balance is $\$2775$.
$\quad P = 2775 \quad n = 45 \quad i = 1\tfrac{1}{4}\% \quad A = ?$

$A = 2775\,(A/P, 1\tfrac{1}{4}\%, 45)^{*} = 2775(0.0292) = \$81.03$

Effective interest rate $= (1 + 0.0125)^{12} - 1 = 0.161 = 16.1\%$

\* note that no interpolation is required as
$(A/P, 1\tfrac{1}{4}\%, 45) = \dfrac{1}{(P/A, i\%, 45)} = \dfrac{1}{34.258} = 0.0292$

# 4-38

$$\text{Effective interest rate} = (1+i)^m - 1$$

$$1.161 = (1+i)^{12}$$

$$\therefore (1+i) = 1.161^{1/12} = 1.161^{0.0833} = 1.0125$$

$$i = 0.0125 = 1\tfrac{1}{4}\%$$

# 4-39

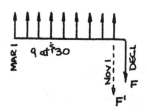

Amount on Nov 1 = $F'$ = 30 (F/A, ½%, 9) = 30(9.182) = 275.46
Amount on Dec 1 = $F$ = 275.46(F/P, ½%, 1) = 275.46(1.005)
$$= 276.84$$

# 4-40

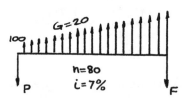

$P$ = 100(P/A, 7%, 80) + 20(P/G, 7%, 80) = 5383.70
$F$ = 5383.70 (F/P, 7%, 80) = 1,207,200

<u>Alternate Solution</u>

$F$ = [100 + 20(A/G, 7%, 80)](F/A, 7%, 80)

= [100 + 20(13.927)](3189.1)    = 1,207,200

# 4-41

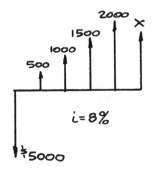

$i = 8\%$

The first four payments will repay
a present sum $P = 500(P/A, 8\%, 4) + 500(P/G, 8\%, 4)$
$$= 500(3.312) + 500(4.650)$$
$$= 3981$$

The unpaid portion of the 5000
is $5000 - 3981 = 1019$

Thus
$$x = 1019 (F/P, 8\%, 5)$$
$$= 1019 (1.469) = 1496.91$$

# 4-42

correct equation is (b)    $\dfrac{50(P/A, i\%, 5) + 10(P/G, i\%, 5) + 50(P/F, i\%, 5)}{100} = 1$

# 4-43

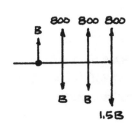

upward (receipts) at black dot
$PW = B + 800(P/A, 12\%, 3) = B + 1921.6$
Downward (expenditures) at black dot
$PW = B(P/A, 12\%, 2) + 1.5P(P/F, 12\%, 3) = 2.757B$
Equating
$$B + 1921.6 = 2.757B \qquad B = \frac{1921.6}{1.757} = 1093.7$$

## 4-44

$F = A(F/A, 10\%, n)$    $35.95 = 1(F/A, 10\%, n)$
$\therefore (F/A, 10\%, n) = 35.95$    From 10% interest table,  $\underline{n = 16}$

## 4-45

$P = A(P/A, 3\frac{1}{2}\%, n)$    $1000 = 50(P/A, 3\frac{1}{2}\%, n)$
$\therefore (P/A, 3\frac{1}{2}\%, n) = 20$    From 3½% interest table,  $\underline{n = 35}$

## 4-46

$P = A(P/A, i\%, n)$    $525 = 15(P/A, 1\frac{1}{2}\%, n)$
$\therefore (P/A, 1\frac{1}{2}\%, n) = \frac{525}{15} = 35$    From 1½% interest table,  $\underline{n = 50 \text{ months}}$

## 4-47

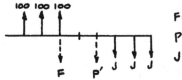

$F = 100(F/A, 10\%, 3) = 100(3.310) = 331$
$P' = 331(F/P, 10\%, 2) = 331(1.210) = 400.51$
$J = 400.51(A/P, 10\%, 3) = 400.51(0.4021)$
$= \underline{161.05}$

*Alternate Solution*:  One may observe that each *J* is equivalent
to the future worth of 100 after five interest periods, or
$J = 100(F/P, 10\%, 5) = 100(1.611) = \$161.10$

## 4-48

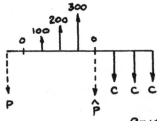

$P = 100(P/G, 10\%, 4) = 100(4.378) = 437.80$
$\hat{P} = 437.80(F/P, 10\%, 5) = 437.80(1.611) = 705.30$
$C = 705.30(A/P, 10\%, 3) = 705.30(0.4021) = \underline{283.60}$

# 4-49

(a) Bill's monthly payment $= \frac{2}{3}(4200)(A/P, \frac{3}{4}\%, 36) = 2800(0.0318)$

$= \$89.04$

(b) Bill owed the Oct 1 payment plus the present worth of the 27 additional payments.

Balance $= 89.04 + 89.04 (P/A, \frac{3}{4}\%, 27) = 89.04 (1 + 24.360) = \underline{2258.05}$

*Alternate Solution:*  Bill made 8 payments prior to October 1st.  These payments would decrease the original $2800 loan by $89.04(P/A,3/4%,8) = $688.90

$2800 - 688.90 = $2111.10 Equivalent unpaid debt, January 1st. The unpaid debt increases in 9 months to $2111.10(F/P,3/4%,9). This equals $2258.88, the amount Bill must pay on October 1st.

# 4-50

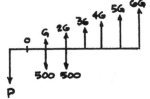

Present Worth P of the two $500 amounts

$P = 500(P/F, 12\%, 2) + 500(P/F, 12\%, 3)$

$= 500(0.7972) + 500(0.7118) = 754.50$

also

$P = G (P/G, 12\%, 7)$

$754.50 = G (11.644)$   $G = \frac{754.50}{11.644} = \$64.80$

# 4-51

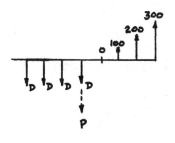

P = present worth of gradient series

$P = 100 (P/G, 10\%, 4) = 100(4.378) = 437.80$

$D = 437.80(A/F, 10\%, 4)$

$= 437.80(0.2155) = \underline{94.35}$

# 4-52

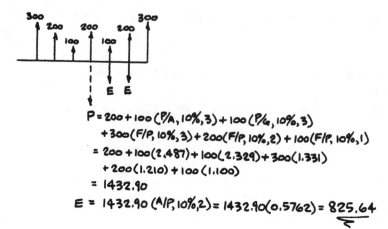

$$P = 200 + 100\,(P/A, 10\%, 3) + 100\,(P/G, 10\%, 3)$$
$$\quad + 300\,(F/P, 10\%, 3) + 200\,(F/P, 10\%, 2) + 100\,(F/P, 10\%, 1)$$
$$= 200 + 100(2.487) + 100(2.329) + 300(1.331)$$
$$\quad + 200(1.210) + 100(1.100)$$
$$= 1432.90$$
$$E = 1432.90\,(A/P, 10\%, 2) = 1432.90(0.5762) = \underline{825.64}$$

# 4-53

$$P = 100\,(P/A, 10\%, 4) + 100\,(P/G, 10\%, 4) = 100(3.170 + 4.378) = 754.8$$

$$P = 4B\,(P/A, 10\%, 4) - B\,(P/G, 10\%, 4) = 754.8$$
$$4B(3.170) - B(4.378) = 754.8$$
$$B = \frac{754.8}{8.30} = \underline{90.94}$$

# 4-54

Amount of each payment $= 1000\,(A/P, 4\tfrac{1}{2}\%, 4) = 1000\,(0.2787)$
$$= \underline{278.70}$$

Effective interest rate $= (1 + 0.045)^4 - 1 = 0.19252 = \underline{19.3\%}$

# 4-55

$$P = F e^{-rn} = 6000\, e^{-(0.12 \times 2.5)} = 6000(0.7408) = \underline{4444.80}$$

**4-56**

Effective interest rate = $(1+i_{mo})^{12} - 1 = 0.18$

$(1+i_{mo}) = (1+0.18)^{1/12} = 1.01389$   $i_{mo} = 0.01388 = \underline{1.388\%}$

**4-57**

Nominal interest rate = $1\frac{3}{4}\% \times 12 = \underline{21\%}$

Effective interest rate = $e^{rn} - 1 = e^{(0.21)(1)} - 1 = 0.2337 = \underline{23.37\%}$

**4-58**

$P = 9500$   $F = 10,000$   $n = 1$ (6 mo interest period)   $i = ?$

$F = P(1+i)$   $(1+i) = \frac{F}{P} = \frac{10,000}{9500} = 1.0526$

$\therefore i = 0.0526 = 5.26\%$

Nominal interest rate = $5.26\% \times 2 = \underline{10.52\%}$

Effective interest rate = $(1+0.0526)^2 - 1 = 0.10797 = \underline{10.80\%}$

**4-59**

WEST BANK

$F = P(1+i)^n = 10,000 \left(1 + \frac{0.065}{365}\right)^{365} = 10,671.53$

EAST BANK

$F = Pe^{rn} = 10,000\, e^{(0.065)(1)} = \underline{10,671.59}$

Difference is   $\underline{6\ cents\ !}$

**4-60**

Effective interest rate = $(1+i)^m - 1 = \left(1 + \frac{0.07}{365}\right)^{365} - 1 = 0.0725 = \underline{7.25\%}$

**4-61**

$P = A\,(P/A, i\%, n)$   $1000 = 91.70\,(P/A, i\%, 12)$

$(P/A, i\%, 12) = \frac{1000}{91.70} = 10.91$

From compound interest tables, $i = 1\frac{1}{2}\%$

Nominal interest rate = $1\frac{1}{2}\% \times 12 = \underline{18\%}$

# 4-62

$$P = Fe^{-rn} = 10{,}000\, e^{-(0.08)(0.5)} = 10{,}000\, e^{-0.04} = 10{,}000(0.9608) = \underline{9608}$$

# 4-63

$$F = P(1+i)^n \qquad 85 = 75(1+i)^1 \qquad (1+i) = \frac{85}{75} = 1.133 \qquad i = 0.133$$

$$\therefore i = 13.3\% \ (\text{per 6 months})$$

Nominal interest rate $= 13.3\% \times 2 = \underline{26.6\%}$

Effective interest rate $= (1+0.133)^2 - 1 = 0.284 = \underline{28.4\%}$

# 4-64

Effective interest rate $= (1+0.0175)^{12} - 1 = 0.2314 = \underline{23.14\%}$

# 4-65

Nominal interest rate $= 1\% \times 12 = \underline{12\%}$

Effective interest rate $= (1+0.01)^{12} - 1 = 0.1268 = \underline{12.7\%}$

# 4-66

monthly payment $= 10{,}000 \,(A/P, \ 3/4\%, 12) = 10{,}000(0.0875) = \$875.00$

Total interest for year $= 875 \times 12 - 10{,}000 = 500.00$

Rule of 78s

with early repayment: interest charge $= \dfrac{12+11+10}{78}(\$500) = 211.54$

Additional sum (in addition to the 3rd $875.00$ payment)

$= 10{,}000 + 211.54 \ \text{interest} - 3 \times 875.00 = \underline{7586.54}$

## Exact Method

Additional Sum equals present worth of the 9 future payments that would have been made.

Additional Sum = $875^{00}(P/A, 3/4\%, 9) = 875^{00}(8.672) \doteq \underline{\underline{7588}}$

**4-67**

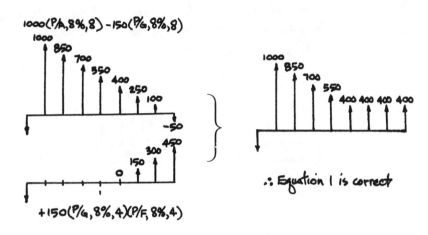

$1000(P/A, 8\%, 8) - 150(P/G, 8\%, 8)$

$+150(P/G, 8\%, 4)(P/F, 8\%, 4)$

$\therefore$ Equation I is correct

# 4-68

$i = 1\frac{1}{2}\%$ per quarter year    $n = 12$ quarterly periods (in 3 years)

$A = 3 \times 100 = \$300$

$F = A\,(F/A, i, n) = 300\,(F/A, 1\frac{1}{2}\%, 12) = 300\,(13.041) = \$3912.30$

note that this is no different from Ann's depositing $300 at the end of each quarter, as her monthly deposits do not earn any interest until the subsequent quarter.

# 4-69

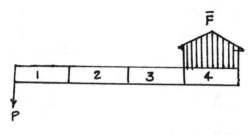

$$P = \bar{F}\left[\frac{e^r - 1}{re^{rn}}\right] = 40{,}000\,\frac{e^{0.07} - 1}{0.07e^{(0.07)(4)}}$$

$$P = 40{,}000\,\frac{0.072508}{0.092619} = \$31{,}314.53$$

**4-70**

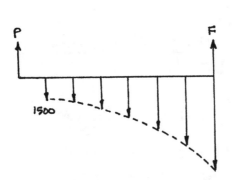

(a)
Since the book only gives a geometric gradient to present worth factor, we must first solve for P, and then F.

$$i = 10\% \quad g = 8\% \quad n = 6$$

$P = A_1 (P/A, g, i, n)$

$$(P/A, g, i, n) = \left[ \frac{1-(1+g)^n(1+i)^{-n}}{i-g} \right] = \left[ \frac{1-(1.08)^6(1.10)^{-6}}{0.02} \right] = 5.212$$

$P = 1500(5.212) = 7818$

$F = P(F/P, i, n) = 7818(F/P, 10\%, 6) = \$13,853$

as a check solve with single payment factors:

$1500(F/P, 10\%, 5) = 1500 (1.611) = 2446.50$

$$1620 (1.464) = 2371.68$$
$$1749.60 (1.331) = 2328.72$$
$$1889.57 (1.210) = 2286.38$$
$$2040.73 (1.100) = 2244.80$$
$$2203.99 (1.000) = \underline{2203.99}$$
$$\$13,852.07$$

(b) Here $i = g$, hence the geometric gradient to present worth equation is:

$$P = A_1 n (1+i)^{-1} = 1500 \times 6 (1+0.08)^{-1} = 8333$$

$$F = P(F/P, 8\%, 6) = 8333(1.587) = \$13,224$$

# 4-71

(a)

Effective $i = (1+i)^m - 1 = (1+0.025)^4 - 1 = 0.1038 = 10.38\%$

(N.B. Effective interest rate is for one year)

(b) Since the effective interest rate is 10.38%, we can work backwards to compute an equivalent $i$ for 1/252 of a year.

$$(1+i)^{252} - 1 = 0.1038 \qquad (1+i)^{252} = 1.1038$$

$$(1+i) = 1.1038^{\frac{1}{252}} = 1.000392$$

∴ Equivalent $i = 0.0392\%$ per $\frac{1}{252}$ year.

(c)

Subscriber's cost/copy

$$A = P\left(A/P, i, n\right) = P\left[\frac{i(1+i)^n}{(1+i)^n - 1}\right]$$

$$A = 206\left[\frac{0.000392(1+0.000392)^{504}}{(1+0.000392)^{504} - 1}\right] = 206\,(0.002187)$$

$$= 0.45 = 45¢/copy$$

as a check,

ignoring interest the cost/copy $= \dfrac{\$206}{2(252)} = 40.8¢/copy.$

Therefore the 45¢ answer looks reasonable.

## 4-72

(a) interest rate /6 months $= \dfrac{20,000}{500,000} = 0.04 = 4\%$

Effective interest rate (per year) $= (1+0.04)^2 - 1 = 0.0816 = 8.16\%$

(b) For continuous compounding

$$F = Pe^{rn} \qquad 520,000 = 500,000\,e^{r(1)}$$

$$r = \ln\left(\frac{520,000}{500,000}\right) = 0.0392 = 3.92\% \text{ per 6 months}$$

nominal interest rate (per year)

$$= 2(3.92\%) = 7.84\%$$

# 4-73

(a) Continuous cash flow - continuous compounding - one period

$$F = \bar{P}\left[\frac{(e^r-1)(e^{rn})}{re^r}\right] = 1\times10^9\left[\frac{(e^{0.005}-1)(e^{0.005\times1})}{0.005\,e^{0.005}}\right]$$

$$F = 1\times10^9\left[\frac{e^{0.005}-1}{0.005}\right] = 1\times10^9\left[\frac{0.00501252}{0.005}\right]$$

$$= 1,002,504,000$$

Thus the interest is $ 2,504,000.

(b) Deposits 4 times/month   A = 250 × 10⁶

continuous compounding.  r = nominal interest rate/¼ month

$$= \frac{0.005}{4} = 0.00125$$

$$F = A\left[\frac{e^{rn}-1}{e^r-1}\right] = 250,000,000\left[\frac{e^{0.00125(4)}-1}{e^{0.00125}-1}\right]$$

$$= 250\times10^6\left[\frac{0.00501252}{0.00125078}\right] = 1,001,879,000$$

Here the interest is $ 1,879,000.
So it pays $ 625,000 a month to move quickly!

# 4-74

Since there are annual deposits, but quarterly compounding, we
need to first compute the effective interest rate (per year)
Effective $i = (1+i)^m - 1 = (1+0.02)^4 - 1 = 0.0824 = 8.24\%$

Since $F = \$1,000,000$ we can find the equivalent $P$ for
$i = 8.24\%$ and $n = 40$

$P = F\ (P/F, 8.24\%, 40) = 1,000,000\ (1+0.0824)^{-40} = \$42,120$

now we can insert these values in the geometric gradient to
present worth equation:

$$P = A_1 \left[ \frac{1-(1+g)^n(1+i)^{-n}}{i-g} \right]$$

$$42,120 = A_1 \left[ \frac{1-(1.07)^{40}(1.0824)^{-40}}{0.0824-0.0700} \right] = A_1\ (29.78)$$

The first IRA deposit
$$A_1 = \frac{42,120}{29.78} = \$1414$$

**4-75**

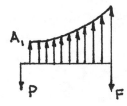

gradient series $i = g$
$A_1 = 5\%(52000) = 2600$
$i = g = 8\%$   $n = 20$

$P = A_1\ n\ (1+i)^{-1} = 2600 \times 20(1+0.08)^{-1} = 48,148.$
$F = P(F/P, i, n) = 48,148\ (1+0.08)^{20} = \$\ 224,416.$

**4-76**

$A_1 =$ Second yr salary $= (1.08)(225,000)$
    $= 243,000$
$g = 8\%$ geometric gradient
$i = 12\%$ interest rate

$$P = A_1 \left[ \frac{1-(1+g)^n(1+i)^{-n}}{i-g} \right] = 243,000 \left[ \frac{1-(1.08)^4(1.12)^{-4}}{0.04} \right]$$

$$P = 243,000 \left[ \frac{0.135385}{0.04} \right] = \$\ 822,462.$$

## 4-77

$$P = \overline{F}\left[\frac{e^r - 1}{r e^{rn}}\right] = 15{,}000\left[\frac{e^{0.08} - 1}{0.08\, e^{(0.08 \times 6)}}\right]$$

$$P = 15000\left[\frac{0.083287}{0.129286}\right] = \$9{,}663.$$

## 4-78

Future Worth (a)

$71 million $= 165{,}000\,(F/P, i, 61)$

$(F/P, i, 61) = \dfrac{\$71 \text{ million}}{165{,}000} = 430.3 \quad 10\% < i < 12\%$

$i \approx 10\% + (2\%)\left(\dfrac{430.3 - 341.7}{1034.5 - 341.7}\right) \approx 10.3\%$    (HP12C = 10.45%)

(b) In 1929 the Consumer Price Index was 17 compared to about 126 in 1990. So $165,000 in 1929 dollars is roughly equivalent to $165000\left(\frac{126}{17}\right) = \$1{,}223{,}000$ in 1990 dollars. The real rate of return is closer to 6.9%

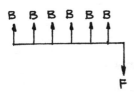

**4-79**

B B B B B B

The solution can follow the general approach of the end-of-year derivation in the book.

F

$$F = B\,(1+i)^n + \cdots + B(1+i)^1 \qquad (1)$$

Divide by $(1+i)$:

$$F\,(1+i)^{-1} = B\,\frac{(1+i)^n}{1+i} + \cdots + B\frac{(1+i)}{1+i} \qquad (2)$$

Subtract (2) from (1)

$$F - F(1+i)^{-1} = B\left[(1+i)^n - 1\right] \qquad (1)-(2)$$

multiply both sides by $(1+i)$

$$F(1+i) - F = B\left[(1+i)^{n+1} - (1+i)\right]$$

So the equation is

$$F = B\left[\frac{(1+i)^{n+1} - (1+i)}{i}\right]$$

applied to the numerical values:

$$F = 100\left[\frac{(1+0.08)^7 - (1.08)}{0.08}\right] = \$792.28$$

**4-80**

$$FW = FW$$
$$1000\,(F/A,\,i,\,10)(F/P,\,i,\,4) = 28000$$

trial & error solution:

try $i = 12\%$   $1000(17.549)(1.574) = 27,622$   $i$ too low

$i = 15\%$   $1000(20.304)(1.749) = 35,512$   $i$ too high

$$i = 12\% + (3\%)\left(\frac{28000 - 27622}{35512 - 27622}\right) = 12.14\%$$

## 4-81

Since $(A/P, i, n) = (A/F, i, n) + i$    (shown on p. 78)

$$0.1728 = 0.0378 + i$$

$$i = 13.5\%$$

## 4-82

Effective $i = (1+i)^m - 1$    $0.0931 = (1+i)^4 - 1$

$$1.0931^{0.25} = (1+i)$$

$$1.0225 = 1 + i \qquad i = 2.25\%/quarter$$

$$i = 9\% \text{ per year}$$

## 4-83

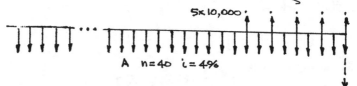

$$A \quad n = 40 \quad i = 4\%$$

Compute F equivalent to the 5–$10,000 withdrawals

$$F = 10,000\left[(F/P, 4\%, 8) + (F/P, 4\%, 6) + (F/P, 4\%, 4) + (F/P, 4\%, 2) + 1\right]$$

$$= 10,000\,(1.369 + 1.265 + 1.170 + 1.082 + 1) = \$58,850$$

Req'd series of 40 deposits

$$A = F(A/F, 4\%, 40) = 58,850(0.0105) = \$618$$

$P = 10,000$    $F = 30000$    $i = 5\%$    $n = ?$      **4-84**

$F = Pe^{rn}$    $30000 = 10000 e^{0.05(n)}$

$$0.05n = \ln\left(\frac{30,000}{10,000}\right) = 1.0986$$

$$n = \frac{1.0986}{0.05} = 21.97 \text{ years}$$

**4-85**

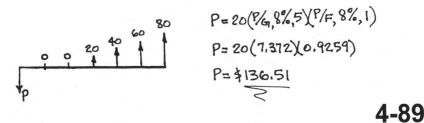

B = 200

n = 15    i = 7%

F

F'

$F = 200(F/A, i, n) = 200 (F/A, 7\%, 15) = 200(25.129) = 5025.80$

$F' = F(F/P, i, n) = 5025.80 (F/P, 7\%, 1) = 5025.80(1.07) = \underline{5377.61}$

**4-86**

44.955

$P = 3000 + 280 (P/A, 1\%, 60) = \underline{\$15,587.}$

**4-87**

$i_{eff} = (1+i)^{m} - 1 = (1+0.03)^{4} - 1 = 0.1255 = \underline{12.55\%}$

**4-88**

80

60

40

20

o    o

P

$P = 20(P/G, 8\%, 5)(P/F, 8\%, 1)$

$P = 20(7.372)(0.9259)$

$P = \underline{\$136.51}$

**4-89**

$P = 1$    $F = 2$    $i = 1\%$    $n = ?$

$2 = 1 (F/P, 1\%, n)$     $(F/P, 1\%, n) = 2$

From the 1% table, $n \approx \underline{70 \text{ months}}$

## 4-90

$$F = 2000 (F/A, 8\%, 10)(F/P, 8\%, 5)$$
$$= 2000 (14.487)(1.469) = \$42,560$$

## 4-91

(a) Effective $i = (1+i)^m - 1 = (1+0.025)^4 - 1 = 0.1038 = 10.38\%$

(b) Effective $i = (1+i)^m - 1 = \left[1 + \dfrac{0.10}{365}\right]^{365} - 1 = 0.10516 = 10.52\%$

(c) Effective $i = e^r - 1 = e^{0.10} - 1 = 0.10517 = 10.52\%$

**4-92**

$P = 1250\ (P/A,10\%,8) - 250\ (P/G,10\%,8) +3000 - 250\ (P/F,10\%,8)$
$= 1250\ (5.335) - 250\ (16.029) + 3000 - 250\ (0.4665)$
$= \$\underline{5545}$

**4-93**

$P = 25{,}000 \qquad i = 18\% \qquad 60\ \text{months}$

*a.* $\quad A = \$25{,}000\ (A/P,\ 1\text{-}\frac{1}{2}\ \%,\ 60)$
$\quad\quad = \$635$

*b.* $\quad P = 25{,}000\ (0.98) = \$24{,}500$
$\quad\quad 24{,}500 = 635\ (P/A,\ i,60)$
$\quad\quad (P/A,\ i,\ 60) = \dfrac{24{,}500}{635} = 38.5827$

| $i\%$ | $(P/A,\ i,\ 60)$ |
|---|---|
| 1 ½ | 39.380 |
| 1 3/4 | 36.964 |

$i\% = 0.015 + (0.0025)\dfrac{(39.380 - 38.5827)}{(39.380 - 36.964)}$
$\quad\quad = 0.015 + 0.000825$
$\quad\quad = 0.015825 = 1.5825\%\ \text{per month}$

$i_a = (1+0.015825)^{12} - 1$
$\quad = 0.2073\ \text{or}\ \underline{20.73\%}$

62    Chapter 4    More Interest Formulas

# 4-94

*a.*      11.98% compounded continuously
$$F = \$10,000\ e^{0.1198 \times 4}$$
$$= \$16,147.82$$

*b.*      12% compounded daily
$$F = \$10,000\ (1 + \frac{0.12}{365})^{365 \times 4}$$
$$= 16,159.47$$

*c.*      12.01% compounded monthly
$$F = \$10,000\ (1 + \frac{0.1201}{12})^{4 \times 12}$$
$$= \$16,128.65$$

*d.*      12.02% compounded quarterly
$$F = \$10,000\ (1 + \frac{0.1202}{4})^{4 \times 4}$$
$$= \$16,059.53$$

*e.*      12.03% compounded yearly
$$F = \$10,000\ (1 + 0.1203)^4$$
$$= \$15,752.06$$
**Decision:  Choose <u>Alt *b.*</u>**

# 4-95

*a.*      $r = i \times m$
$r = (1.25\%)(12)$
$r = 15\%$

*b.*      $i_a = (1+0.0125)^{12} - 1$
$i_a = 16.08\%$

*c.*      $A = 10,000(A/P, 1.25\%, 48)$
$A = 10,000(0.0278)$
$A = \$278$

# 4-96

*a.*      $P = \$1000$
$A = \$90.30$
$m = 12$ months
$1000 = 90.30(P/A, i, 12)$
$(P/A, i, 12) = 1000/90.30 = 11.074$
Find $i$ such that $(P/A, i, 12) = 11.074$
$i = 1.25\%$

*b.*      $r = (1.25\%)(12)$
$r = 15\%$

*c.*      $i_a = (1+0.0125)^{12} - 1$
$i_a = 16.08\%$

# 4-97

*a.*   $P = Fe^{-rn}$
       $P = 8000 \exp(-0.08)(4.5)$
       $P = \$5581.41$

*b.*   $F = Pe^{rn}$
       $F/P = e^{rn}$
       $\ln(F/P) = rn$
       $r = (1/n)\ln(F/P)$
       $r = (1/4.5)\ln(8000/5000)$
       $r = 10.44\%$

# 4-98

$i = 5.25\%; A = \$300; n = 10$ years; $P = ?$
$P = A(P/A, 5.25\%, 10)$

$$P = A\frac{[(1+i)^n - 1]}{i(1+i)^n} = 300\frac{[(1.0525)^{10} - 1]}{0.0525(1.0525)^{10}}$$

$P = 300(7.62884)$
$\;\; = \underline{\$2289}$

# 4-99

Cash Flow number 1.
$P_{0_1} = A(P/A, 12\%, 4)$
Cash Flow number 2.
$P_{0_2} = 150(P/A, 12\%, 5) + 150(P/G, 12\%, 5)$
      Since $P_{0_1} = P_{0_2}$
$A(3.037) = 150(3.605) + 150(6.397)$
$A = (540.75 + 959.55)/3.037$
$\;\; = \$494$

# 4-100

*a.*
       $i = 8\%$
       $n = 15$ years
       $P = 150,000 - 30,000 = \$120,000$
       $A = P(A/P, i, n)$
          $= 120,000(A/P, 8\%, 15)$
          $= 120,000(0.11683)$
          $= \$14,019.55$

$R_y$ = Remaining Balance in any year, $y$.

$2004 = R_7 = ?$

$R_y = A (P/A, i, n - y)$

$R_7 = 14,019.55 (P/A, 8\%, 15 - 7)$

$= 14,019.55 (5.747)$

$= \underline{\$80,570.35}$

*b.*

The quantities in Table 4-100 are computed as follows:  Column 1 shows the number of interest periods. Column 2 shows the equal annual amount as computed in part *a.* above.  The amount $14,019.55 is the total payment which includes the principal and the interest portions for each of the 15 years.  To compute the interest portion for year one, we must first multiply the interest rate in decimal by the remaining balance:

Interest Portion = $(0.08)(120,000) = \$9600$

**TABLE 4-100:   SEPARATION OF INTEREST AND PRINCIPAL**

| YEAR | ANNUAL PAYMENT | INTEREST PORTION | PRINCIPAL PORTION | REMAINING BALANCE |
|---|---|---|---|---|
| 0 | | | | $120,000 |
| 1 | $14,019.55 | $9,600 | $4,419.55 | 115,580.45 |
| 2 | 14,019.55 | 9,246.44 | 4,773.11 | 110,807.34 |
| 3 | 14,019.55 | 8,864.59 | 5,154.96 | 105,652.38 |
| 4 | 14,019.55 | 8,452.19 | 5,567.36 | 100,085.02 |
| 5 | 14,019.55 | 8,006.80 | 6,012.75 | 94,072.27 |
| 6 | 14,019.55 | 7,525.78 | 6,493.77 | 87,578.50 |
| 7* | 14,019.55 | 7,006.28 | 7,013.27 | 80,565.23 |
| 8 | 14,019.55 | 6,445.22 | 7,574.33 | 72,990.90 |
| 9 | 14,019.55 | 5,839.27 | 8,180.28 | 64,810.62 |
| 10 | 14,019.55 | 5,184.85 | 8,834.70 | 55,975.92 |
| 11 | 14,019.55 | 4,478.07 | 9,541.48 | 46,434.44 |
| 12 | 14,019.55 | 3,714.76 | 10,304.79 | 36,129.65 |
| 13 | 14,019.55 | 2,890.37 | 11,129.18 | 25,000.47 |
| 14 | 14,019.55 | 2,000.04 | 12,019.51 | 12,981.00 |
| 15 | 14,019.55 | 1,038.48 | 12,981.00 | 0 |

Subtracting the interest portion of $9600 from the total payment of $14,019.55 gives the principal portion to be $4419.55, and subtracting it from the principal balance of the loan at the end of the previous year (y) results in the remaining balance after the first payment is made in year 1 ($y_1$), of $115,580.45.  This completes the year 1 row.  The other row quantities are computed in the same fashion.  The interest portion for row two, year 2 is:

$(0.08)(115,580.45) = \$9246.44$

*NOTE: Interest is computed on the remaining balance at the end of the preceding year and not on the original principal of the loan amount.  The rest of the calculations proceeds as before.  Also, note that on year 7, the remaining balance as shown on Table 4-100 is approximately equal to the value calculated in *a.* using a formula except for round off error.

# 4-101

Determine the required present worth of the escrow account on January 1, 1998:

$$n = 3 \text{ years}$$
$$i = 5.75\%$$
$$A = \$8000$$
$$PW = ?$$

$$PW = A \ (P/A, i, n)$$
$$= 8000 + 8000(P/A, 5.75\%, 3)$$
$$= 8000 + 8000 \left[\frac{(1 + i)^n - 1}{i (1 + i)^n}\right] = \$8000 + 8000 \left[\frac{(1.0575)^4 - 1}{.0575(1.0575)^3}\right]$$
$$= \underline{\$29,483}$$

It is necessary to have $29,483 at the end of 1997 in order to provide $8000 at the end of 1998, 1999, 2000 and 2001. It is now necessary to determine what yearly deposits should have been over the period 1981-1997 to build a fund of $29,483.

$$n = 18; F = \$29,483; i = 5.75\%; A = ?$$
$$A = F \ (A/F, i, n) = \$29,483 \ (A/F, 5.75\%, 18)$$

$$A = 29,483 \left[\frac{i}{(1 + i)^n - 1}\right]$$

$$= 29,483 \left[\frac{0.0575}{(1.0575)^{18} - 1}\right]$$
$$= 29,483 \ (0.03313) = \$977$$

# 4-102

Compute the effective interest rate per quarterly payment period
$$i_{qtr} = (1 + 0.10/12)^3 - 1 = 0.0252 = 2.52\%$$
Compute the present worth of the 32 quarterly payments
$$P = A \ (P/A, 2.52\%, 32)$$
$$= 3000 \left[\frac{(1.0252)^{32} - 1}{0.0252 \ (1.0252)^{32}}\right]$$
$$= 3000 \ (21.7878)$$
$$= \$65,363$$

# 4-103

*a.* The effective interest rate $i_a = (1 + r/m)^m - 1 = (1 + 0.06/2)^2 - 1$
$$= 0.0609 = 6.09\%.$$
The continuous effective interest rate $= e^{0.06} - 1 = 6.18 \%$.
*b.* The future value of the loan, one period (6 months) before the first
repayment $= 2000(F/P,3\%,5) = 2000(1.159) = \$2318$
The uniform payment $= 2318(A/P,3\%,4) = 2318(0.2690) = \$623.54$ every 6 months.
*c.* Total interest paid $= (4 \times 623.54) - 2000 = \$494.16$

# 4-104

BOP = Beginning of Period.          EOP = End of Period.

|   | A | B | C | D | E | F | G |
|---|---|---|---|---|---|---|---|
| 1 |   |   |   |   |   |   |   |
| 2 |   |   |   |   |   |   |   |
| 3 | Problem |   |   |   |   |   |   |
| 4 |   |   |   |   |   |   |   |
| 5 | Amortization schedule for a $4500 loan at 6% | | | , paid monthly for 24 months | | | |
| 6 |   |   |   |   |   |   |   |
| 7 | P = $4500.00 | | I = 6%/12 mo. = 1/2% per mo. | | n = 24 mo. | | |
| 8 |   |   |   |   |   |   |   |
| 9 | pmnt. | amnt. owed | int. owed | total owed | principal | monthly | |
| 10 | no. | (BOP) | (this pmnt.) | (EOP) | (this pmnt.) | pmnt. | |
| 11 |   |   |   |   |   |   |   |
| 12 | 1 | 4500.00 | 22.50 | 4522.50 | 176.94 | 199.44 | |
| 13 | 2 | 4323.06 | 21.62 | 4344.68 | 177.82 | 199.44 | |
| 14 | 3 | 4145.24 | 20.73 | 4165.96 | 178.71 | 199.44 | |
| 15 | 4 | 3966.52 | 19.83 | 3986.35 | 179.61 | 199.44 | |
| 16 | 5 | 3786.91 | 18.93 | 3805.85 | 180.51 | 199.44 | |
| 17 | 6 | 3606.41 | 18.03 | 3624.44 | 181.41 | 199.44 | |
| 18 | 7 | 3425.00 | 17.13 | 3442.13 | 182.31 | 199.44 | |
| 19 | 8 | 3242.69 | 16.21 | 3258.90 | 183.23 | 199.44 | |
| 20 | 9 | 3059.46 | 15.30 | 3074.76 | 184.14 | 199.44 | |
| 21 | 10 | 2875.32 | 14.38 | 2889.69 | 185.06 | 199.44 | |
| 22 | 11 | 2690.25 | 13.45 | 2703.70 | 185.99 | 199.44 | |
| 23 | 12 | 2504.26 | 12.52 | 2516.79 | 186.92 | 199.44 | |
| 24 | 13 | 2317.35 | 11.59 | 2328.93 | 187.85 | 199.44 | |
| 25 | 14 | 2129.49 | 10.65 | 2140.14 | 188.79 | 199.44 | |
| 26 | 15 | 1940.70 | 9.70 | 1950.40 | 189.74 | 199.44 | |
| 27 | 16 | 1750.96 | 8.75 | 1759.72 | 190.69 | 199.44 | |
| 28 | 17 | 1560.28 | 7.80 | 1568.08 | 191.64 | 199.44 | |
| 29 | 18 | 1368.64 | 6.84 | 1375.48 | 192.60 | 199.44 | |
| 30 | 19 | 1176.04 | 5.88 | 1181.92 | 193.56 | 199.44 | |
| 31 | 20 | 982.48 | 4.91 | 987.40 | 194.53 | 199.44 | |
| 32 | 21 | 787.96 | 3.94 | 791.90 | 195.50 | 199.44 | |
| 33 | 22 | 592.46 | 2.96 | 595.42 | 196.48 | 199.44 | |
| 34 | 23 | 395.98 | 1.98 | 397.96 | 197.46 | 199.44 | |
| 35 | 24 | 198.52 | 0.99 | 199.51 | 198.45 | 199.44 | |
| 36 |   |   |   |   |   |   |   |
| 37 | TOTALS | | 286.63 | | 4499.93 | | |
| 38 |   |   |   |   |   |   |   |
| 39 | B12 = $4500.00   (principal amount) | | | | | | |
| 40 |   |   |   |   |   |   |   |
| 41 | B13 = B12 - E12   (amount owed BOP - principal in this payment) | | | | | | |
| 42 |   |   |   |   |   |   |   |
| 43 | column C = amount owed BOP * 0.005 | | | | | | |
| 44 |   |   |   |   |   |   |   |
| 45 | column D = column B + column C   (principal + interest) | | | | | | |
| 46 |   |   |   |   |   |   |   |
| 47 | column E = column F - column C   (payment - interest owed) | | | | | | |
| 48 |   |   |   |   |   |   |   |
| 49 | column F = uniform monthly payment   (from formula for A/P) | | | | | | |

# 4-105

BOP = Beginning of Period        EOP = End of Period

| | A | B | C | D | E | F | G |
|---|---|---|---|---|---|---|---|
| 1 | | | | | | | |
| 2 | | | | | | | |
| 3 | Problem | | | | | | |
| 4 | | | | | | | |
| 5 | Amortization schedule for a $4500 loan at 6% | | | , paid monthly for 24 months | | | |
| 6 | | | | | | | |
| 7 | P = $4500.00 | | I = 6%/12 mo. = 1/2% per mo. | | n = 24 mo. | | |
| 8 | | | | | | | |
| 9 | pmnt. | amnt. owed | Int. owed | total owed | principal | monthly | |
| 10 | no. | (BOP) | (this pmnt.) | (EOP) | (this pmnt.) | pmnt. | |
| 11 | | | | | | | |
| 12 | 1 | 4500.00 | 22.50 | 4522.50 | 176.94 | 199.44 | |
| 13 | 2 | 4323.06 | 21.62 | 4344.68 | 177.82 | 199.44 | |
| 14 | 3 | 4145.24 | 20.73 | 4165.96 | 178.71 | 199.44 | |
| 15 | 4 | 3966.52 | 19.83 | 3986.35 | 179.61 | 199.44 | |
| 16 | 5 | 3786.91 | 18.93 | 3805.85 | 180.51 | 199.44 | |
| 17 | 6 | 3606.41 | 18.03 | 3624.44 | 181.41 | 199.44 | |
| 18 | 7 | 3425.00 | 17.13 | 3442.13 | 182.31 | 199.44 | |
| 19 | 8 | 3242.69 | 16.21 | 3258.90 | 483.79 | 500.00 | |
| 20 | 9 | 2758.90 | 13.79 | 2772.69 | 185.65 | 199.44 | |
| 21 | 10 | 2573.25 | 12.87 | 2586.12 | 267.13 | 280.00 | |
| 22 | 11 | 2306.12 | 11.53 | 2317.65 | 187.91 | 199.44 | |
| 23 | 12 | 2118.21 | 10.59 | 2128.80 | 188.85 | 199.44 | |
| 24 | 13 | 1929.36 | 9.65 | 1939.01 | 189.79 | 199.44 | |
| 25 | 14 | 1739.57 | 8.70 | 1748.27 | 190.74 | 199.44 | |
| 26 | 15 | 1548.83 | 7.74 | 1556.57 | 191.70 | 199.44 | |
| 27 | 16 | 1357.13 | 6.79 | 1363.92 | 192.65 | 199.44 | |
| 28 | 17 | 1164.48 | 5.82 | 1170.30 | 193.62 | 199.44 | |
| 29 | 18 | 970.86 | 4.85 | 975.71 | 194.59 | 199.44 | |
| 30 | 19 | 776.27 | 3.88 | 780.15 | 195.56 | 199.44 | |
| 31 | 20 | 580.71 | 2.90 | 583.62 | 196.54 | 199.44 | |
| 32 | 21 | 384.18 | 1.92 | 386.10 | 197.52 | 199.44 | |
| 33 | 22 | 186.66 | 0.93 | 187.59 | 186.66 | 187.59 | |
| 34 | 23 | 0.00 | 0.00 | 0.00 | 0.00 | 0.00 | |
| 35 | 24 | 0.00 | 0.00 | 0.00 | 0.00 | 0.00 | |
| 36 | | | | | | | |
| 37 | TOTALS | | 256.95 | | 4500.00 | | |
| 38 | | | | | | | |
| 39 | B12 = $4500.00   (principal amount) | | | | | | |
| 40 | | | | | | | |
| 41 | B13 = B12 - E12    (amount owed BOP - principal in this payment) | | | | | | |
| 42 | | | | | | | |
| 43 | column C = amount owed BOP * 0.005 | | | | | | |
| 44 | | | | | | | |
| 45 | column D = column B + column C    (principal + interest) | | | | | | |
| 46 | | | | | | | |
| 47 | column E = column F - column C    (payment - interest owed) | | | | | | |
| 48 | | | | | | | |
| 49 | column F = uniform monthly payment    (from formula for A/P) | | | | | | |
| 50 | | | | | | | |
| 51 | Payment 22 is final payment. Payment amount = $187.59 | | | | | | |

# 4-106

| | A | B | C | D | E | F | G | H |
|---|---|---|---|---|---|---|---|---|
| 1 | | | | | | | | |
| 2 | | | | | | | | |
| 3 | Problem | | | | | | | |
| 4 | | | | | | | | |
| 5 | Savings Account Balance sheet | | | | | | | |
| 6 | | | | | | | | |
| 7 | Interest is paid at 9%, compounded monthly   (i = 9%/12 = 3/4% per mo.) | | | | | | | |
| 8 | | | | | | | | |
| 9 | month | deposit | acct. bal. | interest | deposit | acct. bal. | | |
| 10 | no. | (BOM) | (BOM) | earned | (EOM) | (EOM) | | |
| 11 | | | | | | | | |
| 12 | 1 | 400.00 | 400.00 | 3.00 | 0.00 | 403.00 | | |
| 13 | 2 | 0.00 | 403.00 | 3.02 | 270.00 | 676.02 | | |
| 14 | 3 | 0.00 | 676.02 | 5.07 | 0.00 | 681.09 | | |
| 15 | 4 | 0.00 | 681.09 | 5.11 | 0.00 | 686.20 | | |
| 16 | 5 | 0.00 | 686.20 | 5.15 | 0.00 | 691.35 | | |
| 17 | 6 | 0.00 | 691.35 | 5.19 | 100.00 | 796.53 | | |
| 18 | 7 | 0.00 | 796.53 | 5.97 | 180.00 | 982.51 | | |
| 19 | 8 | 0.00 | 982.51 | 7.37 | 0.00 | 989.88 | | |
| 20 | 9 | 0.00 | 989.88 | 7.42 | 0.00 | 997.30 | | |
| 21 | 10 | 200.00 | 1197.30 | 8.98 | 0.00 | 1206.28 | | |
| 22 | 11 | 0.00 | 1206.28 | 9.05 | 0.00 | 1215.33 | | |
| 23 | 12 | 0.00 | 1215.33 | 9.11 | 0.00 | 1224.44 | | |
| 24 | | | | | | | | |
| 25 | | | | Total in account @ EOM 12 = | | 1224.44 | | |
| 26 | | | | | | | | |
| 27 | column B = deposits made at the beginning of the month | | | | | | | |
| 28 | | | | | | | | |
| 29 | column C = acct bal @ end of last mo. + dep made beginning of current mo. | | | | | | | |
| 30 | | | | | | | | |
| 31 | column D = interest earned on BOM acct balance | | | | | | | |
| 32 | | | | | | | | |
| 33 | column E = deposits made at the end of the month | | | | | | | |
| 34 | | | | | | | | |
| 35 | column F = column C + column D + column E | | | | | | | |

$$i = \frac{NIR}{M} = \frac{9\%}{12} = \underline{3/4\% / mo.}$$

$$F_{12} = 400\left(F/p, 3/4\%, 12\right) + 270\left(F/p, 3/4\%, 10\right) + 100\left(F/p, 3/4\%, 6\right) + 180\left(F/p, 3/4\%, 5\right) + 200\left(F/p, 3/4\%, 3\right)$$

$$F_{12} = 400\left(1.094\right) + 270\left(1.078\right) + 100\left(1.046\right) + 180\left(1.038\right) + 200\left(1.023\right)$$

$$\boxed{F_{12} = \$1224.70} \implies (\text{SAME AS ABOVE})$$

# 4-107

Int. rate per month $= \dfrac{0.07}{12} = 0.00583 /$ month

Int. rate per day $= 0.07/365 = 0.000192/$ day

Payment $= P\left[\dfrac{i(1+i)^n}{(1+i)^n - 1}\right] = 80,000\left[\dfrac{0.00583(1+0.00583)^{360}}{(1+0.00583)^{360} - 1}\right] = \$532.03$

Principal in first payment $= 532.03 - [(80,000)(0.00583)] = \$65.63$

Loan Principal @ beginning of month 2 $= 80,000 - 65.63 = \$79,934.37$

Int for 33 days $= Pin = (79,934.37)(33)(0.000192) = \$506.46$

Principal in 2nd Payment $= 532.03 - 506.46 = \$25.57$

# 4-108

Given: $P = 10,000$
$F = 30,000$
$i = 12\%$
$n = 4$
$A = ?$

$10,000(F/P,12\%,4) + A\,(F/A,12\%,4) = 30,000$
$10,000(1.574) + A(4.779) = 30,000$
$\underline{A = \$2984}$

# 4-109

Let **X** = toll per vehicle    Then:
$A = 20,000,000\ \mathbf{X}$
$i = 10\%$
$F = 25,000,000$
$n = 3$

Therefore: $20,000,000\ \mathbf{X}\,(F/A,10\%,3) = 25,000,000$
$20,000,000\ \mathbf{X}\,(3.31) = 25,000,000$
$\underline{\mathbf{X} = \$0.38 \text{ per vehicle}}$

# 4-110

Given: $P = 2000$ cars/day
$i = 5\%$
$n = 2$
Find: $F_2 =$ cars/day  two years hence?

$F_2 = P\,e^{in} = 2000\,e^{0.05\,(2)} = \underline{2210 \text{ cars per day}}$

# 4-111

$i = 14\%$
$n = 19$ semiannual periods
$i_{qtr} = 0.14 / 4 = 0.035$
$i_{semiannual} = (1 + 0.035)^2 - 1 = 0.071225$

Can either solve for $P$ or $F$ first. Let's solve for $F$ first:

$$F_{1/05} = A\ (F/A\ ,\ i,\ n) = 1000 \left[ \frac{(1+0.071225)^{19} - 1}{0.071225} \right] = 37{,}852.04$$

Now, we have the Future Worth at January 1, 2005. We need the Present Worth at April 1, 1998. We can use either interest rate, the quarterly or the semiannual. Let's use the quarterly with $n = 27$.

$$P = F\ (1+i)^{-n} = 37{,}852.04\ (1+0.035)^{-27} = 14{,}952$$

This particular example illustrates the concept of these problems being similar to putting a puzzle together. There was no simple formula, or even a complicated formula, to arrive at the solution. While the actual calculations were not difficult, there were several steps required to arrive at the correct solution.

# 4-112

$n = 3$ years    $P = 29{,}000$    $F = ?$

a.  $i_a = 0.13$

$$F = P\ (1+i)^n = 29{,}000\ (1.13)^3 = 29{,}000\ (1.4429) = \$41{,}844$$

b.  $r = 0.1275$

$$F = P\ e^{rn} = 29{,}000\ (e^{0.1275 \times 3}) = 29{,}000\ (1.4659) = \$42{,}511$$

We can see that although the interest rate was less with the continuous compounding, the future amount is greater because of the increased compounding periods (an infinite number of compounding periods). Thus, the correct choice for the company is to choose the 13% interest rate and discrete compounding.

# 4-113

$A = 1200$ per month

$r = 0.14/12 = 0.01167$  nominal rate/period

$n = 7 \times 12 = 84$ compounding subperiods

$$F = A\left[\frac{e^{rn}-1}{e^{r}-1}\right] = 1200\left[\frac{e^{0.01167\times84}-1}{e^{0.01167}-1}\right]$$

$$= 1200\left[\frac{1.66520}{0.011738}\right] = \$170{,}237$$

# 4-114

$$i = \frac{\text{interest rate}}{\text{interest period}} = \frac{0.13}{52} = 0.0025 = \tfrac{1}{4}\%$$

<u>Paco's account</u>:   63 deposits of \$38,000 each

Compute the equivalent weekly deposit

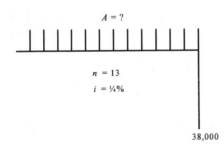

$A = ?$

$n = 13$

$i = \tfrac{1}{4}\%$

38,000

$A = F(A/F, i, n) = 38{,}000\,(A/F, \tfrac{1}{4}\%, 13) = 38{,}000\,(0.0758) = 2880.40$

For 63 deposits:

$$F = 2880.40 \ (F/A \ , \ \tfrac{1}{4}\%, \ 63 \times 13) = 2880.40 \left[ \frac{\left(1+0.0025\right)^{819} - 1}{0.0025} \right]$$

$$= 2880.40 \times 2691.49 \ = \ 7,752,570 \ \text{at} \ 4/1/2012$$

Amount at $1/1/2007 \ = \ 7,752,570 \ (P/F, \ \tfrac{1}{4}\%, \ 273) = \ 7,752,570 \ (0.50578) \ = \ 3,921,000$

Tisha's account:   18 deposits of $18,000 each
Equivalent weekly deposit
$A \ = \ 18,000 \ (A/F, \ \tfrac{1}{4}\%, 26) = 18,000 \ (0.0373) = 671.40$

$$\text{Present worth } P_{1/1/2006} \ = \ 671.40 \ (P/A \ , \ 1/4\%, \ 18 \times 26) = 671.40 \left[ \frac{\left(1+0.0025\right)^{468} - 1}{0.0025\left(1+0.0025\right)^{468}} \right]$$

$$= \ 671.40 \left[ \frac{\left(1+0.0025\right)^{468} - 1}{275.67} \right] \ = \ 185,084$$

Amount at $1/1/2007 \ = \ 185,084 \ (F/P, \ \tfrac{1}{4}\%, \ 52) = 185,084 \ (1.139) \ = 211,000$

Sum of both accounts at $1/1/2007 \ = \ 3,921,000 \ + \ 211,000 \ = \ \$4,132,000$

# 4-115

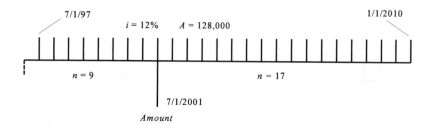

Amount $_{7/1/2001} \ = \ 128,000 \ (F/A, \ 6\%, \ 9) \ + 128,000(P/A, \ 6\%, \ 17)$
$= \ 128,000 \ (11.491) \ (10.477)$
$= \ \$15,410,000$

# 4-116

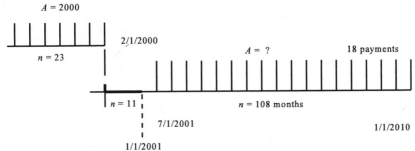

4/1/98

$A = 2000$

$n = 23$

2/1/2000

$A = ?$          18 payments

$n = 11$          $n = 108$ months

7/1/2001                              1/1/2010

1/1/2001

Monthly cash flows

$F_{2/1/2000} = 2000 \, (F/A, 1\%, 23) = 2000 \, (25.716) = 51,432$

$F_{2/1/2001} = 51,432 \, (F/P, 1\%, 11) = 51,432 \, (1.116) = 57,398$

Equivalent $A$ from 2/1/2001 thru 1/1/2010:   $n = 108$   $i = 1\%$
  $A_{equiv} = 57,398 \, (A/P, 1\%, 108) = 57,398 \, (0.01518) = 871.30$

Equivalent semiannual payments required from 7/1/2001 thru 1/1/2010:
  $A_{semiannual} = 871.30 \, (F/A, 1\%,6) = 871.30 \, (6.152) = \$5360$

# 4-117

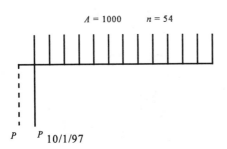

$A = 1000$     $n = 54$

$P$     $P$ 10/1/97

Continuous compounding

Effective interest rate / quarter year $= e^{\left(\frac{0.13}{4}\right)} - 1 = 0.03303$

**Solution One**

$$P_{10/1/97} = 1000 + 1000\ (P/A,\ 3.303\%,\ 53) = 1000 + 1000 \left[ \frac{(1+0.03303)^{53} - 1}{0.03303\ (1+0.03303)^{53}} \right] = \$25{,}866$$

**Solution Two**

$$P_{10/1/97} = 1000\ (P/A,\ 3.303\%,\ 54)\ (F/P,\ 3.303\%,\ 1)$$

$$= 1000 \left[ \frac{(1+0.03303)^{54} - 1}{0.03303\ (1+0.03303)^{54}} \right] (1+0.03303) = \$25{,}866$$

# 4-118

<u>First Bank</u>
Continuous Compounding

Effective interest rate $\quad i_a = e^r - 1 = e^{0.045} - 1 = 0.04603 = 4.603\%$

<u>Second Bank</u>
Monthly Compounding

Effective interest rate $\quad i_a = \left(1 + \frac{0.046}{12}\right)^{12} - 1 = 0.04698 = 4.698\%$

No, Barry should have selected the Second Bank.

# 4-119

Deposits

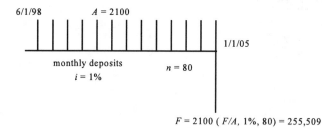

$F = 2100\ (F/A,\ 1\%,\ 80) = 255{,}509$

Withdrawals

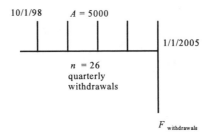

Equivalent quarterly interest $\quad i_{\text{quarterly}} = \left[1 + 0.01\right]^{3} - 1 = 0.0303 = 3.03\%$

$$F_{\text{withdrawals}} = 5000 \ (F/A \ , \ 3.03\%, \ 26) = 5000 \left[\frac{(1 + 0.0303)^{26} - 1}{0.0303}\right] = 193{,}561$$

Amount remaining in the account
on January 1, 2005  = 255,509 - 193,561 = $ 61,948

## 4-120

$i = 18\% / 12 = 1.5\%$ per month
**a.** $A = 100 \ (A/P, \ 1.5\%, \ 24) = 100 \ (0.0499) = \$4.99$
**b.** $P_{13} = 4.99 + 4.99 \ (P/A, \ 1.5\%, \ 11)$

$\overset{\frown}{\phantom{xx}}$ 13th $\qquad \overset{\frown}{\phantom{xx}}$ PW of future 11
payment $\qquad\qquad$ payments

$= 4.99 + 4.99(10.071) = \$55.24$

## 4-121

$i = 6\% / 12 = \frac{1}{2}\%$ per month
**a.** $P = 10 \ (P/A, \ \frac{1}{2}\% \ , \ 48 \ ) = 10 \ (42.580) = \$425.80$
**b.** $P_{24} = 10 \ (P/A, \ \frac{1}{2}\% \ , \ 24 \ ) = 10 \ (22.563) = \$ 225.63$

**c.** $P = 10 \left[\dfrac{e^{(.005)(48)} \quad -1}{e^{\ (.005)(48)} \ (e^{\ .005} -1)}\right] = 10 \ (42.568) = \$425.68$

## 4-122

**a.**  $P = \$500{,}000 - \$100{,}000 = \$400{,}000$
$\qquad r = 9\%$
$\qquad m = 12$

$i = 9\%/12 = 0.75\%$
$A = P(A/P, 0.75\%, 360)$
$A = 400,000(0.00805)$
$A = \$3220$

**b.**   $P = A(P/A, 0.75\%, 240)$
$P = 3220(111.145)$
$P = \$357,887$

**c.**   $A = 400,000 \left[ \dfrac{e^{(.06/12)(360)} \times e^{(0.06/12)} - 1}{e^{(.06/12)(360)} - 1} \right] = 400 \dfrac{(6.05)(0.005)}{(6.05-1)} = \$2396$

# 4-123

**a.** $F_{16} = 10,000 \left( 1 + \dfrac{0.055}{4} \right)^{16}$

$= 12,442.11$

$F_{30} = 12,442.11 \left( 1 + \dfrac{0.065}{4} \right)^{24}$

$= \$\underline{18,319.24}$

**b.** $18,319.24 = ( 1 + i)^{10} (10,000)$
$(1 + i)^{10} = \dfrac{18,319.24}{10,000} = 1.8319$
$10 \ln (1 + i) = \dfrac{\ln 1.8319}{10}$
$= 0.0605$
$1 + i = 1.0624$
$i = 1.0624 - 1$
$= 0.0624 \text{ or } \underline{6.24\%}$

Alternative Solution
$18,319.24 = 10,000 (F/P, i, 10)$
$(F/P, i,10) = 1.832$

| $(F/P, i, 10)$ | $i$ | |
|---|---|---|
| 1.791 | 6% | Interpolate between 6% and 7% |
| 1.967 | 7% | |

$i = 6\% + \dfrac{(1.832 - 1.791)}{(1.967 - 1.791)} = 6.24\%$

**Solutions to Spreadsheet supplement problems are after Chapter 19.**

# Present Worth Analysis

## 5-1

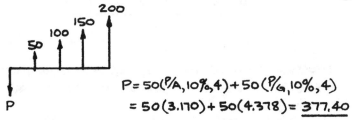

$$P = 50(P/A, 10\%, 4) + 50(P/G, 10\%, 4)$$
$$= 50(3.170) + 50(4.378) = \underline{377.40}$$

## 5-2

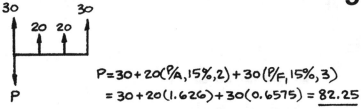

$$P = 30 + 20(P/A, 15\%, 2) + 30(P/F, 15\%, 3)$$
$$= 30 + 20(1.626) + 30(0.6575) = \underline{82.25}$$

## 5-3

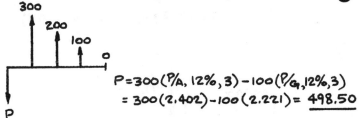

$$P = 300(P/A, 12\%, 3) - 100(P/G, 12\%, 3)$$
$$= 300(2.402) - 100(2.221) = \underline{498.50}$$

## 5-4

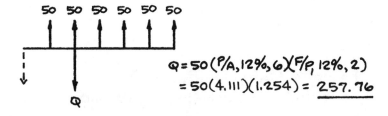

$$Q = 50(P/A, 12\%, 6)(F/P, 12\%, 2)$$
$$= 50(4.111)(1.254) = \underline{257.76}$$

77

## 5-5

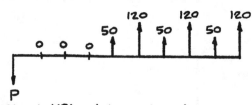

$P = 50(P/A,10\%,6)(P/F,10\%,3) + 70(P/F,10\%,5) + 70(P/F,10\%,7) + 70(P/F,10\%,9)$
$= 50(4.355)(0.7513) + 70(0.6209 + 0.5132 + 0.4241) = \underline{272.67}$
alternate Solution
$P = [50(P/A,10\%,6) + 70(P/F,10\%,2) + 70(P/F,10\%,4) + 70(P/F,10\%,6)](P/F,10\%,3)$
$= [50(4.355) + 70(0.8264 + 0.6830 + 0.5645)](0.7513) = \underline{272.66}$

## 5-6

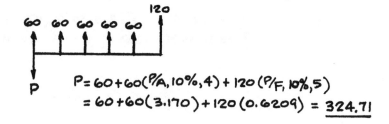

$P = 60 + 60(P/A,10\%,4) + 120(P/F,10\%,5)$
$= 60 + 60(3.170) + 120(0.6209) = \underline{324.71}$

## 5-7

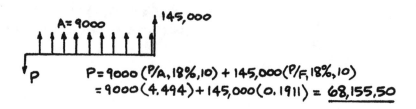

$P = 9000(P/A,18\%,10) + 145,000(P/F,18\%,10)$
$= 9000(4.494) + 145,000(0.1911) = \underline{68,155.50}$

## 5-8

$P = 100(P/A,6\%,6) + 100(P/G,6\%,6)$
$= 100(4.917) + 100(11.459) = \underline{1637.60}$

**5-9**

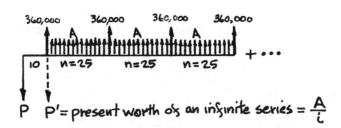

$$A = 6 \times \$60{,}000 \ (A/F, 4\%, 25) = 360{,}000 \ (0.0240) = 8640$$

$$P' = \frac{A}{i} = \frac{8640}{0.04} = 216{,}000$$

$$P = (216{,}000 + 360{,}000)(P/F, 4\%, 10) = 576{,}000 \, (0.6756)$$
$$= \$389{,}150.$$

**5-10**

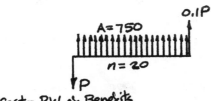

PW of Cost = PW of Benefits
$$P = 750(P/A, 7\%, 20) + 0.1P(P/F, 7\%, 20)$$
$$= 750(10.594) + 0.1P(0.2584) = 7945 + 0.02584P$$
$$P = \frac{7945}{0.97416} = \$8156.$$

# 5-11

By buying the "lifetime" muffler the car owner will avoid paying $50 two years hence.  Compute how much he is willing to pay now to avoid the future $50 disbursement.

$$P = 50\,(P/F, 20\%, 2) = 50(0.6944) = {}^{\frac{3}{5}}34.72$$

Since the lifetime muffler costs an additional $15, it appears to be the desirable alternative.

# 5-12

Compute the PW of Cost for a 25-year analysis period.
Note that in both cases the annual maintenance is $100,000 per year after 25 years.  Thus after 25 years all costs are identical.

Single Stage Construction

$$PW \text{ of Cost} = 22,400,000 + 100,000\,(P/A, 4\%, 25)$$
$$= 22,400,000 + 100,000\,(15.622)$$
$$= 23,962,000.$$

Two Stage Construction

$$PW \text{ of Cost} = 14,200,000 + 75,000(P/A, 4\%, 25)$$
$$+ 12,600,000\,(P/F, 4\%, 25)$$
$$= 14,200,000 + 75,000\,(15.622) + 12,600,000(0.3751)$$
$$= 20,098,000.$$

Choose 2-stage construction

# 5-13

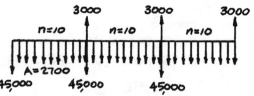

PW of Cost of 30 years of Westinghome
$$= 45000 + 2700\,(P/A, 10\%, 30) + 42000(P/F, 10\%, 10)$$
$$+ 42000\,(P/F, 10\%, 20) - 3000\,(P/F, 10\%, 30)$$

$PW$ of $Cost = 45{,}000 + 2700(9.427) + 42{,}000(0.3855)$
$+ 42{,}000(0.1486) - 3000(0.0573) \overset{\$}{=} 92{,}713.$

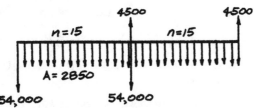

PW of Cost of 30 years of Itis

$= 54{,}000 + 2850\,(P/A, 10\%, 30) + 49{,}500(P/F, 10\%, 15)$
$-4500\,(P/F, 10\%, 30)$

$= 54{,}000 + 2850(9.427) + 49{,}500(0.2394) - 4500(0.0573)$

$= 92{,}459.$

The Itis bid has a slightly lower cost.

## 5-14

There appears to be four alternative plans for the ties.

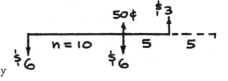

1. Use treated ties initially and as the replacement.

$PW$ of $Cost = \$6 + 5.50(P/F, 8\%, 10) - 3(P/F, 8\%, 15)$
$= \$6 + 5.50(0.4632) - 3(0.3152) = \$7.60$

2. Use treated ties initially. Replace with untreated ties.

$PW$ of $Cost = \$6 + 4(P/F, 8\%, 10) - 0.50(P/F, 8\%, 15)$
$= \$6 + 4(0.4632) - 0.50(0.3152) = \$7.70$

3. Use untreated ties initially. Replace with treated ties.

$PW$ of $Cost = 4.50 + 5.50(P/F, 8\%, 6) - 0.50(P/F, 8\%, 15)$
$= 4.50 + 5.50(0.6302) - 0.50(0.3152) = \$7.81$

4.  Use untreated ties initially. Then two replacements with untreated ties.

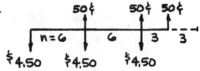

$$PW \text{ of } Cost = 4.50 + 4(P/F, 8\%, 6) + 4(P/F, 8\%, 12) - 0.50(P/F, 8\%, 15)$$
$$= 4.50 + 4(0.6302) + 4(0.3971) - 0.50(0.3152)$$
$$= \$8.45$$

Conclusion: Choose Alt. 1.

# 5-15

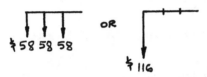

3 One-Year Subscriptions:
$$PW \text{ of } Cost = 58 + 58(P/F, 20\%, 1) + 58(P/F, 20\%, 2)$$
$$= 58(1 + 0.8333 + 0.6944) = \$146.61$$
A three-year Subscription:
$$PW \text{ of } Cost = \$116$$

Choose 3-year Subscription

# 5-16

Determine the cash flow:

| Year | Cash Flow |
|------|-----------|
| 0 | -4400 |
| 1 | +220 |
| 2 | +1320 |
| 3 | +1980 |
| 4 | +1540 |

NPW = PW of Benefits - PW of Cost
$$= 220(P/F, 6\%, 1) + 1320(P/F, 6\%, 2) + 1980(P/F, 6\%, 3)$$
$$+ 1540(P/F, 6\%, 4) - 4400$$
$$= 220(0.9434) + 1320(0.8900) + 1980(0.8396)$$
$$+ 1540(0.7921) - 4400$$
$$= -135.41$$

NPW is negative. Don't purchase equipment.

## 5-17

For end-of-year disbursements,

PW of wage increases $= (\$0.40 \times 8hr \times 250days)(P/A, 8\%, 10)$
$$+ (\$0.25 \times 8hr \times 250days)(P/G, 8\%, 10)$$
$$= \$800(6.710) + \$500(25.977)$$
$$= \$18,356,$$

This $18,356 is the <u>increased</u> justifiable cost of the equipment.

## 5-18

Eight mutually exclusive alternatives.

| Plan | Initial Cost | Net Annual Benefit | x (P/A,10%,10) = PW of Benefit | NPW = PW of Benefit minus Cost |
|------|------|------|------|------|
| 1 | $265 | $51 | $313.4 | $48.4 |
| 2 | 220 | 39 | 239.7 | 19.7 |
| 3 | 180 | 26 | 159.8 | -20.2 |
| 4 | 100 | 15 | 92.2 | -7.8 |
| 5 | 305 | 57 | 350.3 | 45.3 |
| 6 | 130 | 23 | 141.3 | 11.3 |
| 7 | 245 | 47 | 288.8 | 43.8 |
| 8 | 165 | 33 | 202.8 | 37.8 |

6.145

Maximize NPW - Choose Plan 1.

## 5-19

$$P = \frac{A}{i} = \frac{67,000}{0.08} = \$837,500$$

## 5-20

Two assumptions are needed.
1. Value of an urn of cherry blossoms (plus the cost to have the bank administer the trust) -- say $50.00/year.
2. A "conservative" interest rate -- say 5%.

$$P = \frac{A}{i} = \frac{\$50/\ year}{0.05} = \$1000. \quad \text{What a Bargain!}$$

## 5-21

$375 invested at 4% interest produces a perpetual annual income of $15. $A = Pi = 375(0.04) = \$15$   But this is <u>not</u> quite the situation here.

$15

$\ldots$ continuing membership

vs.

$375 ———————— Lifetime membership

An additional $360 now instead of n annual payments
of $15 each. Compute n

$$P = A (P/A, 4\%, n) \qquad 360 = 15 (P/A, 4\%, n)$$

$$(P/A, 4\%, n) = \frac{360}{15} = 24$$

From 4% interest table: n = 82

Lifetime (Patron) membership not economically sound
unless one expects to be active for 82+1 = 83 years.
(But that's probably not why people buy patron memberships
or avoid buying them.)

# 5-22

Since the necessary waste treatment and mercury recovery is
classed as "Fixed Output," choose the alternative with the least
Present Worth of Cost.

Foxhill
PW of Cost = 35,000 + (8000 - 2000)(P/A, 7%, 20) - 20,000(P/F, 7%, 20)

$$= 35000 + 6000(10.594) - 20,000(0.2584)$$

$$= \$93,396.$$

Quicksilver
PW of Cost = 40,000 + (7000 - 2200)(P/A, 7%, 20)

$$= 40,000 + 4800(10.594) = \$90,851.$$

Almaden
PW of Cost = 100,000 + (2000 - 3500)(P/A, 7%, 20)

$$= 100,000 - 1500(10.594) = \$84,109.$$

Select the Almaden bid

## 5-23

Use a 20-year analysis period

Alt. A  NPW = $1625(P/A, 6\%, 20) - 10,000 - 10,000(P/F, 6\%, 10)$

$\qquad = 1625(11.470) - 19000 - 10,000(0.5584)$

$\qquad = 18,639 - 10,000 - 5584 = 3055$

Alt. B  NPW = $1530(P/A, 6\%, 20) - 15,000$

$\qquad = 1530(11.470) - 15000 = 2549$

Alt. C  NPW = $1890(P/A, 6\%, 20) - 20,000$

$\qquad = 1890(11.470) - 20,000 = 1678$

Choose Alternative A

## 5-24

| Fuel | Installed Cost | Annual Fuel Cost |
|------|------|------|
| Natural Gas | $30,000 | $7500 > Fuel Oil |
| Fuel Oil | 55,000 | |
| Coal | 180,000 | 15,000 < Fuel Oil |

For Fixed Output: minimize PW of Cost

Natural Gas:

PW of Cost = $30,000 + 7500(P/A, 8\%, 20)$ + PW of Fuel Oil Cost

$\qquad = 30,000 + 7500(9.818)$ + PW of Fuel Oil Cost

$\qquad = \$103,635$ + PW of Fuel Oil Cost

Fuel Oil:

PW of Cost = $\$55,000$ + PW of Fuel Oil Cost

Coal:

PW of Cost = $180,000 - 15,000(P/A, 8\%, 20)$ + PW of Fuel Oil Cost

$\qquad = 180,000 - 15,000(9.818)$ + PW of Fuel Oil Cost

$\qquad = \$32,730$ + PW of Fuel Oil Cost

Conclusion: Install Coal Fired Steam Boiler.

# 5-25

Compute the Present Worth of Benefit for each stock.

From the 10% interest table, read:

$$(P/A,10\%,4) = 3.170$$
$$(P/F,10\%,4) = 0.683$$

| | PW of Future Price | | PW of Dividends | | | | | | PW of Benefit |
|---|---|---|---|---|---|---|---|---|---|
| Western House | $32 x 0.683 | + | 1.25 x 3.170 | = | 21.86 | + | 3.96 | = | $25.82 |
| Fine Foods | 45 | " | + 4.50 | " | = | 30.74 | + | 14.26 | = | 45.00 |
| Mobile Motors | 42 | " | + 0 | " | = | 28.69 | + | 0 | = | 28.69 |
| Trojan Products | 20 | " | + 0 | " | = | 13.66 | + | 0 | = | 13.66 |
| U.S. Tire | 40 | " | + 2.00 | " | = | 27.32 | + | 6.34 | = | 33.66 |
| Wine Products | 60 | " | + 3.00 | " | = | 40.98 | + | 9.51 | = | 50.49 |

| | PW of Benefit | PW of Cost | NPW per share | NPW per $1 invested |
|---|---|---|---|---|
| Western House | $25.82 | $23.75 | +2.07 | +0.09 |
| Fine Foods | 45.00 | 45.00 | 0 | 0 |
| Mobile Motors | 28.69 | 30.62 | -1.93 | -0.06 |
| Trojan Products | 13.66 | 12.00 | +1.66 | +0.14 |
| U.S. Tire | 33.66 | 33.37 | +0.29 | +0.01 |
| Wine Products | 50.49 | 52.50 | -2.01 | -0.04 |

In this problem, choosing to Maximize NPW per share leads to Western House. But the student should recognize that this is a faulty criterion.

An investment of some lump sum of money (like $1000) will purchase different numbers of shares of the various stock. It would buy 83 share of Trojan Products, but only 42 shares of Western House. The correct criterion, therefore, is to Maximize NPW for the amount invested. This could be stated as Maximize NPW per $1 invested.

Conclusion: Buy Trojan Products stock.

**5-26**

Capitalized Cost = PW of an infinite analysis period

when $n = \infty$ $A = Pi$ or $P = \dfrac{A}{i}$

Capitalized Cost
$$PW = \frac{5000}{0.08} + \frac{150,000(A/P, 8\%, 40)}{0.08}$$

$$= 62,500 + \frac{150,000(0.0839)}{0.08}$$

$$= 219,800$$

**5-27**

NPW = PW of Benefits − PW of Cost

NPW of 8 yrs of alternate A

$$= 1800(P/A, 10\%, 8) - 5300 - 5300(P/F, 10\%, 4)$$

$$= 1800(5.335) - 5300 - 5300(0.6830)$$

$$= +683.10$$

NPW of 8 yrs of alternate B

$$= 2100(P/A, 10\%, 8) - 10,700$$

$$= 2100(5.335) - 10,700 = +503.50$$

SELECT ALTERNATE A

**5-28**

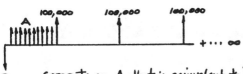

P     Compute an A that is equivalent to $100,000 at end of 10 years
$$A = 100,000 (A/F, 5\%, 10) = 100,000(0.0795) = 7950$$
For infinite series
$$P = \frac{A}{i} = \frac{7950}{0.05} = \$159,000$$

# 5-29

To provide $1000 per month she must deposit

$$P = \frac{A}{i} = \frac{1000}{0.005} = \$200,000$$

∴ when her aunt dies, Susan will receive $200,000

# 5-30

$$P = A_1\left(P/A, g, i, n\right) = A_1\left[\frac{1-(1+0.10)^4(1+0.15)^{-4}}{0.15-0.10}\right]$$

$$P = 200(3.258) = \$651.60$$

# 5-31

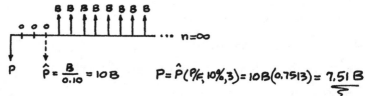

$$P = \hat{P}\left(P/F, 10\%, 3\right) = 10B(0.7513) = 7.51\,B$$

$$\hat{P} = \frac{B}{0.10} = 10B$$

# 5-32

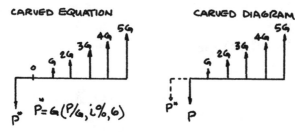

CARVED EQUATION          CARVED DIAGRAM

$$P^* = G(P/G, i\%, 6)$$

$$P = P^*(F/P, i\%, 1)$$

∴ Complete Equation:  $P = G(P/G, i\%, 6)(F/P, i\%, 1)$

# 5-33

The replacement equipment will have the same
NPW = +420 as the original equipment.

$$NPW_{12yrs} = 420 + 420(P/F, 10\%, 6) = +657.09$$

NPW +420   NPW +420

## 5-34

Dec 31, 1997    DEC 31, 1998    DEC 31, 1999
Jan 1, 1998    Jan 1, 1999    Jan 1, 2000

$NPW = -140$

$NPW_{12/31/97} = -140(P/F, 10\%, 2) = -140(0.8264) = -115.7$

## 5-35

$NPW = PW \text{ of Benefits} - PW \text{ of Cost}$

$NPW_A = 0$

$NPW_B = 12(P/A, 10\%, 5) - 50 = 12(3.791) - 50 = -4.51$

$NPW_C = 4.5(P/A, 10\%, 10) - 30 = 4.5(6.145) - 30 = -2.35$

$NPW_D = 6(P/A, 10\%, 10) - 40 = 6(6.145) - 40 = -3.13$

Select alternative A with NPW = 0

## 5-36

$NPW_A = 6(P/A, 8\%, 6) - 20 = +7.74$

$NPW_B = 9.25(P/A, 8\%, 6) - 35 = +7.76$

$NPW_C = 13.38(P/A, 8\%, 6) - 55 = +6.86$

$NPW_D = 13.78(P/A, 8\%, 6) - 60 = +3.70$

$NPW_E = 24.32(P/A, 8\%, 6) - 80 = +32.43$ ← Choose E

$NPW_F = 24.32(P/A, 8\%, 6) - 100 = +12.43$

## 5-37

For Fixed Output, minimize the Present Worth of Cost

Quick Paving

$PW \text{ of Cost} = 42500 + 21,250(P/F, 1\%, 6) + 21,250(P/F, 1\%, 12)$

$= 42500 + 21,250(0.9420) + 21,250(0.8874) = 81,375$

Tartan Paving

$PW \text{ of Cost} = 82,000$

Faultless Paving

$PW \text{ of Cost} = 21000 + 63000(P/F, 1\%, 6) = 21000 + 63000(0.9420)$

$= 80,346$

Award the job to Faultless Paving

# 5-38

(a)  8% interest.   Choose the alternative to maximize NPW.
Alternative
    1.   NPW = 135(P/A,8%,10) - 500 - 500(P/F,8%,5) = +65.55
    2.   NPW = 100(P/A,8%,10) - 600 - 350(P/F,8%,5)
           +250(P/F,8%,10)              = -51.41
    3.   NPW = 100(P/A,8%,10) - 700 + 180(P/F,8%,10)= +54.38
    4.   NPW = 0
                              Choose Alternative 1
(b)  12% interest.
Alternative
    1.   NPW = 135(P/A,12%,10) -500 - 500(P/F,12%,10) = -20.95
    2.   NPW = 100(P/A,12%,10) -600 - 350(P/F,12%,5)
           +250(P/F,12%,10)             = -153.09
    3.   NPW = 100(P/A,12%,10) -700 + 180(P/F,12%,10) = -77.04
    4.   NPW = 0
                              Choose Alternative 4

# 5-39

This is a situation of Fixed Input, therefore Maximize PW of Benefits.

By inspection one can see that C, with its greater benefits, is
preferred over A and B.   Similarly, E is preferred over D.
The problem reduces to choosing between C and E.

Alternative
    C.  PW of Benefits = 100(P/A,10%,5) + 110(P/A,10%,5)(P/F,10%,5)
                       = 100(3.791) + 110(3.791)(0.6209) = 638

    E.  PW of Benefits = 150(P/A,10%,5) + 50(P/A,10%,5)(P/F,10%,5)
                       = 150(3.791) + 50(3.791)(0.6209) = 686.4
                              Choose Alternative E

# 5-40

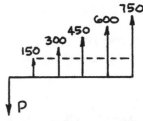

$$P = 150(P/A, 3\%, 5) + 150(P/G, 3\%, 5)$$
$$= 150(4.580) + 150(8.889) = 687.00 + 1333.35 = 2020.35$$

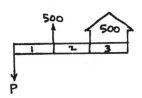

**5-41**

$$P = Fe^{-rn} + \bar{F}\left[\frac{e^r - 1}{re^{rn}}\right] = 500\,e^{-0.05(1)} + 500\left[\frac{e^{0.05} - 1}{0.05\,e^{0.05(3)}}\right]$$

$$\doteq 500\,(0.951229) + 500\left[\frac{0.051271}{0.058092}\right]$$

$$= 475.61 + 441.29 = \$916.90$$

**5-42**

(a) $PW \text{ of Cost} = (26000 + 7500)(P/A, 18\%, 6) = \$117,183.$
                                          $3.498$

(b) $PW \text{ of Cost} = \left(\frac{26000 + 7500}{12}\right)(P/A, 1.5\%, 72) = \$122,400.$
                                          $43.845$

(c) $PW \text{ of Cost} = \bar{F} \sum_{n=1}^{6}\left[\frac{e^r - 1}{re^{rn}}\right] = 33,500\left[\left(\frac{e^{0.18} - 1}{0.18\,e^{0.18(1)}}\right) + \left(\frac{e^{0.18} - 1}{0.18\,e^{0.18(2)}}\right) + \cdots\right]$

$$= 33,500\left[\left(\frac{0.1972}{0.2155}\right) + \left(\frac{0.1972}{0.2580}\right) + \left(\frac{0.1972}{0.3089}\right) + \left(\frac{0.1972}{0.3698}\right)\right.$$

$$\left. + \left(\frac{0.1972}{0.4427}\right) + \left(\frac{0.1972}{0.5300}\right)\right]$$

$$= 33,500\,(0.9151 + 0.7643 + 0.6384 + 0.5333 + 0.4454 + 0.3721)$$

$$= 33,500\,(3.6686) = \$122,897.$$

(**d**) Part (a) assumes end of year payments.  Parts (b) and (c)
assume earlier payments, hence their PW of Cost is greater.

# 5-43

$$\text{Capitalized Cost}_A = 500{,}000 + \frac{35000}{0.12} + \frac{350{,}000 \overset{0.0570}{(A/F, 12\%, 10)}}{0.12}$$

$$= 500{,}000 + 291{,}670 + 166{,}250 = 957{,}920. \longleftarrow$$

$$\text{Capitalized Cost}_B = 700{,}000 + \frac{25000}{0.12} + \frac{450000 \overset{0.0268}{(A/F, 12\%, 15)}}{0.12}$$

$$= 700{,}000 + 208{,}330 + 100{,}500 = 1{,}008{,}830. \longleftarrow$$

Type A with its smaller capitalized cost is preferred.

# 5-44

The amount of money needed now to begin the perpetual payments

$$P' = \frac{A}{i} = \frac{10{,}000}{0.08} = \$125{,}000$$

The amount of money that would need to have been deposited 50 years ago at 8% interest is

$$P = 125{,}000 \,(P/F, 8\%, 50) = 125000 \,(0.0213)$$

$$= \$2662.$$

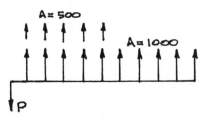

**5-45**

maximum investment = Present worth of benefits
$$= 1000 \,(P/A, 4\%, 10) + 500\,(P/A, 4\%, 5)$$
$$= 1000 \,(8.111) + 500\,(4.452) = \underline{\underline{10,337}}$$

**5-46**

Capitalized cost = \$2 million + $\dfrac{15,000}{0.05}$ = \$$\underline{\underline{2.3 \text{ million}}}$

**5-47**

Effective annual interest rate = $(1+0.025)^2 - 1$
$$= 0.050625 = 5.0625\%$$
Annual withdrawal $A = Pi = 25000\,(0.050625) = \underline{\underline{\$1265.60}}$

**5-48**

PW of Cost$_A$ = \$1300
PW of Cost$_B$ = $100\,(P/A, 6\%, 5) + 100\,(P/G, 6\%, 5)$
$$= 100\,(4.212 + 7.934) = \$1215$$
To minimize PW of Cost, Choose $\underline{\underline{B}}$

**5-49**

$P = 30\,(P/A, 4\%, 40) + 1000\,(P/F, 4\%, 40)$
$$= 30\,(19.793) + 1000\,(0.2083) = \underline{\underline{\$802}}$$

# 5-50

The trust fund has three components:

1. $P = \$1$ million

2. For $n = \infty$    $P = \dfrac{A}{i} = \dfrac{150,000}{0.06} = 2,500,000$

3. $\$100,000$ every 4 years: First compute an equivalent A

100,000   100,000   100,000

Solving one portion of the perpetual series for A

100,000

$$A = 100,000 \,(A/F, 6\%, 4) \overset{0.2286}{=} \$22,860$$

$$P = \frac{A}{i} = \frac{22860}{0.06} = 381,000$$

Req'd money in trust fund
$$= \$1 \text{ million} + \$2.5 \text{ million} + 381,000 = \$3,881,000$$

# 5-51

Full Capacity Tunnel:
$$\text{Capitalized Cost} = 556,000 + \frac{40\,000 \,\overset{0.0724}{(A/F,7\%,10)}}{0.07} = \$597,400$$

First Half Capacity Tunnel:
$$\text{Capitalized Cost} = 402,000 + \frac{32,000 \,(0.0724)}{0.07} + \frac{2000}{0.07} = 463,700$$

Second Half Capacity Tunnel:
20 yrs hence the capitalized cost of the second half-capacity tunnel equals the present capitalized cost of first half

$$\text{Capitalized Cost}_{NOW} = 463,700 \,\overset{0.2584}{(P/F,7\%,20)} = 119,800$$

Capitalized cost for two half-capacity tunnels
$$= 463,700 + 119,800 = \underline{583,500}$$

**Build the full capacity tunnel**

# 5-52

maximum contractor would pay
$$= PW \text{ of benefits} = (5.80 - 4.30) \times 50,000 \, (P/A, 10\%, 5)$$
$$+ 40,000 \, (P/F, 10\%, 5)$$
$$= 1.50 \times 50,000 \, (3.791) + 40,000 \, (0.6209)$$
$$= \underline{309,200}$$

# 5-53

(a)

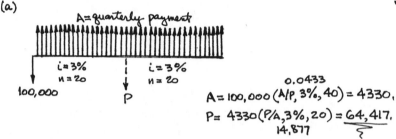

$i = 3\%$
$n = 20$

$i = 3\%$
$n = 20$

100,000

P

$$A = 100,000 \, (A/P, 3\%, 40) = 4330,$$
$$\overset{0.0433}{\phantom{A}}$$
$$P = 4330 \, (P/A, 3\%, 20) = \underline{64,417,}$$
$$\overset{}{14.877}$$

(b) Service charge = 0.05P
Amount of new loan = 1.05 (64,417) = 67,638
Quarterly payment on new loan = 67,638 (A/P, 2%, 80) = $1704
$$\overset{0.0252}{\phantom{A}}$$
Difference in quarterly payments = 4330 - 1704 = $\underline{2626}$

**5-54** Using PW Method the study period is a common multiple of the lives of the alternatives. Thus we use 12 years and assume repeatability of the cash flows.

Alt. *A*

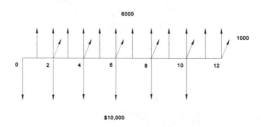

NPW = 6,000 (*P/A*, 10%, 12) + 1,000 (*P/F*, 10%, 12) - 10,000 - [10,000 - 1,000]{[*P/F*, 10%, 2]
        + [*P/F*, 10%, 4] + [*P/F*, 10%, 6] + [*P/F*, 10%, 8] + [*P/F*, 10%,10]}
    = 40,884 + 319 -10,000 - 26, 331
    = $4872

Alt. *B*

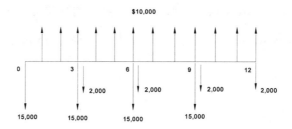

NPW = 10,000 (*P/A*, 10%, 12) - 2000 (*P/F*, 10%, 12) - 15,000 - (15,000 +2000) [(*P/F*, 10%,3)
        + (*P/F*, 10%, 6) + (*P/F*, 10%, 9)]
    =68,140 - 637 - 15,000 - 29,578
    = $22,925

**Alt. *C***

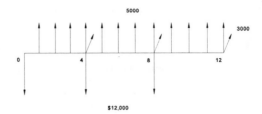

$12,000

NPW = 5000 (*P/A*, 10%, 12) + 3000 (*P/F*, 10%, 12)
        -12,000-[12,000 -3000][(*P/F*, 10%, 4) + (*P/F*, 10%, 8)]
    = 34,070 + 956 - 12,000 - 10,345 = $12,681
Decision:  Choose Alt.*B*

# 5-55

$i = 5\%$
$P = 50/0.05 + 500 \ (A/F, 5\%, 5)/0.05$
$\ \ = 50/0.05 + 500 \ (0.1810)/0.05 = \$2810$

# 5-56

***a.*** $P = 5000 + 200/0.08 + 300 \ (A/F, 8\%, 5)/0.08$
$\ \ \ = 5000 + 2500 + 300(0.1705)/0.08$
$\ \ \ = \$8139$

***b.*** $P = 5000 + 200(P/A, 8\%, 75) + 300(A/F, 8\%, 5)(P/A, 8\%, 75)$
$\ \ \ = 5000 + 200(12.461) + 300(0.1705)(12.461)$
$\ \ \ = \$8130$

# 5-57

The market value of the bond is the present worth of the future interest payments and the face value on the current 6% yield on bonds.
$A = (\$1000)(0.08\% \ / \ 2 \ \text{payments/year}) = \$40$
$P = \$40(P/A, 3\%, 40) + \$1000(P/F, 3\%, 40)$
$P = \$924.60 + \$306.60 = \$1231.20$

# 5-58

The objective is to determine if the Net Present Worth is non negative.
NPW(Benefits) = 50,000 (*P/A*,10%,10) + 10,000 (*P/F*,10%,10)
            = 50,000(6.145) +10,000(0.3855)
            = 311,105
PW(Costs)    = 200,000 + 9,000(*P/A*,10%,10)= 196,144

= 200,000 + 9,000(6.145)        = 255,305
NPW = 311,105 - 255,305 = $ 55,800
Since NPW is positive, the process should be automated.

# 5-59

*a.* PW of Costs = 700,000,000 + 10,000,000*(*P/A*,9%,80)
                = $811,000,000
PW of Receipts = (550,000 x 90)(*P/A*,9%,10) + (50,000 x 90)(*P/G*,9%,10)
                + (1,000,000 x 90)(*P/A*,9%,70)(*P/F*,9%,10)

                = 318,000,000 + 110,000,000 + 421,000,000
NPW = $38,000,000
The project meets the 9% minimum rate of return as NPW is positive.
*b.* Other considerations:
                Engineering feasibility
                Ability to finance the project
                Effect on trade with Brazil
                Military/national security considerations.

# 5-60

Revenues are common; the objective is to minimize cost.
Part *a.*
                Present Worth of Cost for Option 1:
                PW(Cost) = $200,000+$15,000(*P/A*,10%,30)= $341,400
                Present Worth of Cost for Option 2:
                PW(Cost) = $150,000+$150,000(*P/F*,10%,10)
                        +$10,000(*P/A*,10%,30) +
                        $10,000(*P/A*,10%,20)(*P/F*,10%,10)
                = $150,000+$150,000(0.3855) +$10,000(9.427) +
                        $10,000(8.514)(0.3855)
                =$334,900

                Conclusion:      Select option 2 because it has a smaller Present Worth of Cost.
Part *b.*
                The cost for option 1 will not change.  The cost for option 2 will now be higher.
                PW(Cost) =  $150,000+$150,000(*P/F*,10%,5)+10,000(*P/A*,10%,30)
                        +  $10,000(*P/A*,10%,25)(*P/F*,10%,5)
                = $394,300
Therefore, the answer will change to option 1.

# 5-61

Given:                      $A = 100,000$
        $i = 10\%$
        $n = \infty$
        $P = ?$
        $P = A/i = 100,000 / 0.10 = \$1,000,000$

# 5-62

PW of Cost$_{whelled}$   = 50,000 - 2000($P/F$,8%,5)= 48,640.
PW of Cost$_{track}$ =  80,000 - 10,000($P/F$,8%,5) = 73,190.
The wheel mounted backhoe, with its smaller PW of Cost, is preferred.

# 5-63

Given: $A$ = $250
   $i = \dfrac{18}{12}$ = 1.5% per month

   $n$ = 36 months
Find:    $P$
   $P = 250\ (P/A,1.5\%,36) = 250\ (27.661) = \$6,915$

# 5-64

Given:    $P$ = $12,000
   $i = \dfrac{12}{12}$ = 1.0% per month

   $n$ = 60 months
Find:    $A$
   $A = 12,000\ (A/P,1\%,60) = 12,000\ (0.0222) = \$266$
   $\underline{\$266 > 250\ \text{therefore: she cannot afford the car.}}$

# 5-65

Find: $i$
   $(A/P, i, 60) = \dfrac{A}{P} = \dfrac{250}{12,000} = 0.0208$

   From tables, i = 3/4% per month = 9% per year.

# 5-66

   NPW$_A$ =  -50,000 - 2000($P/A$,9%,10) + 9000($P/A$,9%,10) +
          10,000($P/F$,9%,10)
      =  -50,000 -2000(6.418) + 9000(6.418) + 10,000(0.4224)
      =  - $850
   NPW$_B$ = -80,000 - 1000($P/A$,9%,10) + 15,000($P/A$,9%,10) +
          30,000($P/F$,9%,10)
      = -80,000 - 1000(6.418) + 12000(6.418) + 30,000(0.4224)
      = + $3270
a.  <u>Buy Model B,</u> because it gives a positive NPW.
b.  <u>Select null option</u>.  The NPW of Model A is negative therefore it is better to do nothing or look for more alternatives.

# 5-67

$$i_{month} = \left(1 + \frac{0.045}{365}\right)^{30} - 1 = 0.003705$$

$$P = A\left[\frac{(1+i)^n - 1}{i(1+i)^n}\right] = 199\left[\frac{(1+0.003705)^{60} - 1}{0.003705(1+0.003705)^{60}}\right] = \$10,688$$

# 5-68

$P$ = the first cost = 980,000
$F$ = the salvage value = 20,000
$AB$ = the annual benefit = 200,000

Remember our convention of the costs being negative and the benefits being positive.  Also, remember the $P$ occurs at time = 0.

NPW  =  -First cost  + Annual benefit  $(P/A$, 12%, 13)
              + Salvage value  $(P/F$, 12%, 13)
   =  -980,000 + 200,000 (6.424)  + 20,000 (0.2292)
   =  -980.000 + 1,284,800  +  4584
   =  $309,384

Therefore, purchase the machine, as NPW is positive.

# 5-69

*Machine A:*

   NPW  =  - First cost + Annual benefit  $(P/A$, 12%, 5)
                  - Maintenance & operating costs  $(P/A$, 12%, 5)
                  + Salvage value  $(P/F$, 12%, 5)
   NPW  =  -250,000  +  89,000 ( 3.605) - 4000 ( 3.605)
                  + 15,000 ( 0.5674) = $64,936

*Machine B:*

   NPW  =  - First cost  +  Annual benefit $(P/A$, 12%, 5)
                  - Maintenance & operating costs  $(P/A$, 12%, 5)
                  + Salvage value  $(P/F$, 12%, 5)
   NPW  =  -205,000  +  86,000 (3.605) - 4300 ( 3.605)
                  + 15,000 ( 0.5674) = $98,040

Which machine do we choose?  We choose *Machine B*  because its NPW is greater.

# 5-70

*Company A*

$$NPW = -15,000 + (8000 - 1600) (P/A, 15\%, 4) + 3000 (P/F, 15\%, 4)$$
$$= -15,000 + 6400 (2.855) + 3000 (0.5718) = \$4987$$

*Company B*
$$NPW = -25,000 + (13,000 - 400) (P/A, 15\%, 4) + 6000 (P/F, 15\%, 4)$$
$$= -25,000 + 12,600 (2.855) + 6000 (0.5718) = \$14,404$$

*Company C*
$$NPW = -20,000 + (11,000 - 900) (P/A, 15\%, 4) + 4500 (P/F, 15\%, 4)$$
$$= -20,000 + 10,100 (2.855) + 4500 (0.5718) = \$11,409$$

To maximize NPW select *Company B* 's office equipment.

# 5-71

The interest the investor would receive is : $I = 5000 (0.045 / 2) = \$112.50$ every 6 months.

Probably the simplest approach is to resolve the $112.50 payments every 6 months into equivalent payments every 3 months:

$$A = 112.50 (A/F, 2\%, 2) = 112.50 (0.4951) = \$55.70$$

$$PW \text{ of Bond} = 55.70 (P/A, 2\%, 40) + 5000 (P/F, 2\%, 40)$$
$$= 55.70(27.355) + 5000 (0.4529) = \$3788$$

# 5-72

The least common multiple life is 12 years, so this will be used as the analysis period.

*Machine A*
$$NPW_4 = -52,000 + (38,000 - 15,000) (P/A, 12\%, 4)$$
$$+ 13,000 (P/F, 12\%, 4)$$
$$= -52,000 + 69,851 + 8262 = 26,113$$
$$NPW_{12} = NPW_4 [1 + (P/F, 12\%,4) + (P/F, 12\%,8)]$$
$$= 26,113 [1 + (1.12)^{-4} + (1.12)^{-8}] = 53,255$$

*Machine B*
NPW$_6$ = -63,000 + (31,000 - 9000)  (*P/A*, 12%, 6) + 19,000 (*P/F*, 12%,6)
       = -63,000 + 90,442 + 9625  =  37,067
NPW$_{12}$ = NPW$_6$  [1 + (*P/F*, 12%, 6) ]  =  37,067 [1+(1.12)$^{-6}$ ] = 55,846

*Machine C*
NPW$_{12}$ = - 67,000 + (37,000 - 12,000) (*P/A*, 12%, 12) + 22,000 (*P/F*, 12%, 12)
        = -67,000 + 154,850 + 5647 = 93,497

Thus, *Machine C* is the correct choice.

# 5-73

The cycle repeats with a cash flow as below

$P$ = {[400 - 100 (*A/G*,8%,4) + 900 (*A/F*,8%,4)]/(0.08) + 1,000} {*P/F*,8%,5}
   = {[400 - 100 (1.404) + 900 (0.2219)]/(0.08)+ 1,000}  {0.6806}
   = $ 4588

Alt.Solution: An alternate solution may be appropriate if one assumes that the $1000 cash flow is a
repeating annuity from time 13 to infinity (rather than indicating the repeating decreasing gradient series
cycles).
In this case P$_o$ is calculated as:     P$_o$ = [500 -100(A/G,8%,4)](P/A,8%,8)(P/F,8%,4)
                                       + 500(P/F,8%,5)+ 500(P/F,8%,9) +
                                            1000(P/A,8%,∞)(P/F,8%,12) = 7,073

**Solutions to Spreadsheet supplement problems are after Chapter 19.**

# Annual Cash Flow Analysis

$A = 100\left(A/P, 3\tfrac{1}{2}\%, 3\right)$
$= 100(0.3569) = \underline{35.69}$

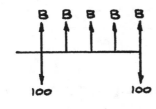

$C = 15 + 15\left(A/G, 10\%, 4\right)$
$= 15 + 15(1.381) = \underline{35.72}$

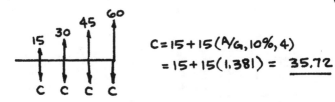

$B = \left[100 + 100(F/P, 15\%, 4)\right](A/F, 15\%, 5)$
$= \left[100 + 100(1.749)\right](0.1483)$
$= \underline{40.77}$

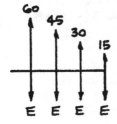

$E = 60 - 15\left(A/G, 12\%, 4\right)$
$= 60 - 15(1.359) = \underline{39.62}$

# 6-5

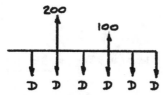

$D = [100 (F/P, 6\%, 2) + 200(F/P, 6\%, 4)](A/F, 6\%, 6)$
$= [100 (1.124) + 200(1.262)](0.1434) = \underline{52.31}$

# 6-6

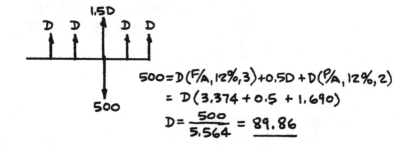

$500 = D(F/A, 12\%, 3) + 0.5D + D(P/A, 12\%, 2)$
$= D(3.374 + 0.5 + 1.690)$
$D = \dfrac{500}{5.564} = \underline{89.86}$

# 6-7

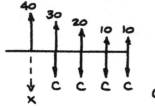

$x = 40 + 10(P/A, 10\%, 4) + 20(P/F, 10\%, 1)$
$\qquad + 10(P/F, 10\%, 2)$
$= 40 + 10(3.170) + 20(0.9091)$
$\qquad + 10(0.8264) = 98.15$
$C = 98.15(A/P, 10\%, 4)$
$= 98.15(0.3155) = \underline{30.97}$

# 6-8

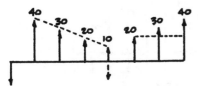

$$P = 40(P/A, 10\%, 4) - 10(P/G, 10\%, 4) + [20(P/A, 10\%, 3) + 10(P/G, 10\%, 3)](P/F, 10\%, 4)$$
$$= 40(3.170) - 10(4.378) + [20(2.487) + 10(2.329)](0.6830) = 132.90$$
$$A = 132.90(A/P, 10\%, 7) = 132.90(0.2054) = \underline{27.30}$$

# 6-9

MACHINE $X$

  EUAC = $5000(A/P, 8\%, 5)$ = $5000(0.2505)$ = \$1252
        Note that this is the same calculation made for
        Plan 3 of Table 4-1.

MACHINE $Y$

  EUAC = $(8000 - 2000)(A/P, 8\%, 12) + 2000(0.08) + 150$ = \$1106

                                              Select Machine $Y$

# 6-10

EUAC = $60,000(0.10) + 3000 + 1000(P/F, 10\%, 1)(A/P, 10\%, 4)$
     = $6000 + 3000 + 1000(0.9091)(0.3155)$ = \$9287

This is the relatively unusual situation where Cost = Salvage Value.
In this situation the annual capital recovery cost equals interest
on the investment.  If anyone doubts this, have them compute
$60,000(A/P, 10\%, 4) - 60,000(A/F, 10\%, 4)$.
This, of course, equals $Pi = 60,000(0.10)$ = \$6000.

# 6-11

Prospective cash flow:

| Year | Cash flow |
|------|-----------|
| 0 | -\$30,000 |
| 1-8 | +A |
| 8 | +35,000 |

EUAC = EUAB

  $30,000(A/P, 15\%, 8) = A + 35,000(A/F, 15\%, 8)$
     $30,000(0.2229) = A + 35,000(0.0729)$
            $6687 = A + 2551.50$

                                 A = \$4135.50

# 6-12

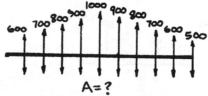

A=?

This problem is much harder than it looks!

$$EUAC = \{600(P/A,8\%,5) + 100(P/G,8\%,5) + [900(P/A,8\%,5)$$
$$-100(P/G,8\%,5)][(P/F,8\%,5)]\}\{(A/P,8\%,10)\}$$

$$= \{600(3.993) + 100(7.372) + [900(3.993) - 100(7.372)]$$
$$[0.6806]\}\{0.1490\}$$

$$= \$756.49$$

# 6-13

$$EUAC = 30,000(A/P,8\%,8) - 1000 - 40,000(A/F,8\%,8)$$
$$= 30,000(0.1740) - 1000 - 40,000(0.0940) = 460$$

The equipment has an annual cost that is $460 greater than the benefits.  The equipment purchase did not turn out to be desirable.

# 6-14

New Machine
$$EUAC = 3700(A/P,8\%,4) - 500 - 200 = 3700(0.3019) - 700$$
$$= 417.03$$

Existing Machine
$$EUAC = 1000(A/P,8\%,4) = 1000(0.3019) = 301.90$$

The new machine should not be purchased.

# 6-15

|  | Around the lake |  |  | Under the lake |  |  |
|---|---|---|---|---|---|---|
| First Cost | $75,000 |  |  | $125,000 |  |  |
| Maintenance | $3,000/yr |  |  | $2,000/yr |  |  |
| Annual Power Loss | $7,500/yr | } | $12,000 | $2,500/yr | } | $7,000 |
| Property Taxes | $1,500/yr |  | per year | $2,500/yr |  | per year |
| Salvage Value | $45,000 |  |  | $25,000 |  |  |
| Useful Life | 15 years |  |  | 15 years |  |  |

Around the lake

EUAC = 75,000(A/P, 7%, 15) + 12,000 − 45,000 (A/F, 7%, 15)

= 75,000(0.1098) + 12,000 − 45,000 (0.0398)

= 18,444.

Under the lake

EUAC = 125,000(A/P, 7%, 15) + 7000 − 25,000(A/F, 7%, 15)

= 125,000 (0.1098) + 7000 − 25,000(0.0398)

= 19,730.

Conclusion: Go around the lake.

**6-16**

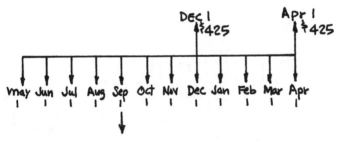

Equivalent total taxes if all were paid on April 1st:

= 425 + 425 (F/P, $\frac{3}{4}$%, 4) = 425 + 425(1.030) = 862.75

Equivalent uniform monthly payment:

= 862.75 (A/F, $\frac{3}{4}$%, 12) = 862.75(0.0800) = 69.02

∴ monthly deposit = $69.02

Amount to deposit September 1:

= Future worth of 5 monthly deposits (May-Sep)

= 69.02 (F/A, $\frac{3}{4}$%, 5) = 69.02 (5.075) = $350.28

Notes:  1.  The fact that the tax payments are for the fiscal
            year, July 1 through June 30, does not affect the
            computations.
         2.  Quarterly interest payments to the savings account
            could have an impact on the solution, but they do
            not in this problem.
         3.  The solution may be verified by computing the amount
            in the savings account on Dec. 1 just before making
            the payment (about $560.03) and the amount on April
            1 after making that payment ($0).

## 6-17

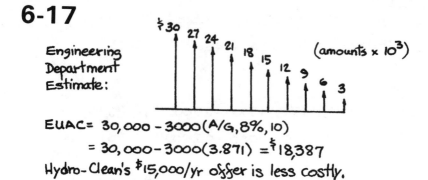

Engineering
Department
Estimate:

$(amounts \times 10^3)$

EUAC = 30,000 − 3000(A/G, 8%, 10)

= 30,000 − 3000(3.871) = $18,387

Hydro-Clean's $15,000/yr offer is less costly.

## 6-18

(a)

A=?

$n = 24 \quad i = 1\%$

9000

A = 9000(A/P, 1%, 24)
= 9000(0.0471)
= 423.90/month

(b)

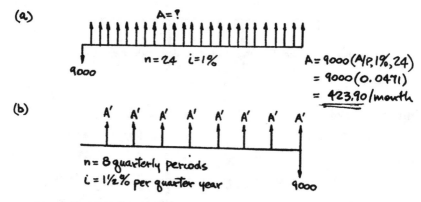

A'  A'  A'  A'  A'  A'  A'  A'

$n = 8$ quarterly periods
$i = 1\frac{1}{2}\%$ per quarter year

9000

Note that interest compounded quarterly

A' = 9000 (A/F, 1½%, 8) = 9000(0.1186) = 1067.40

monthly deposit = ⅓ of A' = 1067.40/3 = 355.80/month

(c)

In Part (a) Bill Anderson's monthly payment includes an interest payment on the loan. The sum of his 24 monthly payments will exceed $9000.

In Part (b) Doug James' savings account monthly deposit earns interest for him that helps to accumulate the $9000. The sum of Doug's 24 monthly deposits will be less than $9000.

# 6-19

Compute equivalent uniform monthly cost for each alternative.

(a) Purchase for cash

Equivalent uniform monthly cost $= (13,000-4000)(A/P, 1\%, 36) + 4000(0.01)$

$$= \$338.80$$

(b) Lease at a monthly cost $= 350.00$

(c) Lease with repurchase option $= 360.00 - 500(A/F, 1\%, 36)$

$$= 348.40$$

Alternative (a) has the least equivalent monthly cost, but non-monetary considerations might affect the decision.

# 6-20

Choose alternative with minimum EUAC.

(a)  12 month tire.   EUAC $= 39.95(A/P, 10\%, 1) = 43.95$
(b)  24 month tire.   EUAC $= 59.95(A/P, 10\%, 2) = 34.54$
(c)  36 month tire.   EUAC $= 69.95(A/P, 10\%, 3) = 28.13 \leftarrow$
(d)  48 month tire.   EUAC $= 90.00(A/P, 10\%, 4) = 28.40$

Buy 36-month tire

# 6-21

Annual cost of diesel fuel $= \dfrac{50\,000\,km}{35\,km/l} \times 0.48/l = \$685.71$

Annual cost of gasoline $= \dfrac{50,000\,km}{28\,km/l} \times 0.51/l = 910.71$

$\text{EUAC}_{diesel} = (13,000-2000)(A/P, 6\%, 4) + 2000(0.06)$
$\qquad + 685.71\ \text{fuel} + 300\ \text{repairs} + 500\ \text{insurance}$
$\qquad = 11,000(0.2886) + 120 + 1485.71 = 4780.31$

$\text{EUAC}_{gasoline} = (12000-3000)(A/P, 6\%, 3) + 3000(0.06)$
$\qquad + 910.71\ \text{fuel} + 200\ \text{repairs} + 500\ \text{insurance}$
$\qquad = 9000(0.3741) + 180 + 1610.71 = 5157.61$

The diesel taxi is more economical

# 6-22

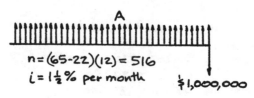

$$n = (65-22)(12) = 516$$
$$i = 1\tfrac{1}{2}\% \text{ per month} \qquad \$1,000,000$$

The 1-1/2% interest table does not contain n = 516.  The problem must be segmented to use the 1-1/2% table.

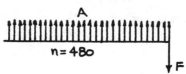

$$n = 480$$
F

Compute the future value F of a series of A's for 480 interest periods.

$$F = A\left(F/A, 1\tfrac{1}{2}\%, 480\right) = A(84,579) = 84,579\,A$$

Substitute 84,579A for the first 480 interest periods and solve for A.

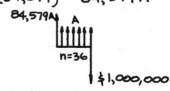

84,579A
A
n=36
\$1,000,000

$$84,579A\left(F/P, 1\tfrac{1}{2}\%, 36\right) + A\left(F/A, 1\tfrac{1}{2}\%, 36\right) = 1,000,000$$
$$84,579A(1.709) + A(47,276) = 1,000,000 \qquad A \doteq 6.92 \;\; \text{monthly investment}$$

# 6-23

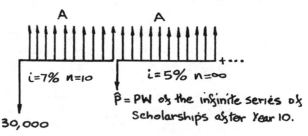

$$i = 7\% \quad n = 10 \qquad i = 5\% \quad n = \infty$$

30,000

$$\hat{P} = \text{PW of the infinite series of Scholarships after Year 10.}$$

$$\hat{P} = \frac{A}{i} = \frac{A}{0.05}$$

$$30,000 = \text{PW of all future scholarships} = A(P/A, 7\%, 10) + \hat{P}\,(P/F, 7\%, 10)$$
$$= A(7.024) + \frac{A}{0.05}(0.5083)$$
$$A = \frac{30,000}{17.190} = 1745.20$$

**6-24**

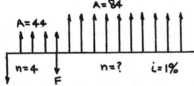

Compute the equivalent future sum for the $2600 and the four $44 payments at F.

$$F = 2600 (F/P, 1\%, 4) - 44 (F/A, 1\%, 4) = 2600(1.041) - 44(4.060)$$
$$= 2527.96$$

This is the amount of money still owed at the end of 4 months. Now solve for the unknown n.

$$2527.96 = 84 (P/A, 1\%, n) \qquad (P/A, 1\%, n) = \frac{2527.96}{84} = 30.09$$

From the 1% interest table n almost exactly 36.
Thus 36-$84.00 payments will be required.

**6-25**

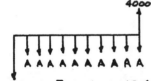

20,000    5 years    n = 10 semiannual periods
                     i = 4% per interest period

First, compute A
$$A = (20,000 - 4000)(A/P, 4\%, 10) + 4000 (0.04)$$
$$= 16,000 (0.1233) + 160 = 2132.80 \text{ per semiannual period}$$

Now, compute the equivalent uniform annual cost

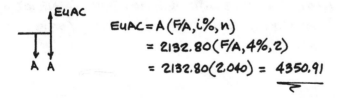

$$EUAC = A (F/A, i\%, n)$$
$$= 2132.80 (F/A, 4\%, 2)$$
$$= 2132.80 (2.040) = 4350.91$$

# 6-26

$A = 1,000,000 \, (A/F, \, 1\frac{1}{4}\%, \, 500)$

But this factor is not available in the compound interest tables. The problem may be solved in parts:

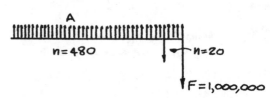

A

$n = 480$ ⟵ $n = 20$

$F = 1,000,000$

$F = A \, (F/A, \, 1\frac{1}{4}\%, \, 480)(F/P, \, 1\frac{1}{4}\%, \, 20) + A \, (F/A, \, 1\frac{1}{4}\%, \, 20)$

$= A \, [(31,017)\,(1.282) + 22.6]$

$= A \, (39,786)$

$$A = \frac{1,000,000}{39,786} = \$25.13$$

# 6-27

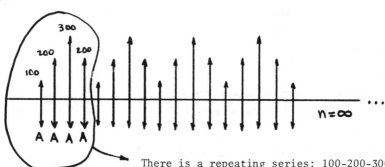

300
200    200
100
A  A  A  A

$n = \infty$

There is a repeating series: 100-200-300-200. Solving this series for A gives us the A for the infinite series.

$A = 100 + \left[ 100 \, (P/F, \, 10\%, \, 2) + 200 \, (P/F, 10\%, 3) + 100 \, (P/F, 10\%, 4) \right] (A/P, \, 10\%, 4)$

$= 100 + \left[ 100 \, (0.8264) + 200 \, (0.7513) + 100 \, (0.6830) \right] (0.3155)$

$= 100 + [301.20](0.3155)$

$= \underline{195.03}$

# 6-28

A:

$EUAC = A = [2000 + 500 (P/F, 12\%, 1)](A/P, 12\%, 5)$

$\qquad = [2000 + 500(0.8929)](0.2774)$

$\qquad = 678.65$

B:

$EUAC = A = 3000(F/P, 12\%, 1)(A/F, 12\%, 5)$

$\qquad = 3000(1.120)(0.1574) = 528.86$

To minimize $EUAC$  select  **B**

# 6-29

machine A
$EUAC = 1000 + \underline{10000(A/P, 10\%, 4) - 10000(A/F, 10\%, 4)}$

$\qquad\qquad\qquad\qquad\qquad = P_i$

$\qquad = 1000 + 1000 = 2000$

machine B
$EUAC = (20,000 - 10,000)(A/P, 10\%, 10) + 10,000(0.10)$

$\qquad = 1627 + 1000 = 2627$

$\qquad\qquad\qquad\qquad\qquad$ Choose  machine A.

# 6-30

(a) $EUAC = 6000(A/P, 8\%, 30) + 3000 \text{ labor} + 200 \text{ material}$

$\qquad - 500(2.30/\text{bale}) - 12 (\$200/\text{mo trucker}) = \$182.80$

$\qquad \therefore$ Bailer is not economical.

(b) The need to recycle materials is an important intangible
consideration.  While the project does not meet the 8% interest
rate criterion, it would be economically justified at a 4%
interest rate.  The bailer probably should be installed.

# 6-31

It is important to note that the customary "identical replacement"
assumption is not applicable here.

A: $EUAB - EUAC = 15 - 50(A/P, 15\%, 10) = 15 - 50(0.1993) = +5.04$

B: $EUAB - EUAC = 60(P/A, 15\%, 5)(A/P, 15\%, 10) - 180(A/P, 15\%, 10) = +4.21$

$\qquad\qquad\qquad\qquad\qquad\qquad$ Choose A

check solution by NPW

A: $NPW = 15(P/A, 15\%, 10) - 50 = +25.28$ ←

B: $NPW = 60(P/A, 15\%, 5) - 180 = +21.12$

# 6-32

Because we may assume identical replacement, we may compare 20 years of $B$ with an infinite life for $A$ by EUAB - EUAC.

alt. A

EUAB-EUAC for an infinite period

$= 16 - 100 (A/P, 10\%, \infty)$   when $n = \infty$  $A = Pi$

$= 16 - 100(0.10) = +6.00$

alt. B

EUAB-EUAC for a 20 year period

$= 24 - 150 (A/P, 10\%, 20) = 24 - 150(0.1175) = +6.38$

<u>choose B</u>

# 6-33

Seven year analysis period:

alt. A

EUAB-EUAC $= 55 - [100 + 100(P/F, 10\%, 3) + 100(P/F, 10\%, 6)](A/P, 10\%, 7)$

$= 55 - [100 + 100(0.7513) + 100(0.5645)](0.2054)$

$= +7.43$

alt. B

EUAB-EUAC $= 61 - [150 + 150(P/F, 10\%, 4)](A/P, 10\%, 7)$

$= 61 - [150 + 150(0.683)](0.2054) = +9.15$

<u>choose B</u>

*Note:* The analysis period is seven years, hence one cannot compare three years of $A$ vs. four years of $B$. If one does, the problem is constructed so he will get the wrong answer.

# 6-34

Original Loan

Annual payment $= 80,000(A/P, 10\%, 25) = 8816$

Balance due at end of 10 years:

method 1

Balance $= 8816(P/A, 10\%, 15) = 67,054$

method 2

Ten payments would repay $8816(P/A, 10\%, 10) = 54,170$, making the unpaid loan at Year 0 $= 80,000 - 54,170 = 25,830$.

At Year 10 this becomes $25,830(F/P, 10\%, 10) = 67,000$.

*Note:* The difference is due to four place accuracy in the compound interest tables. The exact answer is $67,035.80.

New Loan

(Using 67,000 as the existing loan)

amount = $67,000 + 2\%(67000) + 1000 = 69,340$

New payment = $69,340 (A/P, 9\%, 15) = 8605$
$$0.1241$$

New payment < old payment, therefore refinancing desirable.

## 6-35

alt. A
$$\text{EUAB-EUAC} = 10 - 100 (A/P, 8\%, \infty) \qquad \text{when } n = \infty \quad A = Pi$$
$$= 10 - 100(0.08) = +2.00$$

alt. B
$$\text{EUAB-EUAC} = 17.62 - 150 \overset{0.1019}{(A/P, 8\%, 20)} = +2.34$$

alt. C
$$\text{EUAB-EUAC} = 55.48 - 200 \overset{0.2505}{(A/P, 8\%, 5)} = +5.38$$

Select C

## 6-36

(a) $F = 1000 (F/A, 6\%, 10) = 1000 (13.181) = 13,181.$

(b) The equivalent present sum P that is equivalent to \$13,181 is
$$P = 13,181 (P/F, 6\%, 10) = 13,181 (0.5584) = 7360$$

Geometric Series Present Worth Factor

$$P = A_1 \left[ \frac{1-(1+g)^n (1+i)^{-n}}{i-g} \right] \qquad \text{where } i \neq g$$
$$\text{and } A_1 = \text{year 1 deposit}$$

$$7360 = A_1 \left[ \frac{1-(1.07)^{10}(1.06)^{-10}}{0.06-0.07} \right] = A_1 \left[ \frac{1-(1.96715)(0.55839)}{-0.01} \right]$$

$$= A_1 \left[ \frac{-0.09844}{-0.01} \right] = 9.8437 A_1$$

$$A_1 = \frac{7360}{9.8437} = {}^{\$}747.69$$

# 6-37

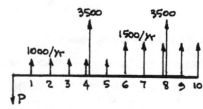

$$P = 1000(P/A, 6\%, 5) + 3500(P/F, 6\%, 4) + 1500(P/A, 6\%, 5)(P/F, 6\%, 5)$$
$$+ 3500(P/F, 6\%, 8)$$

$$P = 1000(4.212) + 3500(0.7921) + 1500(4.212)(0.7473) + 3500(0.6274)$$
$$= 4212 + 2772 + 4721 + 2196 = 13,901$$

Equivalent Uniform Annual Amount $= 13,901(A/P, 6\%, 10) = \$1889$

# 6-38

$$A = F\left[\frac{e^r - 1}{e^{rn} - 1}\right] = 5 \times 10^6\left[\frac{e^{0.15} - 1}{e^{0.15(40)} - 1}\right] = 5 \times 10^6\left[\frac{0.161834}{402.42879}\right]$$

$$A = \underline{2011.}$$

# 6-39

with neither input nor output fixed, maximize $(EUAB - EUAC)$

Continuous compounding capital recovery:

$$A = P\left[\frac{e^{rn}(e^r - 1)}{e^{rn} - 1}\right] \quad \begin{array}{l}\text{For} \\ r = 0.15 \\ n = 5\end{array} \quad \left[\frac{e^{0.15(5)}(e^{0.15} - 1)}{e^{0.15(5)} - 1}\right] = 0.30672$$

alt

A: $EUAB - EUAC = 845 - 3000(0.30672) = -75.16$

B: $EUAB - EUAC = 1400 - 5000(0.30672) = -133.60$

To maximize $(EUAB - EUAC)$ choose alternative with _smaller_ _negative_ _value_.

Choose A.

# 6-40

Provide autos: $P = 18000$  $F = 7000$  $A = 600/yr + 0.12/mile$  $n = 4$ yrs
or pay salesmen: $0.30X$  where $X =$ miles driven

$$0.30X = (18000 - 7000)(A/P, 10\%, 4) + 7000(0.10) + 600 + 0.12X$$
$$0.18X = (11000)(0.3155) + 700 + 600 = 4770$$

$$\text{miles driven } (X) = \frac{4770}{0.18} = \underline{26,500}$$

# 6-41

$EUAC_{gasoline} = (P-S)(A/P, i, n) + Si + \text{Annual Costs}$

$\qquad = (2400-300)(A/P, 10\%, 5) + 300(0.10) + 1200 + 300$

$\qquad = 2100(0.2638) + 30 + 1500$

$\qquad = \$2084$

$EUAC_{electric} = (6000-600)(A/P, 10\%, 10)^{0.1627} + 600(0.10) + 750 + 50$

$\qquad = \$1739$

<u>Select the electric motor</u>

# 6-42

EUAC Comparison

<u>Gravity Plan</u>

Initial investment \$2.8 million $(A/P, 10\%, 40)^{0.1023} = $ 286,400

Annual operations and maintenance $\qquad\qquad\qquad$ 10,000

$\qquad\qquad\qquad$ Annual Cost $\quad$ \$296,400

<u>Pumping Plan</u>

Initial investment \$1.4 million $(A/P, 10\%, 40)^{0.1023} = $ 143,200

Additional investment in 10th year

$\quad$ 200,000 $(P/F, 10\%, 10)(A/P, 10\%, 40) = $ 7,890

$\qquad\qquad$ 0.3855 $\qquad$ 0.1023

Annual operations and maintenance $\qquad = $ 25,000

Power Cost

$\quad$ \$50,000/year for 40 years $\qquad\qquad = $ 50,000

$\qquad$ additional \$50,000/yr for last 30 years

$\qquad$ 50,000 $(F/A, 10\%, 30)(A/F, 10\%, 40) = $ 18,590

$\qquad\qquad$ 164.494 $\qquad$ 0.00226

$\qquad\qquad\qquad$ Annual Cost $\quad$ \$244,680

<u>Select the pumping plan</u>

# 6-43

Use 20 year analysis period.

Net Present Worth Approach

$NPW_{Mas}$ = -250-(250+10)[$(P/F,6\%,4)$ + $(P/F,6\%,8)$ +$(P/F,6\%,12)$ + $(P/F,6\%,16)$]
       +10($P/F,6\%,20$) - 20($P/A,6\%,20$)
   = -250 -240(0.7921 +0.6274 +0.4970 +0.3936)
       +10(0.3118) -20(11.470)
   = -$1031

$NPW_{BRK}$ = -1000 -10($P/A,6\%,20$) + 100($P/F,6\%,20$)
       = -1000 -10(11.470) + 100(0.3118) = -$1083
Choose Masonite to save $52 on Present Worth of Cost.

Equivalent Uniform Annual Cost Approach

$EUAC_{Mas}$ = 20 +250($A/P,6\%,4$) -10($A/F,6\%,4$)
       = 20 +250(0.2886) - 10(0.2286) = $90

$EUAC_{BRK}$ = 10 +1000($A/P,6\%,20$) - 100($A/F,6\%,20$)
       = 10 +1000(0.872) - 100(0.0272) = $94
Choose Masonite to save $4 per year.

# 6-44

*a.* EUAC = 2,500 + 5000($A/F,8\%,4$)
   EUAC = 2,500 + 5000(0.2219) = $3609.50

*b.* $P = A/i$
   P = $3609.50/0.08
   P = $45,119

# 6-45

*a.* EUAC = 5,000 + 35,000(A/P, 6%, 20)
   EUAC = 5,000 + 35,000(0.0872) = $8052

*b.* Since the EUAC of the new pipeline is less than the $5000 annual cost of the existing pipeline, it should be constructed.

## 6-46

A diagram is essential to properly see the timing of the 11 deposits:

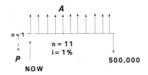

These are <u>beginning of period</u> deposits, so the compound interest factors must be adjusted for this situation.

$P_{now-1} = 500,000(P/F,1\%,12) = 500,000(0.8874) = \$443,700$

$A = P_{now-1} \times (A/P,1\%,11) = 443,700(0.0951) = \$42,196$

Quarterly beginning of period deposit = $42,196

## 6-47

Given:

$P = -\$150,000$

$A = -\$2,500$

$F_4 = -\$20,000$

$F_5 = -\$45,000$

$F_8 = -\$10,000$

$F_{10} = +\$30,000$

Find: EUAC

$EUAC = +150,000(A/P,5\%,10) + 2500 + 20,000(P/F,5\%,4)(A/P,5\%,10)$
$\qquad + 45,000(P/F,5\%,5)(A/P,5\%,10) + 10,000(P/F,5\%,8)(A/P,5\%,10)$
$\qquad - 30,000(A/F,5\%,10)$
$\qquad = 19,425 + 2500 + 2131 + 4566 + 876 - 2385 = \$27,113$

## 6-48

$$i_{month} = \left(1 + \frac{0.1075}{52}\right)^4 - 1 = 0.008295$$

$$P = 0.9\,(178,000) = 160,200$$

$$A = P\left[\frac{i\,(1+i)^n}{(1+i)^n - 1}\right] = 160,200\left[\frac{0.008295\,(1+0.008295)^{300}}{(1+0.008295)^{300} - 1}\right] = \$1450.55$$

# 6-49

*Machine A:*

EUAB - EUAC  = - First cost  $(A/P, 12\%, 7)$
          - Maintenance & operating costs
          + Annual benefit + Salvage value  $(A/F, 12\%, 7)$
          = - 15,000 ( 0.2191) - 1600 + 8000 + 3000 ( 0.0991)
          = $3411

*Machine B:*

EUAB - EUAC  = - First cost  $(A/P, 12\%, 10)$
          - Maintenance & operating costs
          + Annual benefit + Salvage value  $(A/F, 12\%, 10)$
          = - 25,000 ( 0.1770) - 400 + 13,000 + 6000 ( 0.0570)
          = $8517

Which labeling machine do we use?
To maximize (EUAB - EUAC) choose *Machine B.*

# 6-50

*Machine A*

EUAB - EUAC = -700,00 $(A/P, 15\%, 10)$ - 18,000 + 154,000
          -900 $(A/G, 15\%, 10)$ + 142,000  $(A/F, 15\%, 10)$
          = -139,510 - 18,000 + 154,000 - 3044 + 7,000  = 466

*Machine B*

EUAB - EUAC = -1,700,00 $(A/P, 15\%, 20)$ - 29,000 + 303,000
          -750 $(A/G, 15\%, 20)$ + 210,000  $(A/F, 15\%, 20)$
          = -271,660 - 29,000 + 303,000 - 4024 + 2050 = 366

Thus, the choice is *Machine A* , but note that there is very little difference between the alternatives.

Solutions to Spreadsheet supplement problems are after Chapter 19 .

# Rate Of Return Analysis

$3000 = 119.67 \, (P/A, i\%, 30)$     $(P/A, i\%, 30) = \dfrac{3000}{119.67} = 25.069$

| $i$ | $(P/A, i\%, 30)$ |
|------|------|
| 1% | 25.808 |
| 1.25% | 24.889 |

$$i = 1\% + \left(\frac{1}{4}\%\right)\left(\frac{25.808 - 25.069}{25.808 - 24.889}\right) = 1.201\%$$

(a) nominal interest rate $= 1.201 \times 12 = \underline{14.41\%}$

(b) effective interest rate $= (1 + 0.01201)^{12} - 1 = 0.154 = \underline{15.4\%}$

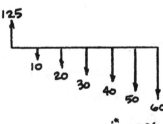

$125 = 10(P/A, i\%, 6) + 10(P/G, i\%, 6)$

at 12%
$\quad 10(4.111) + 10(8.930) = 130.4$

at 15%
$\quad 10(3.784) + 10(7.937) = 117.2$

$$i = 12\% + (3\%)\left(\frac{130.4 - 125}{130.4 - 117.2}\right) = \underline{13.23\%}$$

3000   A=325

n=36

12,375

$9375 = 325(P/A, i\%, 36)$

$\qquad (P/A, i\%, 36) = \dfrac{9375}{325} = 28.846$

From cmpd interest tables: $i = 1.25\%$

Nominal $i = 1.25 \times 12 = \underline{15\%}$

Effective $i = (1 + 0.0125)^{12} - 1 = \underline{16.08\%}$

# 7-4

The algebraic sum of the cash flow equals zero. Therefore, the rate of return is 0%.

# 7-5

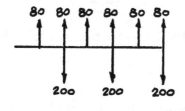

Easiest Solution

Solve one cycle of the repeating diagram.

$$120 = 80(F/P, i\%, 1)$$
$$120 = 80(1+i)^1$$
$$(1+i) = \frac{120}{80} = 1.50$$
$$i^* = 0.50 = \underline{50\%}$$

<u>alternate Solution</u> :   EUAB = EUAC

$$80 = [200(P/F, i\%, 2) + 200(P/F, i\%, 4) + 200(P/F, i\%, 6)](A/P, i\%, 6)$$

Try i = 50%

$$80 = [200(0.4444) + 200(0.1975) + 200(0.0878)](0.5481) = 79.99$$

$$\therefore i^* = \underline{50\%}$$

**7-6**

$$\text{for } n = \infty \quad \hat{P} = \frac{A}{i} = \frac{1000}{i}$$

At Yr0    PW of cost = PW of benefits
$$412 + 5000(P/F, i\%, 10) = \frac{1000}{i}(P/F, i\%, 10)$$
Try $i = 15\%$
$$412 + 5000(0.2472) = \frac{1000}{0.15}(0.2472) \quad 1648 = 1648 \quad \underline{ROR = 15\%}$$

**7-7**

$$1000 = 300(P/A, i\%, 4)(P/F, i\%, 1)$$
Try $i = 5\%$
$$1000 \stackrel{?}{=} 300(3.546)(0.9524)$$
$$\stackrel{?}{=} 1013.16$$
Try $i = 6\%$
$$1000 \stackrel{?}{=} 300(3.465)(0.9434)$$
$$\stackrel{?}{=} 980.66$$
Linear interpolation: $\overset{*}{i} = 5\% + 1\% \left( \frac{1013.16 - 1000}{1013.16 - 980.66} \right) = \underline{5.4\%}$

# 7-8

$1991 - 1626 = 365 \text{ years} = n$

$F = P(1+i)^n \qquad 12 \times 10^9 = 24(1+i)^{365}$

$$(1+i)^{365} = \frac{12 \times 10^9}{24} = 5.00 \times 10^8$$

This may be immediately solved on most hand calculators

$$\overset{*}{i} = \underline{5.64\%}$$

Solution based on compound interest tables:

$(F/P, i, 365) = 5.00 \times 10^8$

$\qquad\qquad = (F/P, i, 100)(F/P, i, 100)(F/P, i, 100)(F/P, i, 65)$

try $i = 6\%$

$\quad (F/P, 6\%, 365) = (339.3)^3(44.14) = 17.24 \times 10^8 \qquad i \text{ too high}$

try $i = 5\%$

$\quad (F/P, 5\%, 365) = (131.5)^3(23.84) = 0.542 \times 10^8 \qquad i \text{ too low}$

Interpolation

$$\overset{*}{i} = 5\% + (1\%)\frac{(5 - 0.54)(10^8)}{(17.24 - 0.54)(10^8)} = 5\% + \frac{4.46}{16.70} = \underline{5.27\%}$$

The linear interpolation is relatively inaccurate.

# 7-9

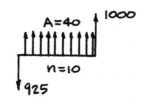

$$A = 40 \qquad \uparrow 1000$$

$$n = 10$$

$$\downarrow 925$$

PW of Cost = PW of Benefits

$\quad 925 = 40(P/A, i\%, 10) + 1000(P/F, i\%, 10)$

try $i = 5\%$

$\quad 925 = 40(7.722) + 1000(0.6139) = 922.78 \qquad i \text{ slightly high}$

try $i = 4\frac{1}{2}\%$

$\quad 925 = 40(7.913) + 1000(0.6439) = 960.42 \qquad i \text{ quite low}$

$$\overset{*}{i} \cong \underline{4.97\%}$$

**7-10**

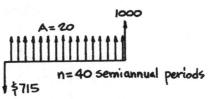

PW of Benefits – PW of Cost = 0

$20(P/A, i\%, 40) + 1000(P/F, i\%, 40) - 715 = 0$

try i=3%

$\qquad 20(23.115) + 1000(0.3066) - 715 = 53.90 \qquad i\ \text{too low}$

try i=3½%

$\qquad 20(21.355) + 1000(0.2526) - 715 = -35.30 \qquad i\ \text{too high}$

Linear interpolation:

$i^* = 3\% + \left(\tfrac{1}{2}\%\right) \dfrac{53.90}{53.90 - (-35.30)} = 3.30\% \qquad \text{Nominal } i^* = 6.60\%$

**7-11**

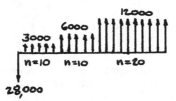

PW of Cost = PW of Benefits

$28,000 = 3000(P/A, i\%, 10) + 6000(P/A, i\%, 10)(P/F, i\%, 10)$
$\qquad\qquad + 12000(P/A, i\%, 20)(P/F, i\%, 20)$

Try i=12%

$28,000 \overset{?}{=} 3000(5.650) + 6000(5.650)(0.3220)$
$\qquad \overset{?}{=} + 12000(7.469)(0.1037)$
$\qquad \overset{.}{=} 37,160$

Try i=15%

$28000 \overset{?}{=} 3000(5.019) + 6000(5.019)(0.2472)$
$\qquad \overset{?}{=} + 12000(6.259)(0.0611)$
$\qquad \overset{.}{=} 27,090$

Linear interpolation

$i^* = 15\% - (3\%)\left(\dfrac{28,000 - 27,090}{37,160 - 27,090}\right) = 15\% - 3\%\left(\dfrac{910}{10,070}\right) = 14.73\%$

# 7-12

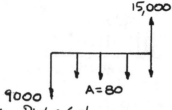

PW of Benefits - PW of Cost = 0

$15000\,(P/F, i, 4) - 9000 - 80\,(P/A, i, 4) = 0$

Try $i = 12\%$

$15000\,(0.6355) - 9000 - 80\,(3.037) = +289.54$

Try $i = 15\%$

$15000\,(0.5718) - 9000 - 80\,(2.855) = -651.40$

Linear Interpolation:

$$i^* = 12\% + (3\%)\,\frac{289.54}{289.54 - (-651.40)} = \underline{12.92\%}$$

# 7-13

The problem requires an estimate for  n  - the expected life of
the infant.   Seventy or seventy-five years might be the range of
reasonable estimates.   Here we will use 71 years.

The purchase of a $200 life subscription avoids the series of
beginning-of-year payments of $ 12.90   Based on 71 beginning-of-
year payments,

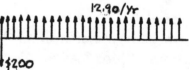

$200 - 12.90 = 12.90\,(P/A, i\%, 70)$

$(P/A, i\%, 70) = \dfrac{187.10}{12.90} = 14.50$

$6\% < i^* < 7\%$

On HP-12C  $i^* = 6.83\%$

# 7-14

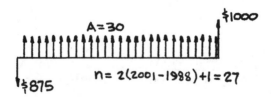

$n = 2(2001 - 1988) + 1 = 27$

PW of Benefits - PW of Cost = 0

$$30(P/A, i\%, 27) + 1000(P/F, i\%, 27) - 875 = 0$$

try

$i = 3\frac{1}{2}\%$   $30(17.285) + 1000(0.3950) - 875 = 38.55$

$i = 4\%$   $30(16.330) + 1000(0.3468) - 875 = -38.30$

∴ $i^* = 3\frac{3}{4}\%$   Nominal rate of return $= 2(3\frac{3}{4}\%) = 7.5\%$

**7-15**

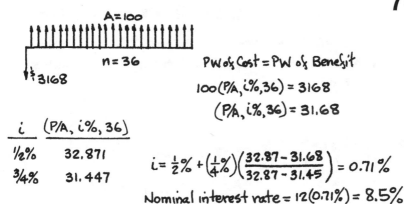

A = 110

n = 24

3500 - 1200

$$(3500 - 1200) = 110(P/A, i\%, 24)$$

$$(P/A, i\%, 24) = \frac{2300}{110} = 20.91$$

From tables:   $1\% < i < 1\frac{1}{4}\%$

On HP-80:  $i = 1.13\%$ per month

Effective interest rate $= (1 + 0.0113)^{12} - 1 = 0.144 = 14.4\%$

**7-16**

A = 100

n = 36

$3168

PW of Cost = PW of Benefit

$$100(P/A, i\%, 36) = 3168$$

$$(P/A, i\%, 36) = 31.68$$

| $i$ | $(P/A, i\%, 36)$ |
|------|------|
| $\frac{1}{2}\%$ | 32.871 |
| $\frac{3}{4}\%$ | 31.447 |

$$i = \frac{1}{2}\% + \left(\frac{1}{4}\%\right)\left(\frac{32.87 - 31.68}{32.87 - 31.45}\right) = 0.71\%$$

Nominal interest rate $= 12(0.71\%) = 8.5\%$

**7-17**

This is a thought-provoking problem for which there is no single answer.  Two possible solutions are provided below.

A.  Assuming the MS degree is obtained by attending graduate school at night while continuing with a full-time job:
      Cost: $1500 per year for 2 years
    Benefit:  $3000 per year for 10 years

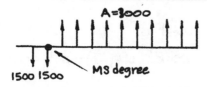

A=3000

1500 1500      MS degree

Computation as of award of MS degree:
$$1500(F/A, i\%, 2) = 3000(P/A, i\%, 10) \qquad i^* > 60\%$$

B.   Assuming the MS degree is obtained by one year of full-time study.

   Cost: <u>Difference</u> between working & going to school. Whether working or at school there are living expenses. The cost of the degree might be $24,000.

   Benefit: $3000 per year for 10 years

$$24,000 = 3000(P/A, i\%, 10) \qquad i^* = 4.3\%$$

# 7-18

(a)

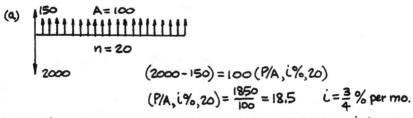

150    A=100

n = 20

2000

$$(2000 - 150) = 100(P/A, i\%, 20)$$
$$(P/A, i\%, 20) = \frac{1850}{100} = 18.5 \qquad i = \frac{3}{4}\% \text{ per mo.}$$

The alternatives are equivalent at a nominal 9% annual interest

(b) Take Alt. 1 - the $2000 - and invest the money at a higher interest rate.

# 7-19

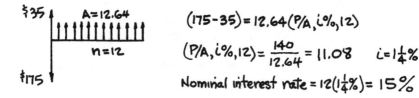

$35    A=12.64

n=12

$175

$$(175 - 35) = 12.64(P/A, i\%, 12)$$
$$(P/A, i\%, 12) = \frac{140}{12.64} = 11.08 \qquad i = 1\frac{1}{4}\%$$
$$\text{Nominal interest rate} = 12(1\frac{1}{4}\%) = 15\%$$

# 7-20

The rate of return exceeds 60% so the interest tables are not useful.

$$F = P(1+i)^n \qquad 25000 = 5000(1+i)^3$$

$$(1+i) = \left(\frac{25000}{5000}\right)^{1/3} = 1.71 \qquad \overset{*}{i} = 0.71$$

$$\text{So } \underline{\text{Rate of Return} = 71\%}$$

# 7-21

| Year | (A)<br>Gas Station | (B)<br>Ice Cream Stand | B-A |
|------|------|------|------|
| 0 | -80,000 | -120,000 | -40,000 |
| 1-20 | +8,000 | +11,000 | +3,000 |
| Computed<br>Rate of Return: | 7.75% | 6.63% | 4.22% |

The rate of return on the incremental investment (B-A) is less than the desired 6%. In this situation the lower cost alternative (A) Gas Station should be selected.

# 7-22

| YEAR | A | B | B-A |
|------|------|------|------|
| 0 | -2000 | -2800 | -800 |
| 1-3 | +800 | +1100 | +300 |
| computed<br>Rate of Return: | 9.7% | 8.7% | 6.1% |

The rate of return on the increment (B-A) exceeds the Minimum Attractive Rate of Return (MARR), therefore the higher cost alternative B should be selected.

# 7-23

This is an unusual problem with an extremely high rate of return. Available interest tables obviously are useless.

One may write:

PW of Cost = PW of Benefits

$$0.5 = 3.5(1+i)^{-1} + 0.9(1+i)^{-2} + 3.9(1+i)^{-3} + 8.6(1+i)^{-4} + \cdots$$

For high interest rates only the first few terms of the series are significant.

Try $i = 650\%$

$$\text{PW of Benefits} = \frac{3.5}{(1+6.50)} + \frac{0.9}{(1+6.5)^2} + \frac{3.9}{(1+6.5)^3} + \frac{8.6}{(1+6.5)^4} + \cdots$$

$$= 0.467 + 0.016 + 0.009 + 0.003 = 0.495$$

Try $i = 640\%$

$$\text{PW of Benefits} = \frac{3.5}{(1+6.40)} + \frac{0.9}{(1+6.4)^2} + \frac{3.9}{(1+6.4)^3} + \frac{8.6}{(1+6.4)^4} + \cdots$$

$$= 0.473 + 0.016 + 0.010 + 0.003 = 0.502$$

(HP-12C Solution: $i = 642.9\%$)

$$\therefore i^* \approx 642\%$$

## 7-24

| YEAR | A | B | A-B | NPW at 7% | NPW at 9% |
|------|------|------|------|------|------|
| 0 | -9200 | -5000 | -4200 | -4200 | -4200 |
| 1 | +1850 | +1750 | +100 | +93 | +92 |
| 2 | +1850 | +1750 | +100 | +87 | +84 |
| 3 | +1850 | +1750 | +100 | +82 | +77 |
| 4 | +1850 | +1750 / -5000 | +5100 | +3891 | +3613 |
| 5 | +1850 | +1750 | +100 | +71 | +65 |
| 6 | +1850 | +1750 | +100 | +67 | +60 |
| 7 | +1850 | +1750 | +100 | +62 | +55 |
| 8 | +1850 | +1750 | +100 | +58 | +50 |
|   |   |   |   | +211 | -104 |

$$\therefore \Delta ROR \approx 8.3\%$$

Choose alternative A

# 7-25

| YEAR | ZAPPO | KICKO | KICKO-ZAPPO |
|------|-------|-------|-------------|
| 0 | -56 | -90 | -34 |
| 1 | -56 | 0 | +56 |
| 2 | 0 | 0 | |

Compute the incremental rate of return on (Kicko-Zappo).
PW of Cost = PW of Benefit
$$34 = 56(P/F, i\%, 1)$$
$$(P/F, i\%, 1) = \frac{34}{56} = 0.6071$$

From interest tables, incremental rate of return > 60%
$(\Delta RoR = 64.7\%)$, hence the increment of investment is desirable.

Buy Kicko

# 7-26

For infinite series: $A = Pi$
EUAC = EUAB
$$3810(i) = 250 + 250(F/P, i\%, 1)(A/F, i\%, 2)^{*}$$
Try $i = 10\%$
$$3810(0.10) \stackrel{?}{=} 250 + 250(1.10)(0.4762)$$
$$381 = 381 \qquad \therefore \text{Interest rate} = 10\%$$

\* alternate equations:
$$3810(i) = 250 + 250(P/F, i\%, 1)(A/P, i\%, 2)$$
$$3810(i) = 500 - 250(A/G, i\%, 2)$$

# 7-27

$$400 = [200(P/A, i\%, 4) - 50(P/G, i\%, 4)](P/F, i\%, 1)$$
Try $i = 7\%$
$$400 \stackrel{?}{=} [200(3.387) - 50(4.795)](0.9346) = 409.03$$
Try $i = 8\%$
$$400 \stackrel{?}{=} [200(3.312) - 50(4.650)](0.9259) = 398.04$$
$$i^{*} = 7\% + 1\%\left(\frac{409.03 - 400}{409.03 - 398.04}\right) = 7.82\%$$

# 7-28

$$100 = 27(P/A, i\%, 10) \qquad (P/A, i\%, 10) = 3.704$$

| $i\%$ | $(P/A, i\%, 10)$ |
|-------|------------------|
| 20% | 4.192 |
| 25 | 3.571 |

Rate of Return

$$= 20\% + (5\%)\left(\frac{4.192 - 3.704}{4.192 - 3.571}\right) = \underline{\underline{23.9\%}}$$

(HP-12C solution: 23.81%)

# 7-29

$$42.55 = 5(P/A, i\%, 5) + 5(P/G, i\%, 5)$$

Try $i = 15\%$

$$42.55 \overset{?}{=} 5(3.352) + 5(5.775) = 45.64$$

Try $i = 20\%$

$$42.55 \overset{?}{=} 5(2.991) + 5(4.906) = 39.49$$

$$\text{Rate of return} = 15\% + (5\%)\left(\frac{45.64 - 42.55}{45.64 - 39.49}\right) = \underline{\underline{17.51\%}}$$

(Exact Answer: 17.38%)

# 7-30

| Year | Cash Flow |
|------|-----------|
| 0 | -500 |
| 1 | -100 |
| 2 | +300 |
| 3 | +300 |
| 4 | +400 |
| 5 | +500 |

$$500 + 100(P/F, i\%, 1) = 300(P/A, i\%, 2)(P/F, i\%, 1)$$
$$+ 400(P/F, i\%, 4) + 500(P/F, i\%, 5)$$

Try $i = 30\%$

$$500 + 100(0.7692) \overset{?}{=} 300(1.361)(0.7692) + 400(0.3501)$$
$$+ 500(0.2693)$$

$$576.92 \overset{?}{=} 588.75 \qquad \Delta = 11.83$$

Try $i = 35\%$

$$500 + 100(0.7407) \overset{?}{=} 300(1.289)(0.7407) + 400(0.3011)$$
$$+ 500(0.2230)$$

$$574.07 \overset{?}{=} 518.37 \qquad \Delta = 55.70$$

$$\text{Rate of Return} = 30\% + (5\%)\left(\frac{11.83}{55.70}\right) = \underline{\underline{31.06\%}}$$
$$(\text{Exact} = 30.81\%)$$

# 7-31

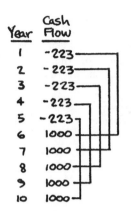

| Year | Cash Flow |
|------|-----------|
| 1 | -223 |
| 2 | -223 |
| 3 | -223 |
| 4 | -223 |
| 5 | -223 |
| 6 | 1000 |
| 7 | 1000 |
| 8 | 1000 |
| 9 | 1000 |
| 10 | 1000 |

The rate of return may be computed by any conventional means. On closer inspection one observes that each 223 increases to 1000 in five years.

$$223 = 1000(P/F, i\%, 5)$$

$$(P/F, i\%, 5) = \frac{223}{1000} = 0.2230$$

From interest tables, Rate of Return = 35%

# 7-32

| YEAR | Cash Flow |
|------|-----------|
| 0 | -640 |
| 1 | 0 |
| 2 | 100 |
| 3 | 200 |
| 4 | 300 |
| 5 | 300 |

$$640 = 100(P/G, i\%, 4) + 300(P/F, i\%, 5)$$

Try $i = 9\%$

$$640 \stackrel{?}{=} 100(4.511) + 300(0.6499) = 646.07$$

Try $i = 10\%$

$$640 \stackrel{?}{=} 100(4.378) + 300(0.6209) = 624.07$$

$$\text{Rate of Return} = 9\% + (1\%)\left(\frac{646.07 - 640}{646.07 - 624.07}\right) = 9.28\%$$

# 7-33

| YEAR | X | Y | X-Y |
|------|------|-------|------|
| 0 | -100 | -50 | -50 |
| 1 | +35 | +16.5 | +18.5 |
| 2 | +35 | +16.5 | +18.5 |
| 3 | +35 | +16.5 | +18.5 |
| 4 | +35 | +16.5 | +18.5 |
| Computed rate of return | 15.0% | 12.1% | 17.8% |

The ΔROR on X-Y is greater than 10%, therefore the increment is desirable.

SELECT X

# 7-34

The fixed output of +$17 may be obtained at a cost of either $50 or $53.   The additional $3 for Alternative B does not increase the benefits, therefore it is not a desirable increment of investment.

Select A

# 7-35

| YEAR | A | B | A-B |
|------|------|------|------|
| 0 | −100.00 | −50.00 | −50.00 |
| 1-10 | +19.93 | +11.93 | +8.00 |
| Computed Rate of Return | 15% | 20% | 9.61% = $\Delta ROR_{A-B}$ |

$$\Delta ROR_{A-B} > MARR \therefore \text{Select A}$$

# 7-36

| YEAR | A | B | A-B |
|------|------|------|------|
| 0 | −9200 | −5000 | −4200 |
| 1 | 1850 | 1750 | 100 |
| 2 | 1850 | 1750 | 100 |
| 3 | 1850 | 1750 | 100 |
| 4 | 1850 | 1750 / −5000 | 100 / 5000 |
| 5 | 1850 | 1750 | 100 |
| 6 | 1850 | 1750 | 100 |
| 7 | 1850 | 1750 | 100 |
| 8 | 1850 | 1750 | 100 |

Rates of Return

A. $9200 = 1850(P/A, i\%, 8)$
    Rate of Return = 11.7%

B. $5000 = 1750(P/A, i\%, 4)$
    Rate of Return = 15%

$\Delta(A-B)$

$4200 = 100(P/A, i\%, 8) + 5000(P/F, i\%, 4)$

$\Delta ROR_{A-B} = 8.3\%$

Select A

## 7-37

| Year | A | B | A-B |
|------|------|------|------|
| 0 | -150 | -100 | -50 |
| 1-10 | +25 | +22.25 | +2.75 |
| 11-15 | +25 | 0 | +25 |
| 15 | +20 | 0 | +20 |
| Computed Rate of Return | 14.8% | 18% | 11.6% |

Rate of Return: A-B

$$50 = 2.75\,(P/A, i\%, 10) + 25\,(P/A, i\%, 5)$$
$$\times\,(P/F, i\%, 10) + 20\,(P/F, i\%, 15)$$

Rate of Return = 11.6%

$$\underline{\text{Select A}}$$

## 7-38

The payment schedule represents a geometric gradient.

There are two possibilities

$$i \neq g \quad \text{and} \quad i = g$$

Try the easier $i = g$ computation first.

$$P = A_1 n (1+i)^{-1} \quad \text{where } i = g = 0.10$$

$$20,000 = 1100 \times 20 (1+0.10)^{-1} = 20,000$$

$\therefore$ Rate of return $\overset{*}{i} = g = \underline{10\%}$

$A_1 = 1100$   $g = 10\%$   $i = ?$

$n = 20$

$P = 20\,000$

## 7-39

| YEAR | X | Y | X-Y |
|------|------|------|------|
| 0 | -5000 | -5000 | 0 |
| 1 | -3000 | +2000 | -5000 |
| 2 | +4000 | +2000 | +2000 |
| 3 | +4000 | +2000 | +2000 |
| 4 | +4000 | +2000 | +2000 |
| Computed ROR: | 16.9% | 21.9% | 9.7% |

Since X-Y difference between alternatives is desirable, Select alt. $\underline{X}$

## 7-40

(a) Using Eqn (4-39): $F = Pe^{rn}$   $4000 = 2000\,e^{r(9)}$

$$2 = e^{r(9)} \quad \text{or} \quad 9r = \ln 2 = 0.693 \quad \therefore r = \underline{7.70\%}$$

(b) Eqn (4-34): $i_{eff} = e^r - 1 = e^{0.077} - 1 = 0.0800 = \underline{8.00\%}$

# 7-41

(a) when $n = \infty$   $i = \dfrac{A}{P} = \dfrac{3180}{100,000} = 3.18\%$

(b) $(A/P, i, 100) = \dfrac{3180}{100,000} = 0.318$   From Interest Tables $i \overset{*}{=} 3\%$

(c) $(A/P, i, 50) = \dfrac{3180}{100000} = 0.318$   From Interest Tables $i \overset{*}{=} 2\%$

(d) The saving in water truck expense is just a small part of the benefits of the pipeline. Convenience, improved quality of life, increased value of the dwellings, etc. all are benefits. Thus the pipeline appears justified.

# 7-42

Since the rate of return exceeds 60%, the tables are useless.

$$F = P(1+i)^n \qquad 4500 = 500(1+i)^4 \qquad (1+i)^4 = \frac{4500}{500} = 9$$

$$\text{or } (1+i) = 9^{0.25} = 1.732$$

$$i \overset{*}{=} 0.732 = \underline{73.2\%}$$

# 7-43

$$A = 50 \quad F = 2242$$

$$n = 4$$

$$P = 1845 \qquad \text{Set PW of Cost = PW of Benefits}$$

$$1845 = 50(P/A, i, 4) + 2242(P/F, i, 4)$$

$i = 7\%$   $1845 \overset{?}{=} 50(3.387) + 2242(0.7629) = 1879$   $i$ too low

$i = 8\%$   $1845 \overset{?}{=} 50(3.312) + 2242(0.7350) = 1813$   $i$ too high

$$\text{Rate of Return} = 7\% + \left(\frac{1879-1845}{1879-1813}\right) = 7.52\% \text{ for 6 months}$$

$$\text{Nominal annual rate of return} = 2 \times 7.52 = 15.0\%$$

$$\text{Equivalent annual rate of return} = (1+0.0752)^2 - 1 = 15.6\%$$

# 7-44

(a) $P = 1$   $F = 5$   $n = 5$

$$F = P(1+i)^n \quad 5 = 1(1+i)^5 \quad (1+i) = 5^{0.20} = 1.38 \quad i \overset{*}{=} \underline{38\%}$$

(b) For a 100% annual rate of return $F = 1(1+1.0)^5 = \$32$, not $\$5$!

Note that the prices Diagonal charges does not necessarily reflect what anyone will pay a collector for his/her stamps!

# 7-45

| Year | Cash flow |
|------|-----------|
| 0 | −9000 |
| 1-4 | +800 |
| 5-8 | +400 |
| 9 | +6000 |

PW of Cost = PW of Benefits

$$9000 = 400(P/A, i, 8) + 400(P/A, i, 4) + 6000(P/F, i, 9)$$

try $i=3\%$   $400(7.020) + 400(3.717) + 6000(0.7664) = 8893$

try $i=2\frac{1}{2}\%$   $400(7.170) + 400(3.762) + 6000(0.8007) = 9177$

Rate of Return

$$= 2\frac{1}{2}\% + \left(\frac{1}{2}\%\right)\left(\frac{9177-9000}{9177-8893}\right) = 2.81\%$$

# 7-46

| YEAR | Cash flow |
|------|-----------|
| 0 | −1000 |
| 3 | +1094.60 |
| 6 | +1094.60 |

$$1000 = 1094.60\left[(P/F, i, 3) + (P/F, i, 6)\right]$$

Try $i=20\%$

$$1000 \stackrel{?}{=} 1094.60(0.5787 + 0.3349) = 1000$$

$$\therefore \text{Rate of Return} = 20\%$$

# 7-47

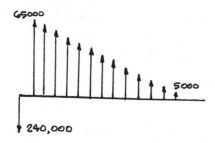

65000

5000

240,000

$$240,000 = 65000 \,(P/A, i, 13) - 5000 \,(P/G, i, 13)$$

Solve by trial & error

try $i = 15\%$

$$= 65000 \,(5.583) - 5000 \,(23.135) = 247,220.$$

try $i = 18\%$

$$= 65000 \,(4.910) - 5000 \,(18.877) = 224,765$$

$$\text{Rate of Return} = 15\% + (3\%) \left( \frac{247\,220 - 240,000}{247\,220 - 224,765} \right)$$

$$= 15 + 0.96 = \underline{15.96\%}$$

# 7-48

(a) Present Worth analysis — maximize NPW

$$NPW_A = 746 \,(P/A, 8\%, 5) - 2500 = +479$$
$$\phantom{NPW_A = 746 \,(}3.993$$

$$NPW_B = 1664 \,(P/A, 8\%, 5) - 6000 = +644$$

$$\underline{\text{Select } B}$$

(b) Annual Cash Flow Analysis — maximize (EUAB − EUAC)

alternative A

$$EUAB - EUAC = 746 - 2500 \,(A/P, 8\%, 5) = +120$$
$$\phantom{EUAB - EUAC = 746 - 2500 \,(}0.2505$$

alternative B

$$EUAB - EUAC = 1664 - 6000 \,(A/P, 8\%, 5) = +161$$

$$\underline{\text{Select } B}$$

(c) Rate of Return Analysis. Compute the rate of return on the B-A increment of investment and compare to 8% MARR.

| YEAR | A | B | B-A |
|------|------|------|------|
| 0 | -2500 | -6000 | -3500 |
| 1-5 | + 746 | +1664 | + 918 |

$3500 = 918(P/A, i, 5)$    Try $i = 8\%$

$$3500 \overset{?}{=} 918\,(3.993) = 3666$$

Try $i = 10\%$

$$= 918\,(3.791) = 3480$$

$$\therefore \Delta \text{ Rate of Return} \approx 9.8\%$$

Since $\Delta ROR > MARR$, B-A increment desirable.  **Select B**

# 7-49

$3000 = 30(P/A, i^* , 120)$
$(P/A, i, 120) = 3000/30 = 100$

| $i$ | $(P/A, i , 120)$ |
|------|------------------|
| 1/4 % | 103.563 |

| $i^*$ | 100 |
|-------|-----|
| ½ % | 90.074 |

$i^* = 0.0025 +0.0025\{(103.562\text{-}100) / (103.563\text{-}90.074)\}$
$= 0.00316$ per month

Nominal Annual Rate $= 12 (0.00316) = 0.03792 \Rightarrow$ **3.79%**

# 7-50

|    | Case  1 (incl. Deposit) |
|----|--------------------------|
| 0  | ($39,264.00) |
| 1  | $599.00 |
| 2  | $599.00 |
| 3  | $599.00 |
| 4  | $599.00 |
| 5  | $599.00 |
| 6  | $599.00 |
| 7  | $599.00 |
| 8  | $599.00 |
| 9  | $599.00 |
| 10 | $599.00 |
| 11 | $599.00 |
| 12 | $599.00 |
| ... | |
| 33 | $599.00 |
| 34 | $599.00 |
| 35 | $599.00 |
| 36 | $27,854.00 ($625.00) $27,229.00 |

| IRR | 0.86% |
|-----|-------|
| IRRnominal | 10.32% |
| IRR effective | 10.83% |

# 7-51

$P = \$30,000$; $n = 35$ years; MARR = 5%
Alternative 1: Withdraw $15,000 today and lose $15,000
Alternative 2: Wait, leave your fund in the system until retirement
Equivalency seeks to determine what future amount is equal to $15,000 now.
$$F = P(1 + i)^n$$
$$= \$30,000(1.05)^{35}$$

$= \$30,000(5.516015) = \$165,480.46$

$\therefore \$15,000 = \$165,480.46(1 + i)^{-35}$

$\$15,000(1 + i)^{35} = \$165,400.46$

$\therefore 1 + i = [(165480.46/15000)]^{1/35}$

$\quad i = 1.071 -1$ or $7.1002\% > 5\%$

$\therefore$ Unless \$15,000 can be invested with a return higher than 7.1%, it is better to wait for 35 years for the retirement fund. \$15,000 now is only equivalent to \$165,480.46  35 years from now if the interest rate now is 7.1% instead of the quoted 5%.

# 7-52

Using incremental analysis, compute the internal rate of return for the difference between the two alternatives.

| Year ($n$) | Alternative B - Alternative A |
|---|---|
| 0 | + $12000 |
| 1 | - 3000 |
| 2 | - 3000 |
| 3 | - 3000 |
| 4 | - 3000 |
| 5 | - 3000 |
| 6 | - 3000 |
| 7 | - 3000 |
| 8 | - 4200 |

Note: Internal Rate of Return (IROR) equals the interest rate that makes the PW of costs minus the PW of benefits equal to zero.

$12,000 - 3000(P/A, i^*, 7) - 4200(P/F, i^*, 8) = 0$

Try $i^* = 18\%$: $12,000 - 3000(3.812) - 4200(0.2660) = -553$

Try $i^* = 17\%$: $12,000 - 3000(3.922) - 4200(0.2848) = 962$

By str. line interp.: $i^* = 17\%+(1\%)(962)/(962 +553)= 17.6\%$

THE CONTRACTOR SHOULD CHOOSE ALT. *B* AND LEASE; 17.6% > 15% MARR.

# 7-53

Total Annual Revenues  $500*12$ months $* 4$ apt. =   \$24,000

Annual Revenues - Expenses = \$24,000 - \$8,000  =   \$16,000

To find Internal Rate of Return the Net Present Worth must be 0.

NPW = $\$16,000(P/A, i^*,5)+\$160,000(P/F,i^*,5)-\$140,000$

Try  $i=12\%$   NPW = \$8464

Try  $i= 15\%$  NPW = -\$6816

IROR = $12\% + (3\%)[8464/(8464+6816)] = 13.7\%$

Part *b.* At 13.7% the apartment building is more attractive than the other options.

# 7-54

$2000 = 91.05 \ (P/A,i^*,30)$
$(P/A,i^*,30) = \ 2000/91.05 = 21.966$
from tables:

| $i\%$ | $(P/A,i,30)$ |
|-------|--------------|
| 2     | 22.396       |
| 2 ½   | 20.930       |

$i_{mo} = 2\% + 1/2\%((22.396\text{-}21.966)/(22.396\text{-}20.930)) = 2.15\% \ / \ mo.$
Nominal ROR received by finance company $= 12(2.15\%) = 25.8\%$

# 7-55

$3000 = 118.90 \ (P/A,i^*,36)$
$\qquad\qquad (P/A,i^*,36) = 3000/112.06 = 26.771$
from tables:

| $i\%$ | $(P/A,i,36)$ |
|-------|--------------|
| 1 ½   | 27.661       |
| 1 3/4 | 26.543       |

$i_{month} = 1 \ ½ \ \% + (1/4\%)(27.661\text{-}26.771)/(27.661\text{-}26.543) = 1.699\%$
Nominal annual ROR $= 12(1.699) = 20.4\%$

# 7-56

$NPW = -300,000 + 20,000 \ (P/F, \ i^*, \ 10)$
$\qquad\qquad + (67,000 - 3000) \ (P/A, \ i^*, \ 10) \ - 600 \ (P/G, \ i^*, \ 10)$

Try $i = 10\%$
$NPW = -300,000 + 20,000 \ (0.3855) + 64,000 \ (6.145) - 600 \ (22.891)$
$\qquad\qquad = 87,255$
NPW greater than zero.  The interest rate used is too low.

Try $i = 18\%$
$NPW = -300,000 + 20,000 \ (0.1911) + 64,000 \ (4.494) - 600 \ (14.352)$
$\qquad\qquad = -17,173$
$\qquad\qquad\qquad$ NPW negative.  Reduce $i$.

Try $i = 15\%$
$NPW = -300,000 + 20,000 \ (0.2472) + 64,000 \ (5.019) - 600 \ (16.979) \ = 9130$

So the rate of return is between 15% and 18%.  By linear interpolation:

$$i^* \ = \ 15\% + \left(18\% - 15\%\right) \left( \frac{9130}{9130 + 17173} \right) = 16.0\%$$

# 7-57

|  | Alternative | | |
|---|---|---|---|
|  | B | A | A-B |
| First cost | $300,000 | $615,000 | $315,000 |
| Maintenance & operating costs | 25,000 | 10,000 | -15,000 |
| Annual benefit | 92,000 | 158,000 | 66,000 |
| Salvage value | -5,000 | 65,000 | 70,000 |

$\Delta ROR_{A-B}$

$NPW = 0$

$NPW = -315,000 + [66,000 - (-15,000)] (P/A, i^*, 10)$
$+ 70,000 (P/F, i^*, 10) = 0$

Try $i = 15\%$
$-315,000 + 81,000 (5.019) + 70,000 (0.2472) \stackrel{?}{=} 0$
$108,840 > 0$

$\therefore \Delta$ ROR > MARR (=15%).  The higher cost alternative $A$ is the more desirable alternative.

Solutions to Spreadsheet supplement problems are after Chapter 19 .

# Difficulties Solving
# For An Interest Rate

## 7A-1

| Year | Cash Flow |
|------|-----------|
| 0 | +4,000 |
| 1-9 | +4,000 |
| 10 | -71,000 |
| 11-19 | +4,000 |

There are 2 sign changes in the cash flow indicating there may be 2, 1, or zero positive interest rates.

At i = 0%  NPW = +5000
At i = ∞%  NPW = +4000

This suggests the NPW plot may look like one of the following:

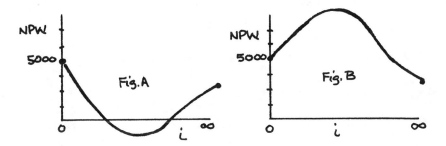

After making a number of calculations, one is forced to conclude that Figure B is the general form of the NPW plot, and there is no positive interest rate for the cash flow.

There is external investment until the end of the tenth year. If an external interest rate (we will call it e* in Chapter 18) is selected, we can proceed to solve for the interest rate i for the investment phase of the problem.

For external interest rate = 6%
Future worth of $4000 a year for 10 years (11 payments)
   = 4000(F/A,6%,11) = 4000(14.972) = $59,888

At Year 10 we have +59,888 - 75,000 = -15,112

The altered cash flow becomes:

| Year | Cash Flow |
|------|-----------|
| 0 | 0 |
| 1-9 | 0 |
| 10 | -15,112 |
| 11-19 | +4,000 |

At the beginning of Year 10:
   PW of Cost = PW of Benefits
      $15,112 = 4000(P/A,i\%,9)$   $(P/A,i\%,9) = \dfrac{15,112}{4,000} = 3.78$
   By linear interpolation from interest tables:
                                          i = 22.1%

The internal interest rate is sensitive to the selected external interest rate.

| For external interest rate | Computed internal interest rate |
|------|------|
| 0% | 3.1% |
| 6% | 22.1% |
| 8% | 45.9% |

# 7A-2

The problem statement may be translated into a cash flow table.

| Year | Cash Flow |
|------|-----------|
| 0 | +80,000 |
| 1 | -85,000 |
| 2 | -70,000 |
| 3 | 0 |
| 4 | +80,000 |

There are two sign changes in the cash flow indicating there may be as many as two positive rates of return.

To search for positive rates of return compute the NPW for the cash flow at several interest rates. This is done on the next page by using single payment present worth factors to compute the PW for each item in the cash flow. Then, their algebraic sum represents NPW at the stated interest rate.

| Year | Cash Flow | PW at 0% | PW at 8% | PW at 9% | PW at 25% | PW at 30% |
|------|-----------|----------|----------|----------|-----------|-----------|
| 0 | +80,000 | +80,000 | +80,000 | +80,000 | +80,000 | +80,000 |
| 1 | -85,000 | -85,000 | -78,700 | -77,980 | -68,000 | -65,380 |
| 2 | -70,000 | -70,000 | -60,010 | -58,920 | -44,800 | -41,420 |
| 3 | 0 | 0 | 0 | 0 | 0 | 0 |
| 4 | +80,000 | +80,000 | +58,800 | +56,670 | +32,770 | +28,010 |
| | | +5,000 | +90 | -230 | -30 | +1,210 |

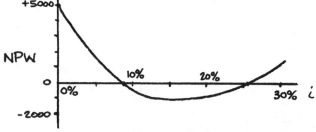

The plot of NPW vs. i shows two positive interest rates.

$$i \approx 8.2\% \quad \text{AND} \quad i \approx 25\%$$

Using an external interest rate of 6%, the Year 0 cash flow is invested and accumulates to +80,000(1.06) = $84,800 at the end of Year 1.  The revised cash flow becomes:

| Year | Cash Flow | |
|------|-----------|---|
| 0 | 0 | With only 1 sign change we know there no longer |
| 1 | -200 | is more than 1 positive interest rate. |
| 2 | -70,000 | |
| 3 | 0 | |
| 4 | +80,000 | |

PW of Benefit - PW of Cost = 0

Try   80,000(P/F,i%,4) - 200(P/F,i%,1) - 70,000(P/F,i%,2) = 0
i = 7%   80,000(0.7629) - 200(0.9346) - 70,000(0.8734) = -293
i = 6%   80,000(0.7921) - 200(0.9434) - 70,000(0.8900) = +879

By interpolation $i = 6\frac{3}{4}\%$

# 7A-3

(a)

| Quarter | Quarterly Cash Flow | PW at 0% | PW at 20% | PW at 40% | PW at 45% |
|---------|---------------------|----------|-----------|-----------|-----------|
| 0 | -75 | -75 | -75.0 | -75.0 | -75.0 |
| 1 | +75 | +75 | +62.5 | +53.6 | +51.7 |
| 2 | -50 | -50 | -34.7 | -25.5 | -23.8 |
| 3 | +50 | +50 | +28.9 | +18.2 | +16.4 |
| 4 | +125 | +125 | +60.3 | +32.5 | +28.3 |
| | | +125 | +42.0 | +3.8 | -2.4 |

By interpolation i ≅ 43% per quarter

Nominal rate of return = 4(43%) = 172%

(b)

| Quarter | Quarterly Cash Flow | | Transformed Cash Flow |
|---------|---------------------|---|----------------------|
| 0 | -$75 | Let X = amount required at end | -$75 |
| 1 | +75 | of 1 to produce 50 at end of 2 | +26.46 |
| 2 | -50 | X(1.03) ⤸   X = 50/1.03 = -48.54 | 0 |
| 3 | +50 | +50 | +50 |
| 4 | +125 | | +125 |

Solve the Transformed Cash Flow for the rate of return:

| Quarter | Transformed Cash Flow | PW at 35% | PW at 40% |
|---------|----------------------|-----------|-----------|
| 0 | -$75 | -$75.00 | -$75.00 |
| 1 | +26.46 | +19.60 | +18.90 |
| 2 | 0 | 0 | 0 |
| 3 | +50 | +20.32 | +18.22 |
| 4 | +125 | +37.64 | +32.54 |
| | | +2.56 | -5.34 |

$$\text{Rate of return} = 35\% + (5\%)\left(\frac{2.56}{2.56 - (-5.34)}\right) = 36.6\% \text{ per Quarter}$$

Nominal annual rate of return = 36.6% x 4 = <u>146%</u>

*NOTE:* Although there are three sign changes in the cash flow, the accumulated cash flow sign test, (described in Chapter 18) indicates there is only a single positive rate of return for the untransformed cash flow.  It is 43%.


(c)   In Part (a) the required external investment in Quarter 1, for return in Quarter 2, is assumed to be at the internal rate of return (which we found is 43% per Quarter).

In Part (b) the required external investment is at 3% per Quarter.

The "correct" answer is the one for the computation whose assumptions more closely fit the actual problem.  Even though there is only one rate of return, there still exists the required external investment in Quarter 1 for Quarter 2. On this basis the Part (b) solution appears to have more realistic assumptions than Part (a).

# 7A-4

This same cash flow is used in Problem 18-1.

| Year | Cash Flow |
|------|-----------|
| 0 | -500 |
| 1 | +2000 |
| 2 | -1200 |
| 3 | -300 |
| Sum = | 0 |

There are two sign changes in the cash flow indicating as many as two positive rates of return.

The required disbursement in Year 2 & 3 indicate that money must be accumulated in an external investment to provide the necessary Year 2 & 3 disbursements.

Before proceeding, we will check for multiple rates of return. This, of course, is not necessary here.

Since the algebraic sum of the cash flow = 0, we know that NPW at 0% = 0, and 0% is a rate of return for the cash flow.

Looking for the other (possible) rate of return:

| Year | Cash Flow | PW at 5% | PW at 50% | PW at 200% | PW at 219% | PW at 250% | PW at ∞ % |
|------|-----------|----------|-----------|------------|------------|------------|-----------|
| 0 | -500 | -500 | -500 | -500 | -500 | -500 | -500 |
| 1 | +2000 | +1905 | +1333 | +667 | +627 | +571 | 0 |
| 2 | -1200 | -1088 | -533 | -133 | -118 | -98 | 0 |
| 3 | -300 | -259 | -89 | -11 | -9 | -7 | 0 |
| | NPW = | +58 | +211 | +23 | 0 | -34 | -500 |

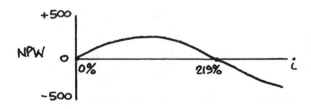

Solution using an external interest rate e* = 6%.

How much of the +2000 at Year 1 must be set aside in an external investment at 6% to provide for the Year 2 and Year 3 disbursements?
Amount to set aside = 1200(P/F,6%,1) + 300(P/F,6%,2)
                    = 1200(0.9434) + 300(0.8900) = $1399.08

The altered cash flow becomes:

| Year | Cash Flow |
|------|-----------|
| 0 | -500 |
| 1 | +2000 - 1399.08 = +600.92 |
| 2 | 0 |
| 3 | 0 |

Solve the altered cash flow for the unknown i:

$$500 = 600.92(P/F,i\%,1) \qquad (P/F,i\%,1) = \frac{500}{600.92} = 0.8321$$

From tables: $i = 20.2\%$

# 7A-5

This same cash flow is used in Problem 18-2.

| Year | Cash Flow | | Altered Cash Flow | PW at 18% | PW at 20% |
|------|-----------|--|------------------|-----------|-----------|
| 0 | -500 | | -500 | -500 | -500 |
| 1 | +200 | 200(1.06) ⟶ | 0 | 0 | 0 |
| 2 | -500 | +212 | -288 | -207 | -200 |
| 3 | +1200 | | +1200 | +730 | +694 |
| | | | +412 | +23 | -6 |

The rate of return is $18\% + (2\%)\left(\dfrac{23}{23 + 6}\right) = 19.6\%$

# 7A-6

| Year | Cash Flow | PW at 20% | PW at 35% | PW at 50% |
|------|-----------|-----------|-----------|-----------|
| 0 | -100 | -100 | -100 | -100 |
| 1 | +360 | +300 | +267 | +240 |
| 2 | -570 | -396 | -313 | -253 |
| 3 | +360 | +208 | +146 | +107 |
| | +50 | +12 | 0 | -6 |

There is a single positive rate of return at 35%.

| Year | Cash Flow | | Altered Cash Flow | PW at 12% | PW at 15% |
|------|-----------|--|------------------|-----------|-----------|
| 0 | -100 | | -100 | -100 | -100 |
| 1 | +360 | 360(1.06) ⟶ | 0 | 0 | 0 |
| 2 | -570 | +382 | -188 | -150 | -142 |
| 3 | +360 | | +360 | +256 | +237 |
| | | | +72 | +6 | -5 |

Rate of return $\approx 13.6\%$

For further computations, see the solution to Prob. 18-4.

# 7A-7

Some money flowing out of the cash flow in Year 2 will be
required for the Year 3 investment of 100.  At 10% external
interest, $90.91 at Year 2 becomes the required $100 at Year 3.

| YEAR | Cash Flow | | Transformed Cash Flow | NPW at 20% | NPW at 25% |
|------|-----------|--|-----------------------|------------|------------|
| 0 | −110 | | −110 | −110.00 | −110.00 |
| 1 | −500 | | −500 | −416.65 | −400.00 |
| 2 | +300 | −90.91(1.10) ⌐ | +209.09 | +145.19 | +133.82 |
| 3 | −100 | +100 | 0 | 0 | 0 |
| 4 | +400 | | +400 | +192.92 | +163.84 |
| 5 | +500 | | +500 | +200.95 | +163.85 |
| | | | | +12.41 | −48.49 |

The rate of return on the transformed cash flow is 21%.

(This is only slightly different from the 21.4% rate of return
on the original cash flow because the external investment is
small and of short duration.)

# 7A-8

| Year | Cash Flow | | Transformed Cash Flow | PW at 15% |
|------|-----------|--|-----------------------|-----------|
| 0 | −$50.0 | | −50.0 | −$50.0 |
| 1 | +20.0 | 20(1.10) ⌐ | 0 | 0 |
| 2 | −40.0 | +22 | −18.0 | −13.6 |
| 3 | +36.8 | | +36.8 | +24.2 |
| 4 | +36.8 | | +36.8 | +21.0 |
| 5 | +36.8 | | +36.8 | +18.3 |
| | | | | −0.1 |

From the computations we see that the rate of return on the
internal investment is 15%.

# 7A-9

| Year | Cash Flow | | | Transformed Cash Flow |
|------|-----------|--|--|-----------------------|
| 0 | -$15,000 | | | -$15,000 |
| 1 | +10,000 | $Y \times 1.12^2$ | $\therefore Y = 1020$ | +8,980 |
| 2 | +6,000 $\times 1.12$ | | | 0 |
| 3 | -8,000 | +6720 | +1280 | 0 |
| 4 | +4,000 | | | +4,000 |
| 5 | +4,000 | | | +4,000 |
| 6 | +4,000 | | | +4,000 |

| Year | Transformed Cash Flow | PW at 10% | PW at 12% |
|------|-----------------------|-----------|-----------|
| 0 | -$15,000 | -$15,000 | -$15,000 |
| 1 | +8,980 | +8,164 | +8,018 |
| 2 | 0 | 0 | 0 |
| 3 | 0 | 0 | 0 |
| 4 | +4,000 | +2,732 | +2,542 |
| 5 | +4,000 | +2,484 | +2,270 |
| 6 | +4,000 | +2,258 | +2,026 |
| | | +638 | -144 |

$$\text{Rate of return} = 10\% + 2\% \left( \frac{638}{638 + 144} \right) = \underline{11.6\%}$$

# 7A-10

The compound interest tables are for positive interest rates and are not useful here. (Tables could be produced, of course, for negative values.)

PW of Cost = PW of Benefits
$$50 = 20(1+i)^{-1} + 20(1+i)^{-2}$$

let $x = (1+i)^{-1}$

$$50 = 20x + 20x^2 \quad \text{or} \quad x^2 + x - 2.50 = 0$$

$$x = \frac{-1 \pm \sqrt{1^2 - 4(-2.50)}}{2} = \frac{-1 \pm \sqrt{11}}{2} = +1.159, \ -2.158$$

Solve for $i$

$$x = (1+i)^{-1} = +1.159 \quad 1+i = \frac{1}{+1.159} = 0.863 \quad i = -0.137 = \underline{-13.7\%}$$

$$x = (1+i)^{-1} = -2.158 \quad 1+i = \frac{1}{-2.158} = -0.463 \quad i = -1.463 = \underline{-146\%}$$

# 7A-11

| Year | Cash Flow | | | Transformed Cash Flow |
|------|-----------|---|---|-----------------------|
| 0 | 0 | | | 0 |
| 1 | 0 | | | 0 |
| 2 | -20 | | | -20 |
| 3 | 0 | | | 0 |
| 4 | -10 | | | -10 |
| 5 | +20 | X(1.15) ⟶ | X= 10/1.15 = 8.7 | +11.3 |
| 6 | -10 | +10 | | 0 |
| 7 | +100 | | | +100 |

| Year | Transformed Cash Flow | PW at 35% | PW at 40% |
|------|-----------------------|-----------|-----------|
| 0 | 0 | 0 | 0 |
| 1 | 0 | 0 | 0 |
| 2 | -20 | -11.0 | -10.2 |
| 3 | 0 | 0 | 0 |
| 4 | -10 | -3.0 | -2.6 |
| 5 | +11.3 | +2.5 | +2.1 |
| 6 | 0 | 0 | 0 |
| 7 | +100 | +12.2 | +9.5 |
| | | +0.7 | -1.2 |

$$\text{Rate of return} = 35\% + 5\% \left( \frac{0.7}{0.7 + 1.2} \right) = \underline{36.8\%}$$

# 7A-12

| Year | Cash Flow | | | Transformed Cash Flow | PW at 25% |
|------|-----------|---|---|-----------------------|-----------|
| 0 | -$800 | | | -$800 | -$800 |
| 1 | +500 | | | +500 | +400 |
| 2 | +500 | X(1.10) ⟶ | X = 272.73 | +227.27 | +145.5 |
| 3 | -300 | +300 | | 0 | 0 |
| 4 | +400 | | | +400 | +163.8 |
| 5 | +275 | | | +275 | +90.1 |
| | | | | | -0.6 |

From the Present Worth computation it is clear that the rate of return is <u>very close to 25%</u>  (HP-12C says 24.96%)

# 7A-13

(a)    The cash flow has two positive values of i:    10% and 30%.

(b)    Some of the money received at the end of Year 1 must be set
aside to pay the Year 2 disbursement.    X = amount to set aside.

$X(1+0.12) = 143$    $X = 127.68$

So cash flow becomes

| YEAR | Cash Flow |
|------|-----------|
| 0 | -100 |
| 1 | +240-127.68 = 112.32 |

Since 100 increases to 112.32 in 1 year, Rate of Return = 12.32%

(c)    Project should be undertaken as $i^* >$ MARR.

# 7A-14

Determine what portion of the cash flow must be invested
externally to allow for the final -1500.

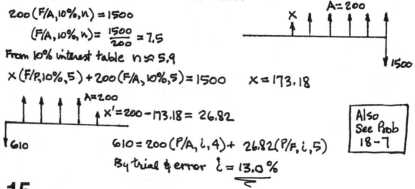

$200(F/A, 10\%, n) = 1500$

$(F/A, 10\%, n) = \dfrac{1500}{200} = 7.5$

From 10% interest table $n \approx 5.9$

$X(F/P, 10\%, 5) + 200(F/A, 10\%, 5) = 1500$    $X = 173.18$

$X' = 200 - 173.18 = 26.82$

Also See Prob 18-7

$610 = 200(P/A, i, 4) + 26.82(P/F, i, 5)$

By trial & error $i = 13.0\%$

# 7A-15

| Yr | Cash Flow | External Investment: | Altered Cash Flow |
|----|-----------|----------------------|-------------------|
| 0 | -500 | | -500 |
| 1 | +800 | $300(1+0.10)$ | +500 |
| 2 | +170 | $(170 + 330)(1+0.10)$ | 0 |
| 3 | -550 | +550 | 0 |
| $\Sigma =$ | -80 | | |

The algebraic sum of the cash flow is -80, suggesting there may
not be a positive rate of return.    300 from year 1 and 170 from year
2 are invested externally at 10% to provide the needed 550 in year 3.
By inspection we see the altered cash flow has a <u>0% rate of return</u>.

# 7A-16

(a) The cash flow for the problem was created as follows

$(x-1.0)(x-1.2)(x-1.4) = 0$

$(x^2 - 2.2x + 1.2)(x-1.4) = 0$

$x^3 - 2.2x^2 + 1.2x - 1.4x^2 + 3.08x = 0$

$x^3 - 3.6x^2 + 4.28x - 1.68 = 0$

multiply by -100 :   $-100x^3 + 360x^2 - 428x + 168 = 0$

Solution continued on next page

This may be rewritten as

$$-100(1+i)^3 + 360(1+i)^2 - 428(1+i) + 168 = 0$$

This represents the future worth of the cash flow

| Year | Cash Flow |
|------|-----------|
| 0 | -$100 |
| 1 | +360 |
| 2 | -428 |
| 3 | +168 |

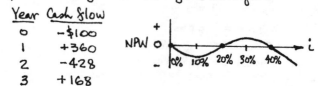

Thus the cash flow has rates of return of 0%, 20%, and 40%

(b) First, transform the cash flow to reduce the number of sign changes to one

| YEAR | Cash Flow | Transformed Cash Flow |
|------|-----------|-----------------------|
| 0 | -100 | -100 |
| 1 | +360 × (1+0.10) ↴ | 0 |
| 2 | -428 | +396   -32 |
| 3 | +168 | +168 |

Since the NPW only varies from about ±0.20 between 0% and 40%, solving the transformed cash flow isn't easy.   HP12C says ROR=9.92%

Try i=9.92% on transformed cash flow

NPW = 168(0.75296) -100 -32(0.82765)

= +126.49 -100 -26.49 = 0

So Rate of Return = 9.92%

# 7A-17

Transform the cash flow to reduce the number of sign changes to one.

| Year | Cash Flow | Transformed Cash Flow |
|------|-----------|-----------------------|
| 0 | -1200 | -1200 |
| 1-3 | +358 | +358 |
| 4 | +358 -0.17(1.1)² ↴ | +357.83 |
| 5 | +358 ×(1.1) ↴ | 0 |
| 6 | -394  +393.8 +0.2 | 0 |

approximately:

$$358 \, (P/A, i, 4) - 1200 = 0$$

Exactly:

$$358 \, (P/A, i, 3) + 357.83 \, (P/F, i, 4) - 1200 = 0$$

Either way: Rate of Return = 7.46%

# 7A-18

This cash flow was actually constructed by combining two cash flows that each have a 10% rate of return:

| Cash Flow Year | 0 | 1 | 2 | 3 | 4 | 5 | 6 | 7 | 8 |
|---|---|---|---|---|---|---|---|---|---|
| A | -3570 | 1000 | 1000 | 1000 | 0 | 500 | 500 | 500 | 500 |
| B |  |  |  |  | -3170 | 1000 | 1000 | 1000 | 1000 |
| combined: | -3570 | 1000 | 1000 | 1000 | -3170 | 1500 | 1500 | 1500 | 1500 |

Thus there are three sign changes, but only one rate of return. Not knowing this, one can only proceed as described in 7A.

| YEAR | Cash Flow | Transformed Cash Flow |
|---|---|---|
| 0 | -3570 | -3570 |
| 1 | 1000   Y(1.08)³ ⟶ Y=733.20 | 266.8 |
| 2 | 1000 × (1.08)² | 0 |
| 3 | 1000 × (1.08) | 0 |
| 4 | -3170 + 1080 + 1166.40 + 923.60 | 0 |
| 5-8 | 1500 | 1500 |

Solving transformed cash flow

$$-3570 + 266.8 \, (P/F, i, 1) + 1500 \, (P/A, i, 4)(P/F, i, 4) = 0$$

Try i = 9%

$$-3570 + 266.8 \, (0.9174) + 1500 \, (3.240)(0.7084) = +117.6$$

Try i = 10%

$$-3570 + 266.8 \, (0.9091) + 1500 \, (3.170)(0.6830) = -79.8$$

$$\text{Rate of Return} = 9\% + (1\%)\left(\frac{117.6}{117.6 + 79.8}\right) = 9.6\%$$

# 7A-19

Total Investment = $800 + 40(55.00)$ payments $\cong 3000$

Total Income $= \$2500$.

So - there is no positive rate of return.

Solving for negative rate of return

$-800 - 55(P/A, i, 40) + 2500(P/F, i, 40) = 0$          (1)

try $i = 0.75\%$ (per month)

$$(P/A, -0.75\%, 40) = \frac{0.9925^{40} - 1}{-0.0075(0.9925)^{40}} = 46.851$$

$$(P/F, -0.75\%, 40) = (0.9925)^{-40} = 1.351$$

using Eqn(1)

$-800 - 55(46.851) + 2500(1.351) = +0.7$

So Rate of Return $\cong -0.75\%/$ month or $\underline{-9\% \text{ per year}}$

# 7A-20

(a)

| YEAR | Cash flow |
|------|-----------|
| 0 | -850 |
| 1 | 600 |
| 2-9 | 200 |
| 10 | -1800 |
| | $\Sigma = -450$ |

So, two ROR for the cash flow are about 13% & 20%

NPW = 0

$-850 + 600(P/F, i, 1) + 200(P/A, i, 8)(P/F, i, 1)$
$-1800(P/F, i, 10) = 0$

NPW at $i = 20\%$

$-850 + 600(0.8333) + 200(3.837)(0.8333)$
$-1800(0.1615) = -1.2$

NPW at $i = 12\%$

$-850 + 600(0.8929) + 200(4.968)(0.8929)$
$-1800(0.3220) = -6.7$

(b) NPW at $i = 10\%$

$-850 + 600(0.9091) + 200(5.335)(0.9091)$
$-1800(0.3855) = \underline{-28.4}$

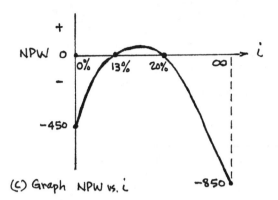

(c) Graph  NPW vs. $i$

(d) Rate of return on internal investment.
    Transform the cash flow.

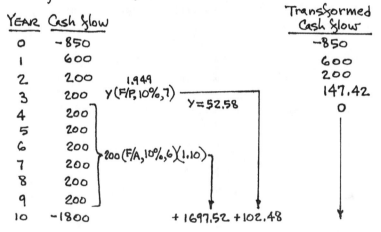

| YEAR | Cash flow | | Transformed Cash flow |
|---|---|---|---|
| 0 | -850 | | -850 |
| 1 | 600 | | 600 |
| 2 | 200 | | 200 |
| 3 | 200 | $Y(F/P,10\%,7)$ 1.949 | 147.42 |
| 4 | 200 | $Y=52.58$ | 0 |
| 5 | 200 | | |
| 6 | 200 | $200(F/A,10\%,6)(1.10)$ | |
| 7 | 200 | | |
| 8 | 200 | | |
| 9 | 200 | | |
| 10 | -1800 | +1697.52 +102.48 | |

Solve transformed cash flow

| YEAR | Transformed Cash flow | NPW at 7% | NPW at 8% |
|---|---|---|---|
| 0 | -850 | -850 | -850 |
| 1 | 600 | 560.8 | 555.5 |
| 2 | 200 | 174.7 | 171.5 |
| 3 | 147.42 | 120.3 | 117.0 |
| | | +5.8 | -6.0 |

∴ Rate of Return = 7.5%

# 7A-21

There are three sign changes. Therefore, there are at most three roots. Transforming the cash flows requires some expertise. How can we negate two of the sign changes?

Move the 7000 into period 3: $P = -7000 (1 + 0.12)^{-1} = -6250$

| | | | | | | |
|---|---|---|---|---|---|---|
| Original | -16,000 | -8000 | 11,000 | 13,000 | -7000 | 8950 |
| Alteration | | | | -6250 | +7000 | |
| Altered | -16,000 | -8000 | 11,000 | 6750 | 0 | 8950 |

With only one sign change in the cash flow there cannot be more than one positive rate of return. Compute the rate of return

$NPW = -16,000 - 8000 \ (P/F,i, \ 1) + 11,000 \ (P/F,i, \ 2) + 6750 \ (P/F,i, \ 3) + 8950 \ (P/F,i, \ 5) = 0$

Try $i = 3\frac{1}{2}\%$

$NPW = -16,000 - 8000 \ (0.9662) + 11,000 \ (0.9335) + 6750 \ (0.9019) + 8950 \ (0.8420)$

$\quad = -16,000 - 7730 + 10,268 + 6088 + 7536 = +162 \qquad i \ \text{too low}$

Try $i = 4\%$

$NPW = -16,000 - 8000 \ (0.9615) + 11,000 \ (0.9246) + 6750 \ (0.8890) + 8950 \ (0.8219)$

$\quad = -16,000 - 7692 + 10,171 + 6001 + 7356 \ = -164 \qquad i \ \text{too high}$

By inspection we see that the rate of return is almost exactly 3.75 %

# 7A-22

| Year | Cash Flow |
|---|---|
| 1 | -15,000 |
| 2 | 10,000 |
| 3 | -8,000 * move into year 2 |
| 4 | 11,000 |
| 5 | 13,000 |

| Year | Transformed Cash Flow |
|---|---|
| 1 | - 15,000 |
| 2 | 10,000  - 8000 $(P/F, 13\%, 1) =$ |
| 3 | 0 |
| 4 | 11,000 |
| 5 | 13,000 |

$$\text{NPW} = \frac{15,000}{\left(1+i^*\right)} + \frac{2920.35}{\left(1+i^*\right)^2} + 0 + \frac{11,000}{\left(1+i^*\right)^4} + \frac{13,000}{\left(1+i^*\right)^5}$$

| $i^*$ | NPW |
|------|---------|
| 0 | 11920.35 |
| 0.20 | 57.22 |
| 0.21 | -258.41 |

So  $20\% < i^* < 21\%$

# 7A-23

Move the year 4 expenditure into year 3.

Year 3 = 62,000 - 31,000 (*P/F*, 12%, 1) = 62,000 - 31,000 (0.8929)
         = 34,320

Using the altered cash flow:

NPW = 0
   -210,000 + 88,000 (*P/F*, *i**, 1) + 68,000 (*P/F*, *i**, 2) + 34,320 (*P/F*, *i**, 3)
      + 30,000 (*P/F*, *i**, 5) + 55,000 (*P/F*, *i**, 6) + 65,000 (*P/F*, *i**, 7) = 0

Try  *i* = 15 %
   -210,000 + 76,525 + 51,415 + 22,565 + 14,916 + 23,776 + 24,434
      = +3631

The interest rate is too low.

Try  *i* = 18 %
   -210,000 + 74,580 + 48,838 + 20,887 + 13,113 + 20,372 + 20,404
      = -11,806

So  *i* * is between 15% and 18%

$$i^* = 15\% + 3\%\left(\frac{3631}{11806 + 3631}\right) = 15.7\%$$

# 7A-24

| Year | Cash Flow | | |
|------|-----------|---|---|
| 0 | -$103,000 | | |
| 1 | 102,700 | - 87,000 (P/F, 18%, 1) = 28,968 | |
| 2 | 0 | | |
| 3 | 94,500 | - 8300 (P/F, 18%, 1) = 87,466 | |
| 4 | 0 | | |
| 5 | 38,500 | | |

NPW = -103,000 + 28,968 (P/F, $i$ *, 1) + 87,466 (P/F, $i$ *, 3)
　　　+ 38,500 (P/F, $i$ *, 5)

Try $i$ = 12 %
　-103,000 + 25,866 + 62,258 + 21,845 = + 6969

Try $i$ = 15 %
　-103,000 + 25,191 + 53,232 + 16,828 = - 7749

So

$$i* = 12\% + 3\% \left( \frac{6969}{6969 + 7749} \right) = 13.4\%$$

The project produced a rate of return less than the company's MARR; hence it has not been acceptable.

# Incremental Analysis

| Plant Location | P | A | (P/A,i%,8) = P/A | Computed i | |
|---|---|---|---|---|---|
| 1. Denver | 300 | 52 | 5.77 | 7.9% | Reject |
| 2. Dallas | 550 | 137 | 4.01 | 18.5% | |
| 3. San Antonio | 450 | 117 | 3.85 | 19.9% | |
| 4. Los Angeles | 750 | 167 | 4.49 | 15.0% | |
| 5. Cleveland | 150 | 18 | 8.33 | < 0% | Reject |
| 6. Atlanta | 200 | 49 | 4.08 | 18.0% | |
| 7. Chicago | 0 | 0 | 0 | 0% | Reject |

Rearrange remaining alternatives in order of increasing cost.
Incremental Analysis.

| | | P | A | Increment | $\Delta$P | $\Delta$A | $\Delta$i | |
|---|---|---|---|---|---|---|---|---|
| 6. | Atlanta | 200 | 49 | | | | | |
| | | | | 3-6 | 250 | 68 | 21.5% | Retain 3 |
| 3. | San Antonio | 450 | 117 | | | | | |
| | | | | 2-3 | 100 | 20 | 11.8% | Retain 2 |
| 2. | Dallas | 550 | 137 | | | | | |
| | | | | 4-2 | 200 | 30 | 4.2% | Retain 2 |
| 4. | Los Angeles | 750 | 167 | | | | | |

Decision: Select Dallas.

| Yr | A | B | B-A | C | C-A | D | D-C | PW(D-C) at 8% |
|---|---|---|---|---|---|---|---|---|
| 0 | -1300 | -1300 | 0 | -1300 | 0 | -1300 | 0 | 0 |
| 1 | +100 | +10 | -90 | +260 | +160 | +450 | +190 | +175.9 |
| 2 | +130 | +60 | -70 | +260 | +130 | +400 | +140 | +120.0 |
| 3 | +160 | +110 | -50 | +260 | +100 | +350 | +90 | +71.4 |
| 4 | +190 | +160 | -30 | +260 | +70 | +300 | +40 | +29.4 |
| 5 | +220 | +210 | -10 | +260 | +40 | +250 | -10 | -6.8 |
| 6 | +250 | +260 | +10 | +260 | +10 | +200 | -60 | -37.8 |
| 7 | +280 | +310 | +30 | +260 | -20 | +150 | -110 | -64.2 |
| 8 | +310 | +360 | +50 | +260 | -50 | +100 | -160 | -86.4 |
| 9 | +340 | +410 | +70 | +260 | -80 | +50 | -210 | -105.0 |
| 10 | +370 | +460 | +90 | +260 | -110 | 0 | -260 | -120.4 |
| | | | 0* | | +250** | | -350 | -23.9*** |

*By inspection, incremental rate of return = 0%.
  Reject B.
**No positive value of i in this borrowing increment. The C-A
  increment is highly desirable. Reject A.
***This borrowing increment has an i greater than 8%. This is not
  a desirable increment. Reject D.

Decision: Choose Alternative C

| Alt. | Cost | Annual Benefit | Useful Life | Increment | $\Delta$P | $\Delta$A | $\Delta$i | |
|---|---|---|---|---|---|---|---|---|
| C | $1300 | $260 | 10 yr | | | | | |
| | | | | E-C | $1700 | $228 | 5.7% | Retain C |
| E | 3000 | 488 | 10 yr | | | | | |
| | | | | F-C | $4550 | $740 | 10.0% | Retain F |
| F | 5850 | 1000 | 10 yr | | | | | |

Decision: Choose Alternative F

# 8-4

This problem is one of neither fixed input nor fixed output.
When the estimated resale value equals the present total investment
we have the special case where

$$A = Pi \quad \text{or} \quad i = \frac{A}{P}$$

| Alternative | P* | A* | i | ΔP | ΔA | Δi | |
|---|---|---|---|---|---|---|---|
| Sell Parking Lot | 0 | 0 | 0% | | | | |
| | | | | $200 | $22 | 11.0% | Keep Lot |
| Keep Parking Lot | $200 | $22 | 11.0% | | | | |
| | | | | 200 | 38 | 19.0% | I Story |
| 1 Story Bldg | 400 | 60 | 15.0% | | | | |
| | | | | 155 | 12 | 7.7% | I Story |
| 2 Story Bldg | 555 | 72 | 12.9% | | | | |
| | | | | 350 | 40 | 11.4% | 3 Story |
| 3 Story Bldg | 750 | 100 | 13.3% | | | | |
| | | | | 125 | 5 | 4.0% | 3 Story |
| 4 Story Bldg | 875 | 105 | 12.0% | | | | |
| | | | | 250 | 20 | 8.0% | 3 Story |
| 5 Story Bldg | 1000 | 120 | 12.0% | | | | |

*All values in thousands.

Conclusion: Build 3 Story Building

# 8-5

| Plan | Cost of Improvements and Land | Net Annual Income | Salvage Value | Computed Rate of Return | Decision |
|---|---|---|---|---|---|
| A | $145,000 | $23,300 | $70,000 | 15% | |
| B | 300,000 | 44,300 | 70,000 | 12.9% | |
| C | 100,000 | 10,000 | 70,000 | 9% | Fails to meet the 10% criterion.  Reject. |
| D | 200,000 | 27,500 | 70,000 | 12% | |

Rank the three remaining projects in order of cost and examine each
separable increment of investment.

Plan D rather than Plan A

| Δ Investment | Δ Annual Income | Δ Salvage Value |
|---|---|---|
| $55,000 | $4200 | $0 |

$$\$55,000 = 4200(P/A,i\%,15)$$
$$(P/A,i\%,15) = \frac{\$55,000}{\$4,200} = 13.1$$

From interest tables: i = 1-3/4%
This is an unacceptable increment of investment.
Reject D and retain A.

Plan B rather than Plan A

| △ Investment | △ Annual Income | △ Salvage Value |
|:---:|:---:|:---:|
| $155,000 | $21,000 | $0 |

$$155,000 = 21,000(P/A,i\%,15)$$

$$(P/A,i\%,15) = \frac{155,000}{21,000} = 7.38$$

From interest tables: i = 10.5%

This is a desirable increment of investment.
Reject A and accept B.

Conclusion: Select Plan B

# 8-6

| Year | Plan A Cash Flow | Plan B Cash Flow | Plan B Rather Than Plan A | Plan C Cash Flow | Plan C Rather Than Plan B |
|:---:|:---:|:---:|:---:|:---:|:---:|
| 0 | -10,000 | -15,000 | -5,000 | -20,000 | -5,000 |
| 1-10 | +1,625 | +1,625 | 0 | +1,890 | +265 |
| 10 | -10,000 | 0 | +10,000 | 0 | 0 |
| 11-20 | +1,625 | +1,625 | 0 | +1,890 | +265 |
| Rate of Return | 10%* | 8.8% | 7.2%** | 7% | 0.6%*** |

*The computation may be made for a 10-year period:
    $10,000 = 1625(P/A,i\%,10)$    i = 10%
 The second 10-year period has the same rate of return.

**The computation is:
    $5,000 = 10,000(P/F,i\%,10)$    $(P/F,i\%,10) = \frac{5,000}{10,000} = 0.5$

                                        i = 7.2%

***Here the computation is:
    $5000 = 265(P/A,i\%,20)$    i = 0.6%

The table above shows two different sets of computations.
 1.  The rate of return for each Plan is computed.

| Plan | Rate of Return |
|:---:|:---:|
| A | 10% |
| B | 8.8% |
| C | 7% |

 2.  Two incremental analyses are performed.

| Increment | Rate of Return | |
|---|:---:|---|
| Plan B - Plan A | 7.2% | A desirable increment. Retain Plan B.  Reject Plan A. |
| Plan C - Plan B | 0.6% | An undesirable increment. Adopt Plan B.  Reject Plan C. |

Conclusion: Select Plan B

# 8-7

Looking at Alternatives B & C it is apparent that B dominates C. Since at the same cost B produces a greater annual benefit, it will always be preferred over C.  C may, therefore, be immediately discarded.

| Alternative | Cost | Annual Benefit | $\Delta$ Cost | $\Delta$ Annual Benefit | $\Delta$ Rate of Return |
|---|---|---|---|---|---|
| B | $50 | $12 | | | |
| | | | $25 — $4 | | 9.6%  This is greater than the 8% MARR.  Retain A. |
| A | $75 | $16 | | | |
| | | | $10 — $1 | | 0%.  < 8% MARR. Retain A. |
| D | $85 | $17 | | | |

Conclusion: Select Alternative A

# 8-8

Like all situations where neither input nor output is fixed, the key to the solution is incremental rate of return analysis.

| Alternative: | A | B | C |
|---|---|---|---|
| Cost: | $200 | $300 | $600 |
| Annual Benefit: | 59.7 | 77.1 | 165.2 |
| Useful Life: | 5 yr | 5 yr | 5 yr |
| Computed Rate of Return: | 15% | 9% | 11.7% |

| | B-A | C-B | C-A |
|---|---|---|---|
| $\Delta$ Cost | $100 | $300 | $400 |
| $\Delta$ Annual Benefit | 17.4 | 88.1 | 105.5 |
| $\Delta$ Rate of Return | < 0% | 14.3% | 10% |

Knowing the 6 rates of return above, we can determine the preferred alternative for the various levels of MARR.

| MARR | Test: Alternative Rate of Return | Test: Examination of separable increments |
|---|---|---|
| 0% ≤ 9% | Reject no alternatives. | B-A increment unsatisfactory. C-A increment satisfactory. Choose C. |
| 9% ≤ 10% | Reject B | C-A increment satisfactory Choose C. |
| 10% ≤ 11.7% | Reject B | C-A increment unsatisfactory. Choose A |
| 11.7% ≤ 15% | Reject B & C | Choose A |

∴ Alternative C preferred when 0% ≤ MARR ≤ 10%

# 8-9

Incremental Rate of Return Solution

|  | A | B | C | D | C-D | B-C | A-C |
|---|---|---|---|---|---|---|---|
|  |  |  |  |  | *Increment* | | |
| Cost | $1000 | $800 | $600 | $500 | $100 | $200 | $400 |
| Uniform Annual Benefit | 122 | 120 | 97 | 122 | -25 | 23 | 25 |
| Salvage Value | 750 | 500 | 500 | 0 | 500 | 0 | 250 |
| Computed Incremental Rate of Return | | | | | 10% | <0% | ¬1.8% |

The *C-D* increment is desirable.   Reject *D* and retain *C*.

The *B-C* increment is undesirable.  Reject *B* and retain *C*.

The *A-C* increment is undesirable.  Reject *A* and retain *C*.

Select Alternative *C*

Net Present Worth Solution

$$\text{Net Present Worth} = \frac{\text{Uniform}}{\text{Annual Benefit}}(P/A,8\%,8) + \frac{\text{Salvage}}{\text{Value}}(P/F,8\%,8) - \text{First Cost}$$

$NPW_A = 122(5.747) + 750(0.5403) - 1000 = +106.36$

$NPW_B = 120(5.747) + 500(0.5403) - 800 = +159.79$

$NPW_C = 97(5.747) + 500(0.5403) - 600 = +227.61$

$NPW_D = 122(5.747) - 500 = +201.13$

Select Alternative *C*

# 8-10

| Year | A | B | B-A | C | C-B |
|------|-----|-----|-----|-----|-----|
| 0 | -$1000 | -$2000 | -$1000 | -$3000 | -$1000 |
| 1 | +150 | +150 | 0 | 0 | -150 |
| 2 | +150 | +150 | 0 | 0 | -150 |
| 3 | +150 | +150 | 0 | 0 | -150 |
| 4 | +150 | +150 | 0 | 0 | -150 |
| 5 | { +150 / +1000 | +150 | -1000 | 0 | -150 |
| 6 | | { +150 / +2700 | +2850 | 0 | -2850 |
| 7 | | | | +5600 | +5600 |

Computed
Incremental
Rate of Return    9.8%                                   6.7%

The B-A incremental rate of return of 9.8% indicates a desirable increment of investment. Alternative B is preferred over alternative A.

The C-B incremental rate of return of 6.7% is less than the desired 8% rate. Reject C.

Select Alternative B

Check solution by NPW

$NPW_A = 150(P/A,8\%,5) + 1000(P/F,8\%,5) - 1000 = +279.55$

$NPW_B = 150(P/A,8\%,6) + 2700(P/F,8\%,6) - 2000 = +394.99$ ◄——

$NPW_C = 5600(P/F,8\%,7) - 3000 \qquad\qquad = +267.60$

# 8-11

Compute rates of return

alt. X    $100 = 31.5(P/A, i\%, 4)$; $(P/A, i\%, 4) = 3.17$    $ROR_X = 9.9\%$

alt. Y    $50 = 16.5(P/A, i\%, 4)$; $(P/A, i\%, 4) = 3.03$    $ROR_Y = 12.1\%$

Incremental Analysis

YEAR    X-Y    (Note: Larger X -Smaller Y)

| 0 | -50 |
|---|-----|
| 1-4 | +15 |

$50 = 15(P/A, i\%, 4)$    Solving: $\Delta ROR_{X-Y} = 7.7\%$

(a) At MARR = 6% the x-y increment is desirable.  Select x.

(b) At MARR = 9% x-y increment undesirable.  Select Y

(c) At MARR = 10% reject alt. x as $ROR_x$ < MARR.  Select Y

(d) At MARR = 14% both alternatives have ROR < MARR.

.: Do Nothing

# 8-12

Compute rates of return

alt. A  100 = 30($P/A, i\%, 5$)  ($P/A, i\%, 5$) = 3.33  $ROR_A$ = 15.2%

alt. B  150 = 43($P/A, i\%, 5$)  ($P/A, i\%, 5$) = 3.49  $ROR_B$ = 13.3%

Incremental Analysis

| YEAR | B-A |
|------|-----|
| 0 | -50 |
| 1-5 | +13 |

50 = 13($P/A, i\%, 5$)  Solving: $\Delta ROR_{B-A}$ = 9.4%

(a) At MARR = 6% the B-A increment is desirable.  Select B

(b) At MARR = 8% the B-A increment still desirable.  Select B

(c) At MARR = 10% B-A increment undesirable.  Select A

# 8-13

This is a chapter 5 homework problem
with A and B reversed and slight modification.

| YEAR | A | B | A-B |
|------|-----|-----|------|
| 0 | -10,700 | -5,500 | -5200 |
| 1-4 | +2100 | +1800 | +300 |
| 4 | | -5,500 | +5500 |
| 5-8 | +2100 | +1800 | +300 |
| Computed Rate of Return | 11.3% | 11.7% | 10.8% |

Since $\Delta ROR_{A-B}$ > MARR, the increment is desirable.

Select A

# 8-14

| YEAR | A | B | C | Increment B-C |
|------|-----|------|------|------|
| 0 | -300 | -600 | -200 | -400 |
| 1-10 | 41 | 98 | 35 | 63 |
| Computed Rate of Return | 6.1% | 10.1% | 11.7% | 9.2% |

Reject    OK    OK

as $ROR_A$

less than MARR

$ROR_{\Delta B-C}$ > MARR

∴ Select B

# 8-15

| YEAR | X | Y | Y-X |
|------|-----|-----|-----|
| 0 | -10 | -20 | -10 |
| 1 | 15 | 28 | +13 |
| computed rate of return | 50% | 40% | 30% |

$ROR_{\Delta Y-X}$ = 30%, therefore Y is preferred for all values of MARR < 30%

0% ≤ MARR ≤ 30%

# 8-16

Since *B* has a higher initial cost and higher rate of return, it dominates *A* with the result that there is no interest rate at which *A* is the preferred alternative.  Assuming this is not recognized, one would first compute the rate of return on the increments *B-A* and then *C-B*.  The problem has been worked out to make the computations relatively easy.

| YEAR | A | B | B-A |
|------|------|---------|---------|
| 0 | -770 | -1406.3 | -636.30 |
| 1 | +420 | +420 | 0 |
| 2 | { +420 / -770 | { +420 / 0 | { +770.0 |
| 3 | +420 | +420 | 0 |
| 4 | +420 | +420 | 0 |

Cash flows repeat for next four years.

Rate of Return on B-A

$636.30 = 770(P/F, i\%, 2)$

$\Delta ROR_{B-A} = 10\%$

| YEAR | B | C | C-B |
|---|---|---|---|
| 0 | -1406.3 | -2563.3 | -1157.0 |
| 1-3 | +420 | +420 | 0 |
| 4 | $\left\{\begin{array}{l}+420\\-1406.3\end{array}\right.$ | $\left\{\begin{array}{l}+420\\0\end{array}\right.$ | $\left\{\begin{array}{l}0\\+1406.3\end{array}\right.$ |
| 5-8 | +420 | +420 | 0 |

Rate of Return
on C-B

$1157 = 1406.3 (P/F, i\%, 4)$

$\Delta ROR_{C-B} = 5\%$

Summary of rates of return:

| A | B-A | B | C-B | C | D |
|---|---|---|---|---|---|
| 6.0% | 10% | 7.5% | 5% | 6.4% | 0% |

Value of MARR

| | |
|---|---|
| 0%-5% | C is preferred |
| 5%-7.5% | B is preferred |
| >7.5% | D is preferred |

∴ B is preferred for values
of MARR from $5\% - 7\frac{1}{2}\%$

# 8-17

| | A | B | A-B | C | C-B |
|---|---|---|---|---|---|
| Cost | -1500 | -1000 | -500 | -2035 | -1035 |
| Annual Benefit first 5 years | +250 | +250 | 0 | +650 | +400 |
| Annual Benefit next 5 years | +450 | +250 | +200 | +145 | -105 |
| Computed Rate of Return | 16.3% | 21.4% | $\Delta ROR$ 9.2% Reject A Keep B | 21.6% | Two sign changes in C-B cashflow ∴ transform it. |

C-B

$P = 105 (P/A, 10\%, 5) = 398$

Transformed cash flow

| YEAR | C-B |
|---|---|
| 0 | -1035 |
| 1-4 | +400 |
| 5 | +2 |

$-1035 = 400 (P/A, i\%, 4) + 2 (P/F, i\%, 5)$

$\Delta ROR_{C-B} = 20\%$ ∴ Increment is desirable

SELECT C

# 8-18

monthly payment on new warehouse loan $= 350,000(A/P, 1\frac{1}{4}\%, 60)$

$$= 8330$$

| month | alt. 1 | alt. 2 | 1-2 | alt. 3 | 1-3 |
|-------|--------|--------|------|--------|------|
| 0 | -100,000 | -100,000 | 0 | 0 | -100,000 |
| 1-60 | $\begin{cases} -8330 \\ +2500 \\ -1000 \end{cases}$ | $\begin{cases} -8330 \\ 0 \\ 0 \end{cases}$ | +1500 | -2700 | -4130 |
| 60 | +600,000 | +600,000 | 0 | 0 | +600,000 |

By Inspection
1-2 Increment
is desirable.
Reject 2
keep 1

$\Delta ROR = 1.34\%/mo$
Nominal ROR
$= 1.34(12) = 16.1\%$
Effective ROR
$= (1+0.0134)^{12}-1 = 17.3\%$

Being less desirable than Alt. 1, Alt. 2 may be rejected.
The 1-3 increment does not yield the required 20% MARR, so it
is not desirable.  Reject 1 and select 3 (continue as is).

# 8-19

Part One - Identical Replacements
            Infinite Analysis period

$$NPW_A = \frac{UAB}{i} - PW \text{ of Cost} = \frac{10}{0.08} - 100 = +25.00$$

$NPW_B$

$$EUAC = 150(A/P, 8\%, 20) = 15.29$$
$$EUAB = 17.62 \text{ (given)}$$

$$NPW_B = \frac{EUAB - EUAC}{i} = \frac{17.62 - 15.29}{0.08} = +29.13$$

$NPW_C$ - using same method as alternate B

$$EUAC = 200 (A/P, 8\%, 5) = 50.10$$

$$NPW_C = \frac{EUAB - EUAC}{i} = \frac{55.48 - 50.10}{0.08} = +67.25$$

<u>SELECT C</u>

<u>Part Two</u> - Replacements provide 8% rate of return

Infinite analysis period

Since the replacemEnts have an 8% rate of return, it follows that their NPW at 8% = 0.

$$NPW_A = \frac{UAB}{i} - PW \text{ of Cost} = \frac{10}{0.08} - 10 = +25.00$$

$$NPW_B = PW \text{ of Benefits} - PW \text{ of Cost}$$
$$= 17.62 (P/A, 8\%, 20) - 150 + 0 = +22.99$$

$$NPW_C = 55.48 (P/A, 8\%, 5) - 200 + 0 = +21.53$$

<u>SELECT A</u>

# 8-20

| YEAR | Pump 1 | Pump 2 | Increment 2-1 | transformation |
|------|--------|--------|---------------|----------------|
| 0 | -100 | -110 | -10 | |
| 1 | 70 | 115 | +45 | $X(1+0.10)^1$ |
| 2 | 70 | 30 | -40 | 40 |

Solve for $X$    $X = \frac{40}{1.10} = 36.36$

| YEAR | Transformed Increment 2-1 |
|------|---------------------------|
| 0 | -10 |
| 1 | +8.64 |
| 2 | 0 |

Obviously an undesirable increment as $\Delta ROR < 0\%$, Select Pump 1

# 8-21

| YEAR | A | B | C | A-B | C-B |
|------|------|------|------|------|------|
| 0 | -20000 | -20000 | -20000 | 0 | 0 |
| 1 | 10000 | 10000 | 5000 | 0 | -5000 |
| 2 | 5000 | 10000 | 5000 | -5000 | -5000 |
| 3 | 10000 | 10000 | 5000 | 0 | -5000 |
| 4 | 6000 | 0 | 15000 | 6000 | 15000 |
| computed ROR | 21.3% | 23.4% | 15.0% | 9.5% | 0% |
| | | | | Reject A | Reject C |

Choose alt. B

# 8-22

| | South End | Both Stores | North End |
|------|------|------|------|
| New Store Cost | | | -500,000 |
| Annual Profit | 170,000 | 260,000 | +90,000 |
| Salvage Value | | | +500,000 |

Where the investment ($500,000) is fully recovered, as in this case, the rate of return = $\frac{A}{P} = \frac{90,000}{500,000} = 0.18 = 18\%$. Open The North End.

# 8-23

| Year | Neutralization | Precipitation | Neut.- Prec. |
|------|------|------|------|
| 0 | -700,000 | -500,000 | -200,000 |
| 1-5 | -40,000 | -110,000 | +70,000 |
| 5 | +175,000 | +125,000 | +50,000 |

Solve (Neut.- Prec.) for rate of return.

$$200,000 = 70(P/A, i, 5) + 50(P/F, i, 5)$$
$$\text{M} \qquad \text{M}$$

Try i = 25%.

$$200,000 \doteq 70,000(2.689) + 50,000(0.3277) = 204,615 \quad \therefore ROR > 25\%$$

Computed rate of return = 26%. Choose Neutralization.

# 8-24

| YEAR | Gen Dev | RJR | RJR-Gen Dev |
|------|------|------|------|
| 0 | -480 | -630 | -150 |
| 1-15 | +94 | +140 | +46 |
| 15 | +1000 | +1000 | 0 |
| computed Rate of Return | 21.0% | 22.8% | 30.0% |

Neither bond yields the desired 25% MARR – so Do NOTHING.

Note that simply examining the (RJR-Gen Dev) increment might lead one to the wrong conclusion!

# 8-25

The ROR of each alternative $\geq$ MARR.
Proceed with incremental analysis. Examine increments of investment.

| | C | B | B-C |
|---|---|---|---|
| Initial Investment | 15,000 | 22,000 | 7,000 |
| Annual Net Income | 1,643 | 2,077 | 434 |

$$7000 = 434(P/A, i, 20)$$
$$(P/A, i, 20) = \frac{7000}{434} = 16.13 \qquad \Delta ROR_{B-C} = 2.1\%$$

Since $\Delta ROR_{B-C} < 7\%$, Reject B-C, and hence B.

| | C | A | A-C |
|---|---|---|---|
| Initial Investment | 15000 | 50000 | 35000 |
| Annual Net Income | 1643 | 5093 | 3450 |

$$35000 = 3450(P/A, i, 20)$$
$$(P/A, i, 20) = \frac{35000}{3450} = 10.14 \qquad \Delta ROR_{A-C} \doteq 7.6\%$$

Since $\Delta ROR_{A-C} > 7\%$, Reject C.

$$\underline{\text{Select A}}$$

# 8-26

Since there are alternatives with ROR > 8% MARR, alternative 3 may be immediately rejected as well as alternative 5. Note also that Alt 2 dominates Alt 1 since its ROR > ROR Alt 1. Thus $\Delta ROR_{2-1} > 15\%$, so alternative 1 can be rejected. This leaves alternatives 2 and 4. Examine the (4-2) increment.

| | 2 | 4 | 4-2 |
|---|---|---|---|
| Initial Cost | \$130.00 | \$330.00 | \$200.00 |
| Uniform Annual Benefit | 38.78 | 91.55 | 52.77 |

$$200 = 52.77(P/A, i, 5)$$
$$(P/A, i, 5) = \frac{200}{52.77} = 3.79 \qquad \Delta ROR_{4-2} = 10\%$$

Since $\Delta ROR_{4-2} > 8\% MARR$, $\underline{\text{Select alt. 4}}$

# 8-27

Check to see if all alternatives have a ROR > MARR.
**Alt. *A***
NPW = 800 $(P/A, 6\%, 5)$ + 2000 $(P/F, 6\%, 5)$ - 2,000
= 800 (4.212) + 2000 (0.7473) -2000 = +2864 ROR > MARR
**Alt.*B***
NPW = 500 $(P/A, 6\%, 6)$ + 1500 $(P/F, 6\%, 6)$ -5,000 - =
= 500(4.917) + 1500(0.7050) -5000 = -1484 ROR < MARR Reject ***B***

**Alt. *C***
NPW = 400 $(P/A, i\%, 7)$ +1400 $(P/F, i\%, 7)$ - 4000
= 400 (5.582) + 1400(0.6651) -4000 = -610 ROR < MARR Reject ***C***
**Alt. D**
NPW =1300 $(P/A, 6\%, 4)$ + 3,000 $(P/A, 6\%, 4)$- 3,000
=1300 (3.465) + 3,000 (0.7921)- 3,000 = +3881 ROR > MARR

So only Alternatives *A* and *D* remain.

| Yr | A | D | D-A |
|----|------|------|------|
| 0 | -2000 | -3000 | -1000 |
| 1 | +800 | +1300 | +500 |
| 2 | +800 | +1300 | +500 |
| 3 | +800 | +1300 | +500 |
| 4 | +800 | +4300 | +3500 |
| 5 | +2800 | | -2800 |

so the increment ***D-A*** has a cash flow with two sign changes.
Move the ***Yr5*** disbursement back to ***Yr4*** at MARR = 6%
***D-A*** Year 4 = +3500 -2800$(P/F,6\%,1)$ = +858
Now compute the incremental ROR on ***D-A***
NPW = -1000 +500$(P/A, i,3)$ +858$(P/F, i,4)$
Try i = 40%
NPW = -1000 + 500(1.589) + 858(0.2603) = +18
So the ▵ROR on ***D-A*** is slightly greater than 40%
Choose Alt. ***D.***

# 8-28

Using Equivalent Uniform Annual Cost

$EUAC_{Th}$ = -5 -20$(A/P,12\%,3)$ =-5 -20(0.4163) = - \$13.33
$EUAC_{SL}$ = -2 -40$(A/P,12\%,5)$ = -2 - 40(0.2774) = -\$13.10
Fred should choose slate over thatch to save \$0.23/year.

To Find incremental ROR, Find $i$ such that $EUAC_{SL}$ - $EUAC_{TH}$ = 0

$0 = -2 -40(A/P, i^*,5) -[ -5 -20(A/P,i^*,3)]$
$\quad = 3 -40(A/P, i^*,5) + 20(A/P, i^*,3)$

@12%
$0 \stackrel{?}{=} 3 - 40(0.2774) + 20(0.4163) = \$0.23$   12% too low.

@15%
$0 \stackrel{?}{=} 3 -40(0.2983) + 20(0.4380) = -\$0.172$  15% too high.
$\triangle ROR = 12 + 3[(0.23/(0.23-(-0.172))] = 13.72\%$

# 8-29

*a.*    For the Atlas mower the cash flow table is:

| Year | Net cash flow (Atlas) |
|------|----------------------|
| 0    | -$6700               |
| 1    | $2500                |
| 2    | $2500                |
| 3    | $2500                |

$NPW = -6700 +2500 (P/A, i^*, 2) +3500 (P/F, i^*, 3) =0$
To solve this for $i^*$, construct a table as follows:

| i    | NPW     |
|------|---------|
| 12%  | +$16    |
| i*   | 0       |
| 15%  | -$334   |

Use linear interpolation to determine ROR
ROR = 12% + 3% x ($16 - $0) / ($16 + $334)
ROR = 12.1%

*b.*    For the Zippy mower the cash flow table is:

| Year | Net cash flow (Zippy) |
|------|----------------------|
| 0 | -$16,900 |
| 1 | $3300 |
| 2 | $3300 |
| 3 | $3300 |
| 4 | $3300 |
| 5 | $3300 |
| 6 | $6,800 |

NPW = -16,900 + 3,300(P/A, i, 5) + 6800(P/F, i, 6)
   At MARR = 8%
NPW = -16,900 + 3300(3.993) +6800(0.6302) = +562
Since NPW is positive at 8%, the ROR > MARR

c.    Look at the incremental cash flow

| Year | Net cash flow (Zippy) | Net cash flow (Atlas) | Difference (Zippy - Atlas) |
|------|----------------------|----------------------|----------------------------|
| 0 | -$16,900 | -$6,700 | -$10,200 |
| 1 | +3,300 | +2,500 | +800 |
| 2 | +3,300 | +2,500 | +800 |
| 3 | +3,300 | +3,500-6700 | +6500 |
| 4 | +3,300 | +2,500 | +800 |
| 5 | +3,300 | +2,500 | +800 |
| 6 | +6,800 | +3,500 | +3300 |

NPW = -10,200 +800 (P/A, i*, 5) +5700 (P/F, i*, 3) +3300 (P/F, i*, 6)
      Compute the ΔROR
Try i=6%
NPW = -10,200 +800(4.212) +5700(0.8396) + 3300(0.7050) = +282
Try i=7%
NPW = -10,200 +800(4.100) +5700(0.8163) + 3300(0.6663) = -68
ΔROR = 6% +(1%)(282-0) / (282+68) = 6.8%
The ΔROR< MARR, so choose the lower cost alternative, the Atlas.

# 8-30

1.    Arrange the alternatives in ascending order of investment

|            | Company A | Company C | Company B |
|------------|-----------|-----------|-----------|
| First cost | 15,000    | 20,000    | 25,000    |

2.    Compute the rate of return for the least cost alternative (*Company A*) or at least, insure that the $ROR_A > MARR$.

At $i = 15\%$

$NPW_A = -15,000 + (8000 - 1600)(P / A, 15\%, 4) + 3000 (P / F, 15\%, 4)$

$= -15,000 + 6400 (2.855) + 3000 (0.5718) = \$4987$

The $NPW_A$ at $i = 15\%$ is positive, hence $ROR_A > 15\%$

3.    Consider the increment   (*Company C - Company A*)

|                                | C - A |
|--------------------------------|-------|
| First cost                     | 5000  |
| Maintenance & operating costs  | -700  |
| Annual benefit                 | 3000  |
| Salvage value                  | 1500  |

Determine whether the rate of return for the increment   (*C -A* ) is more or less than the 15% MARR.

At $i = 15\%$

$NPW_{C-A} = - 5000 + [3000 - (-700)] (P/A, 15\%, 4) + 1500 (P/F, 15\%, 4)$

$= - 5000 + 3700 (2.855) + 1500 (0.5718) = \$6421$

Since the ( *C - A* ) increment is positive at the MARR%, it is desirable.  Reject *Company A*.

4.    Consider the increment ( *Company B - Company C* )

|                                | B - C |
|--------------------------------|-------|
| First cost                     | 5000  |
| Maintenance & operating costs  | -500  |
| Annual benefit                 | 4000  |
| Salvage value                  | 1500  |

At $i = 15\%$

$NPW_{B-C} = - 5000 + [4000 - (-500)] (P/A, 15\%, 4) + 1500 (P/F, 15\%, 4)$

$= - 5000 + 4500 (2.855) + 1500 (0.5718) = \$8705$

So ( *B - C* ) increment is desirable.  Reject *Company C* .

Conclusion:  Select *Company B* 's widget machine.

# 8-31

MARR = 15 %   $n$ = 10   RANKING:    0 < *Economy* < *Regular* < *Deluxe*
△ *(Economy - 0)*
         NPW = -75,000 + (28,000 - 8000) ($P/A, i^*$, 10) + 3000 ($P/F, i^*$, 10)

| $i^*$ | NPW |
|-------|-----|
| 0 | 128,000 |
| 0.15 | 26,120 |
| ∞ | -75,000 |

∞   -75,000        $i^*$ > MARR , so *Economy*  is better than doing nothing.

△ *(Regular - Economy )*
NPW = - (125,000 - 75,000) + ((43,000 - 28,000)
              - (13,000 - 8000)) ($P/A, i^*$, 10) + (6900 - 3000)  ($P/F, i^*$, 10)

| $i^*$ | NPW |
|-------|-----|
| 0 | 53,900 |
| 0.15 | 1,154 |
| ∞ | -50,000 |

∞   -50,000        $i^*$ > MARR, so *Regular*  is better than *Economy*

△ *(Deluxe - Regular)*
NPW = - (220,000 - 125,000) + ((79,000 - 43,000) - (38,000 - 13,000))
($P/A, i^*$, 10) + (16,000 - 6900) ($P/F, i^*$, 10)

| $i^*$ | NPW |
|-------|-----|
| 0 | 24,100 |
| 0.15 | -37,540 |
| ∞ | -95,000 |

∞   -95,000        $i^*$ < MARR, so *Deluxe*  is less desirable than *Regular*.
The correct choice is the *Regular* model.

# 8-32

Put the four alternatives in order of increasing cost:
    *Do Nothing* --  *U-Sort-M* --  *Ship-R*  --  *Sort-Of*
Incremental Analysis

*U-SORT-M  -  Do Nothing*

| First cost | $180,000 |
|---|---|
| Annual Benefit | 68,000 |
| Maintenance & operating costs | 12,000 |
| Salvage value | 14,400 |

$NPW_{15\%} = -180,000 + (68,000 - 12,000)$
$(P/A, 15\%, 7) + 14,400 (P/F, 15\%, 7)$
$= -180,000 + 232,960 + 5413$
$= +58,373$

$\therefore$ ROR > MARR.  Reject *Do Nothing*

*Ship-R  -  U-SORT-M*

| First cost | $4,000 |
|---|---|
| Annual benefit | 23,900 |
| Maintenance & operating costs | 7,300 |
| Salvage value | 9,000 |

$NPW_{15\%} = -4,000 + (23,900 - 7300)$
$(P/A, 15\%, 7) + 9000 (P/F, 15\%, 7)$
$= -4000 + 69,056 + 3383$
$= +68,439$

$\therefore$ ROR > MARR.  Reject *U-Sort-M*

*Sort-Of  -  Ship-R*

| First cost | $51,000 |
|---|---|
| Annual benefit | 13,700 |
| Maintenance & operating costs | 0 |
| Salvage value | 5700 |

$NPW_{15\%} = -51,000 + (13,700)$
$(P/A, 15\%, 7) + 5700 (P/F, 15\%, 7)$
$= -51,000 + 56,992 + 2143$
$= +8135$

$\therefore$  ROR > MARR.    Reject   *Ship-R*
Conclusion: Select *Sort-Of*

**Conclusion: Select *Sort-of***

# Other Analysis Techniques

**9-1**

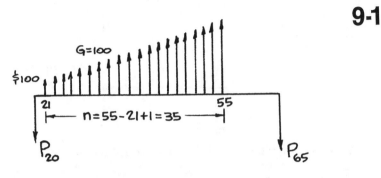

$P_{20} = 100(P/A, 12\%, 35) + 100(P/G, 12\%, 35)$

$= 100(8.176) + 100(62.605) = 7078.10$

$P_{65} = P_{20}(F/P, 12\%, 45) = 7078.10(163.988) = 1,160,700$

**9-2**

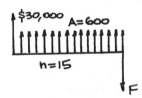

$F = 30,000(F/P, 10\%, 15) + 600(F/A, 10\%, 15)$

$= 30,000(4.177) + 600(31.772) = \$144,373$

**9-3**

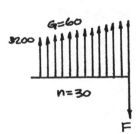

$F = 3200(F/A, 7\%, 30) + 60(P/G, 7\%, 30)(F/P, 7\%, 30)$

$= 3200(94.461) + 60(120.972)(7.612)$

$= \$357,526$

183

# 9-4

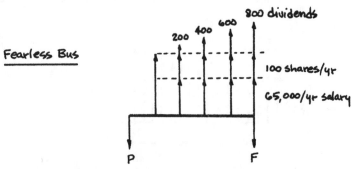

$P = 65,000\, (P/A, 9\%, 5) + 200\, (P/G, 9\%, 5) + 500\ \text{shares stock}$
$\qquad\qquad\quad 3.890 \qquad\qquad\quad 7.111$

$= 254,272 + 500\ \text{shares stock}$

Future Worth $F = 254,272\,(F/P, 9\%, 5) + 500\,(\$60/\text{share})$
$\qquad\qquad\qquad\qquad\quad 1.539$

$\qquad\qquad = 421,325$

Generous Electric

Future Worth $= 62,000\,(F/A, 9\%, 5) + 600\ \text{shares GE stock}$
$\qquad\qquad\qquad\quad 5.985$

$\qquad\qquad\quad = 371,070 + 600\ \text{shares GE stock}$

Set $FW_{GE} = FW_{Fearless}$

$\quad 600\ \text{shares GE stock} + 371,070 = 421,325$

$\qquad\qquad\text{Required value of GE stock} = \dfrac{50,255}{600} = \underline{\$83.76\ \text{per share}}$

# 9-5

$EUAC_{American} = (8900-1700)(A/P, 8\%, 3) + 1700(0.08) + 12,000\ \text{Km}\,(0.09)$

$\qquad\qquad = 4010$

$EUAC_{Fiasco} = (8000 - X)(A/P, 8\%, 3) + X\,(0.08) + 12,000\ \text{km}\,(0.08)$

$\qquad\qquad = 3104 - 0.3880X + 0.08X + 960$

Set $EUAC_{American} = EUAC_{Fiasco}$

$\qquad\quad 4010 = 3104 - 0.308X + 960$

Minimum Fiasco resale value $X = \dfrac{54}{0.308} = \underline{\$175}$

**9-6**

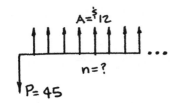

$$A = \$12$$
$$n = ?$$
$$P = 45$$

$$45 = 12\,(P/A, i\%, n)$$
$$(P/A, i\%, n) = \frac{45}{12} = 3.75$$

| n | i |
|---|-----|
| 4 | 2.6% |
| 5 | 10.4% |
| 6 | 15.3% |
| 7 | 18.6% |
| 8 | 20.8% |

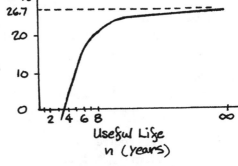

RATE OF Return

Useful Life
n (years)

when $n = \infty$

$$i = \frac{A}{P} = \frac{12}{45} = 26.7\%$$

(b) For a 12% rate of return, useful life must be $5\frac{1}{4}$ years

(c) $n = \infty$, Rate of Return $= 26.7\%$

**9-7**

Investment $= \$67,000$   Annual Benefit $= 26,000/\text{yr}$ for 2 years

Payback Period $= \dfrac{67,000}{26,000} = 2.6$ years.

Don't Buy.
Total Benefits $(2 \times \$26,000) <$ Cost.

**9-8**

Payback Period $= \dfrac{\text{Cost}}{\text{Annual Benefit}} = \dfrac{3800}{4 \times 400} = 2.4$ years

$$A = 400/\text{mo}$$
$$\$3800 \qquad n = 60 \text{ mo.}$$

$$3800 = 400(P/A, i\%, 4) + 400(P/A, i\%, 4)(P/F, i\%, 12)$$
$$\qquad + 400(P/A, i\%, 4)(P/F, i\%, 24) + 400(P/A, i\%, 4)(P/F, i\%, 36)$$
$$\qquad + 400(P/A, i\%, 4)(P/F, i\%, 48)$$

$$3800 = 400(P/A, i\%, 4)\left[1 + (P/F, i\%, 12) + (P/F, i\%, 24) + (P/F, i\%, 36) + (P/F, i\%, 48)\right]$$

Try $i = 3\%$
$$= 400(3.717)\left[1 + 0.7014 + 0.4919 + 0.3450 + 0.2420\right]$$
$$= 1486.80 \,[2.7803] = 4134 \qquad i \text{ too low}$$

Try $i = 4\%$
$$= 400(3.630)\left[1 + 0.6246 + 0.3901 + 0.2437 + 0.1522\right]$$
$$= 1452 \,[2.4106] = 3500 \qquad i \text{ too high}$$

Try $i = 3\frac{1}{2}\%$
$$= 400(3.673)\left[1 + 0.6618 + 0.4380 + 0.2898 + 0.1918\right]$$
$$= 1469.20 \,[2.5814] = 3793$$

$$\therefore i \approx 3\tfrac{1}{2}\% \text{ per month}$$
$$\text{Nominal Rate of Return} = 12(3\tfrac{1}{2}\%) = 42\%$$

# 9-9

|                | A    | B    | C    |
|----------------|------|------|------|
| Cost           | 50   | 150  | 110  |
| Annual Benefit | 28.8 | 39.6 | 39.6 |
| Useful Life    | 2 yr | 6 yr | 4 yr |

(a)  Solve by Future Worth analysis.  In future worth analysis there
must be a common future time for all calculations.  In this case
12 years hence is a practical future time.

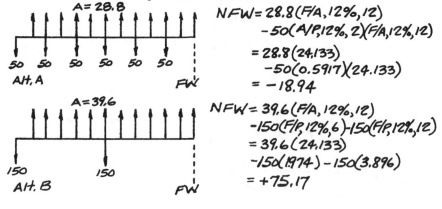

$$NFW = 28.8(F/A, 12\%, 12)$$
$$\qquad - 50(A/P, 12\%, 2)(F/A, 12\%, 12)$$
$$= 28.8(24.133)$$
$$\qquad - 50(0.5917)(24.133)$$
$$= -18.94$$

$$NFW = 39.6(F/A, 12\%, 12)$$
$$\qquad - 150(F/P, 12\%, 6) - 150(F/P, 12\%, 12)$$
$$= 39.6(24.133)$$
$$\qquad - 150(1.974) - 150(3.896)$$
$$= +75.17$$

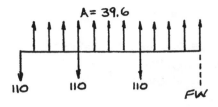

$$FW = 39.6(F/A, 12\%, 12)$$
$$-110(F/P, 12\%, 4) - 110(F/P, 12\%, 8)$$
$$-110(F/P, 12\%, 12)$$
$$= 39.6(24.133) - 110(1.574)$$
$$-110(2.476) - 110(3.896)$$
$$= +81.61$$

Choose alternative that maximizes Future Worth
Choose Alt. C

(b)  Solve by Benefit-Cost ratio analysis.

With neither input nor output fixed, incremental analysis
is required.

Alternative C - Alternative A

| Year | Alt. C | Alt. A | C - A |
|------|--------|--------|-------|
| 0 | -110 | -50 | -60 |
| 1 | +39.6 | +28.8 | +10.8 |
| 2 | +39.6 | {+28.8 / -50} | +60.8 |
| 3 | +39.6 | +28.8 | +10.8 |
| 4 | +39.6 | +28.8 | +10.8 |

Four years is a
suitable analysis period
for alternatives C and A

Increment C-A
PW of Cost = 60
PW of Benefits = $10.8(P/A, 12\%, 4) + 50(P/F, 12\%, 2)$
$$= 10.8(3.037) + 50(0.7972) = 72.66$$
$$\frac{\Delta B}{\Delta C} = \frac{PW \text{ of Benefits}}{PW \text{ of Cost}} = \frac{72.66}{60} > 1$$

The increment of investment is acceptable and
therefore Alternative C is preferred over Alternative A.

Increment B-C

| Year | Alt. B | Alt. C | B - C |
|------|--------|--------|-------|
| 0 | -150 | -110 | -40 |
| 1-4 | +39.6 | +39.6 | 0 |
| 4 | 0 | -110 | +110 |
| 5-6 | +39.6 | +39.6 | 0 |
| 6 | -150 | 0 | -150 |
| 7-8 | +39.6 | +39.6 | 0 |
| 8 | 0 | -110 | +110 |
| 9-12 | +39.6 | +39.6 | 0 |

For these alternatives
12 years is a suitable
analysis period.

Ignoring the potential difficulties signalled by 3 sign changes in the B - C cash flow:

PW of Cost = $40 + 150(P/F, 12\%, 6) = 40 + 150(0.5066) = 115.99$
PW of Benefits = $110(P/F, 12\%, 4) + 110(P/F, 12\%, 8)$
$= 110(0.6355) + 110(0.4039) = 114.33$

$$\frac{\Delta B}{\Delta C} = \frac{PW \text{ of Benefits}}{PW \text{ of Cost}} = \frac{114.33}{115.99} < 1$$

The increment is undesirable.
Alternative C is preferred over Alternative B

Alternative Analysis of the Increment B - C.

An examination of the B-C cash flow suggests there is an external investment of money at the end of Year 4. Using an external interest rate (say, 12%) the +110 at Year 4 becomes:
+110(F/P,12%,2) = +110(1.254) = +137.94 at the end of Year 6.
The altered cash flow becomes:

| Year | B - C |
|------|-------|
| 0 | -40 |
| 1-6 | 0 |
| 6 | -150 + 137.94 = -12.06 |
| 7-8 | 0 |
| 8 | +110 |

For the altered B-C cash flow:
PW of Cost = $40 + 12.06(P/F, 12\%, 6) = 40 + 12.06(0.5066) = 46.11$
PW of Benefits = $110(P/F, 12\%, 8) = 110(0.4039) = 44.43$

$$\frac{\Delta B}{\Delta C} = \frac{PW \text{ of Benefits}}{PW \text{ of Cost}} = \frac{44.43}{46.11} < 1$$

The increment is undesirable.
Alternative C is preferred over Alternative B
Solution for Part (b): Choose Alt. C

(c)  Payback Period

A.  Payback = $\frac{50}{28.8}$ = 1.74 year

B.  Payback = $\frac{150}{39.6}$ = 3.79 years

C.  Payback = $\frac{110}{39.6}$ = 2.78 years

To minimize the Payback Period, Choose Alt. A

(d)   Payback period is the time required to recover the investment. Here we have three alternatives that have rates of return varying from 10% to 16.4%. Thus each generates uniform annual benefits in excess of the cost, during the life of the alternative. From this it must follow that the alternative with a 2-year life has a payback period less than 2 years. The alternative with a 4-year life has a payback period less than 4 years, and the 6-year alternative less than 6 years.

Thus we see that the shorter lived asset automatically has an advantage over longer lived alternatives in a situation like this. While Alternative A takes the shortest amount of time to recover its investment, Alternative C is best for long term economic efficiency.

## 9-10

|  | 2 Stories | 5 Stories | 10 Stories |
|---|---|---|---|
| Cost (including Land) | $500,000 | $900,000 | $2,200,000 |
| Annual Income (A) | 70,000 | 105,000 | 256,000 |
| Salvage Value (F) | 200,000 | 300,000 | 400,000 |

**B/C Ratio Analysis**

| | 2 Stories | 5 Stories | 10 Stories |
|---|---|---|---|
| Cost | 500,000 | 900,000 | 2,200,000 |
| $-$ PW of Salvage Value $= F(P/F, 8\%, 20) = 0.2145F$ | 42,900 | 64,350 | 85,800 |
| PW of Cost | 457,100 | 835,650 | 2,114,200 |
| PW of Benefit $= A(P/A, 8\%, 20) = 9.818A$ | 687,260 | 1,030,890 | 2,513,410 |
| B/C Ratio $= \dfrac{\text{PW of Benefits}}{\text{PW of Cost}} =$ | 1.50 | 1.23 | 1.19 |

**INCREMENTAL B/C Ratio Analysis**

|  | 5 Stories Rather than 2 Stories | 10 Stories Rather than 2 Stories |
|---|---|---|
| $\Delta$ PW of Cost: | $835,650 - 457,100 = 378,550$ | $2,114,200 - 457,100 = 1,657,100$ |
| $\Delta$ PW of Benefit: | $1,030,890 - 687,260 = 343,630$ | $2,513,410 - 687,260 = 1,826,150$ |

$$\frac{\Delta B}{\Delta C} = \frac{\Delta \text{ PW of Benefits}}{\Delta \text{ PW of Cost}}$$

= 0.91

<1 undesirable increment.
Reject 5 Stories

= 1.10

>1
Desirable
Increment

With $\Delta B/\Delta C$ = 0.91 the increment of 5 stories rather than 2 is not desirable.  The 10 stories rather than 2 stories is desirable.

Conclusion: Choose the 10 story alternative.

# 9-11

Note that the three alternatives have been rearranged below in order of increasing cost.

|  | C | B | A |
|---|---|---|---|
| First Cost | $120 | $340 | $560 |
| Uniform |  |  |  |
| Annual Benefit | 40 | 100 | 140 |
| Salvage Value | 0 | 0 | 40 |
|  |  |  |  |
| Computed |  |  |  |
| B/C Ratio | 1.45 | 1.28 | 1.13 |

|  | B−C | A−B |
|---|---|---|
| Δ First Cost | $220 | $220 |
| Δ Uniform |  |  |
| Annual Benefit | 60 | 40 |
| Δ Salvage Value | 0 | 40 |
|  |  |  |
| Computed |  |  |
| ΔB/ΔC Ratio | 1.19 | 0.88 |

Benefit-Cost Ratio Computations:

For A   $B/_C = \dfrac{140(P/A,10\%,6)}{560-40(P/F,10\%,6)} = \dfrac{140(4.355)}{560-40(0.5645)} = 1.13$

For B   $B/_C = \dfrac{100(P/A,10\%,6)}{340} = 1.28$

For C   $B/_C = \dfrac{40(P/A,10\%,6)}{120} = 1.45$

Incremental Analysis:

B−C   $ΔB/_{ΔC} = \dfrac{60(P/A,10\%,6)}{220} = 1.19$   a desirable increment of investment

A−B   $ΔB/_{ΔC} = \dfrac{40(P/A,10\%,6)}{220-40(P/F,10\%,6)} = 0.88$   an undesirable increment

Conclusión: Do B

The solution may be checked by Net Present Worth or Rate of Return

NPW Solution

$NPW_A$ = 140(P/A,10%,6) + 40(P/F,10%,6) - 560
         = 140(4.355) + 40(0.5645) - 560 = +72.28

$NPW_B$ = 100(P/A,10%,6) - 340 = +95.50

$NPW_C$ =  40(P/A,10%,6) - 120 = +54.20

                                              Do B

Rate of Return Solution

|  | B - C | A - B |
|---|---|---|
| **Δ**Cost | $220 | $220 |
| **Δ**Uniform Annual Benefit | 60 | 40 |
| **Δ**Salvage Value | 0 | 40 |
| Computed **Δ**ROR | 16.2% | 6.6% |
|  | > 10% | < 10% |
|  | accept B | reject A |
|  | reject C | |

                              Do B

# 9-12

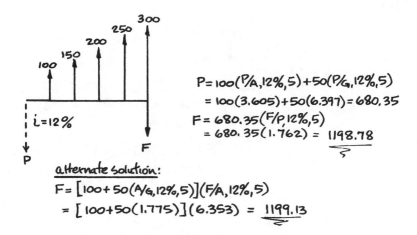

$P = 100(P/A,12\%,5) + 50(P/G,12\%,5)$
$= 100(3.605) + 50(6.397) = 680.35$
$F = 680.35(F/P,12\%,5)$
$= 680.35(1.762) = 1198.78$

alternate solution:
$F = [100 + 50(A/G,12\%,5)](F/A,12\%,5)$
$= [100 + 50(1.775)](6.353) = 1199.13$

## 9-13

$$F = \tfrac{1}{2}100(F/A, \tfrac{1}{2}\%, 24)(F/P, \tfrac{1}{2}\%, 60)$$
$$= 100(25.432)(1.349) = \underline{3430.78}$$

## 9-14

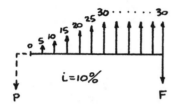

$$F = 5(P/G, 10\%, 6)(F/P, 10\%, 12)$$
$$+ 30(F/A, 10\%, 6)$$
$$= 5(9.684)(3.138) + 30(7.716)$$
$$= \underline{383.42}$$

## 9-15

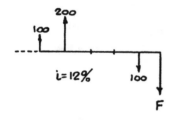

$$F = 100(F/P, 12\%, 5) + 200(F/P, 12\%, 4)$$
$$- 100(F/P, 12\%, 1)$$
$$= 100(1.762) + 200(1.574) - 100(1.120)$$
$$= \underline{379.00}$$

## 9-16

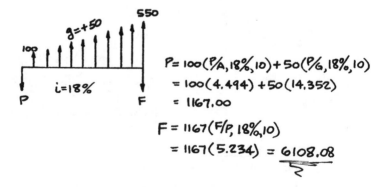

$$P = 100(P/A, 18\%, 10) + 50(P/G, 18\%, 10)$$
$$= 100(4.494) + 50(14.352)$$
$$= 1167.00$$

$$F = 1167(F/P, 18\%, 10)$$
$$= 1167(5.234) = \underline{6108.08}$$

**9-17**

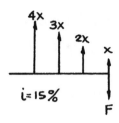

$$F = \left[4x - x\left(A/G, 15\%, 4\right)\right]\left(F/A, 15\%, 4\right)$$
$$= \left[4x - x(1.326)\right](4.993)$$
$$= \underline{\underline{13.35X}}$$

<u>alternate solution</u>

$$F = 4x\left(F/P, 15\%, 3\right) + 3x\left(F/P, 15\%, 2\right)$$
$$+ 2x\left(F/P, 15\%, 1\right) + x$$
$$= 4x(1.521) + 3x(1.323) + 2x(1.150) + x$$
$$= \underline{\underline{13.35X}}$$

**9-18**

$$F = £100(1+0.10)^{800} = £\underline{\underline{1.3 \times 10^{35}}}$$

**9-19**

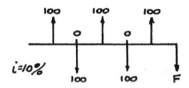

$$F = 100(F/P, 10\%, 5) + 100(F/P, 10\%, 3) + 100(F/P, 10\%, 1)$$
$$- 100(F/P, 10\%, 4) - 100(F/P, 10\%, 2)$$
$$= 100(1.611 + 1.331 + 1.100 - 1.464 - 1.210) = \underline{\underline{136.80}}$$

**9-20**

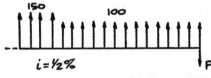

$$F = 150(F/A, \frac{1}{2}\%, 4)(F/P, \frac{1}{2}\%, 14) + 100(F/A, \frac{1}{2}\%, 14)$$
$$= 150(4.030)(1.072) + 100(14.464) = \underline{\underline{2094.42}}$$

# 9-21

using single payment compound amount factors

$$F = 1000\left[(F/P, 4\%, 12) + (F/P, 4\%, 10) + (F/P, 4\%, 8) + (F/P, 4\%, 6)\right.$$
$$\left. + (F/P, 4\%, 4) + (F/P, 4\%, 2)\right]$$
$$= 1000(1.601 + 1.480 + 1.369 + 1.265 + 1.170 + 1.082) = \$7967$$

Alternate Solution:

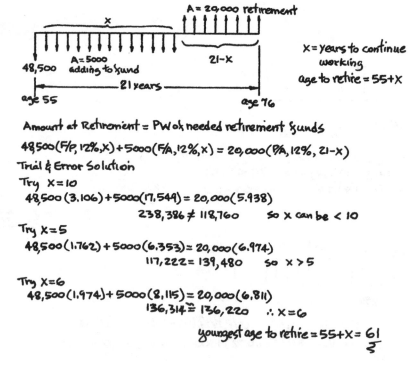

$$A = 1000(A/P, 4\%, 2) = 1000(0.5302) = 530.20$$
$$F = 530.20(F/A, 4\%, 12) = 530.20(15.026) = \$7966.80$$

# 9-22

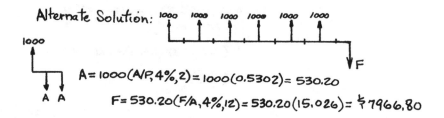

$x =$ years to continue working
age to retire $= 55 + x$

A = 20,000 retirement
A = 5000 adding to fund
48,500
21 years
age 55
age 76

Amount at Retirement = PW of needed retirement funds
$$48,500(F/P, 12\%, x) + 5000(F/A, 12\%, x) = 20,000(P/A, 12\%, 21-x)$$
Trial & Error Solution
Try x = 10
$$48,500(3.106) + 5000(17.549) = 20,000(5.938)$$
$$238,386 \ne 118,760 \qquad \text{so } x \text{ can be} < 10$$
Try x = 5
$$48,500(1.762) + 5000(6.353) = 20,000(6.974)$$
$$117,222 = 139,480 \qquad \text{so } x > 5$$
Try x = 6
$$48,500(1.974) + 5000(8,115) = 20,000(6.811)$$
$$136,314 \approx 136,220 \qquad \therefore x = 6$$

youngest age to retire $= 55 + x = \underline{61}$

# 9-23

| | A | B | C |
|---|---|---|---|
| Cost | 600 | 500 | 200 |
| Uniform annual Benefit | 158.3 | 138.7 | 58.3 |

$$B/c_{of\,A} = \frac{158.3}{600(A/P,10\%,5)} = 1.00 \qquad B/c_{of\,B} = \frac{138.7}{500(A/P,10\%,5)} = 1.05$$

$$B/c_{of\,C} = \frac{58.3}{200(A/P,10\%,5)} = 1.11$$

All alternatives have a B/c ratio $\geqslant 1.00$
Proceed with incremental analysis.

| | B-C | | | A-B |
|---|---|---|---|---|
| Cost | 300 | | Cost | 100 |
| Uniform annual benefit | 80.4 | | Uniform annual benefit | 19.6 |

$$B/c\,of_{B-C} = \frac{80.4}{300(A/P,10\%,5)} = 1.02 \qquad B/c\,of_{A-B} = \frac{19.6}{100(A/P,10\%,5)} = 0.74$$

Desirable increment, so reject C.

undesirable increment reject A

conclusion:  Select B

# 9-24

This is an above-average difficulty problem.  An incremental Uniform Annual Benefit becomes a cost rather than a benefit.

Compute B/c for each alternative

Form of computation used: $\dfrac{PW\,of\,B}{PW\,of\,C} = \dfrac{UAB(P/A,8\%,8)}{cost-S(P/F,8\%,8)}$

$$\quad \overset{5.747}{\phantom{x}} \quad \overset{0.5403}{\phantom{x}}$$

$$B/c_A = \frac{12.2(5.747)}{100-75(0.5403)} = 1.18$$

$$B/c_B = \frac{12(5.747)}{80-50(0.5403)} = 1.30$$

$$B/c_C = \frac{9.7(5.747)}{60-50(0.5403)} = 1.69$$

$$B/c_D = \frac{12.2(5.747)}{50} = 1.40$$

So all alternatives have a B/c > 1.
Proceed with $\Delta$ analysis

Incremental Analysis

$$
\begin{array}{ll}
 & \dfrac{C-D}{} \\
\Delta\text{Cost} & 10 \\
\Delta\text{UAB} & -2.5 \;\; \therefore \text{ this is a COST, not a Benefit} \\
\Delta S & 50
\end{array}
$$

The apparent confusion may be cleared up by a detailed examination of the cash flows:

| YEAR | Cash Flow C | Cash Flow D | Cash Flow C-D |
|------|-------------|-------------|---------------|
| 0 | -60.0 | -50.0 | -10.0 |
| 1-7 | +9.7 | +12.2 | -2.5 |
| 8 | $\left\{ \begin{array}{l} +9.7 \\ +50.0 \end{array} \right.$ | $+12.2$ | $\left. \begin{array}{c} \\ \end{array} \right\} +47.5$ |

$$
C-D: \;\; B/c \text{ ratio} = \frac{47.5(P/F,8\%,8)}{10+2.5(P/A,8\%,7)} = \frac{47.5(0.5403)}{10+2.5(5.206)} = 1.11
$$

$\qquad\qquad\qquad\qquad\qquad\qquad\qquad \underset{\text{NOTE}}{\underbrace{\phantom{xxxx}}}$

The C-D increment is desirable. Reject D.

B-C

$$
\begin{array}{ll}
 & \dfrac{B-C}{} \\
\Delta\text{Cost} & 20.0 \\
\Delta\text{UAB} & 2.3 \\
\Delta S & 0
\end{array}
\qquad
B/c = \frac{2.3(5.747)}{20} = 0.66 \;\; \text{Reject B}
$$

A-C

$$
\begin{array}{ll}
 & \dfrac{A-C}{} \\
\Delta\text{Cost} & 40.0 \\
\Delta\text{UAB} & 2.5 \\
\Delta S & 25.0
\end{array}
\qquad
B/c = \frac{2.5(5.747)}{40-25(0.5403)} = 0.54 \;\; \text{Reject A}
$$

$\qquad\qquad\qquad\qquad\qquad\qquad$ conclusion: Select C

Check the solution by NPW

$$
NPW_A = 12.2\overset{5.747}{(P/A,8\%,8)} + 75\overset{0.5403}{(P/F,8\%,8)} - 100 = +10.64
$$

$$
NPW_B = 12\,(P/A,8\%,8) + 50(P/F,8\%,8) - 80 = +15.98
$$

$$
NPW_C = 9.7\,(P/A,8\%,8) + 50\,(P/F,8\%,8) - 60 = +22.76 \longleftarrow \text{Select C}
$$

$$
NPW_D = 12.2(P/A,8\%,8) - 50 \qquad\qquad = +20.11
$$

**9-25**

(a) $Payback_A = 4\,yrs$      $Payback_B = 1 + \dfrac{200}{125} = 2.6\,yrs$

$Payback_C = 2\,yrs$      To minimize payback choose C

(b) check B/c ratios

$$B/c_A = \frac{100(P/A,10\%,6) + 100(P/F,10\%,1)}{500} = 1.05$$

$$B/c_B = \frac{125(P/A,10\%,5) + 75(P/F,10\%,1)}{400} = 1.36$$

$$B/c_C = \frac{100(P/A,10\%,4) + 100(P/F,10\%,1)}{300} = 1.36$$

Incremental analysis

| YEAR | B−C |
|------|------|
| 0 | −100 |
| 1 | 0 |
| 2 | +25 |
| 3 | +25 |
| 4 | +25 |
| 5 | +125 |

$$\Delta B/\Delta C_{B-C} = \frac{25(P/A,10\%,3)(P/F,10\%,1) + 125(P/F,10\%,5)}{100}$$

$$= 1.34 \quad \text{Desirable increment}$$
$$\text{reject C}$$

| YEAR | A−B |
|------|------|
| 0 | −100 |
| 1 | 0 |
| 2 | −25 |
| 3 | −25 |
| 4 | −25 |
| 5 | −25 |
| 6 | +100 |

By inspection we see that $\Delta B/\Delta C < 1$
computation:

$$\Delta B/\Delta C_{A-B} = \frac{100(P/F,10\%,6)}{100 + 25(P/A,10\%,4)(P/F,10\%,1)} = 0.33$$

Reject A      choose B

**9-26**

$$B/c_A = \frac{142(P/A,10\%,10)}{800} = 1.09 \qquad B/c_B = \frac{60(P/A,10\%,10)}{300} = 1.23$$

$$B/c_C = \frac{33.5(P/A,10\%,10)}{150} = 1.37$$

Incremental analysis

| $\Delta$ Cost | B-C |
|---|---|
| | 150 |
| $\Delta$ UAB | 26.5 |

$$\Delta B/\Delta C = \frac{26.5(P/A,10\%,10)}{150} = 1.09$$

DESIRABLE INCREMENT

Reject C

| $\Delta$ Cost | A-B |
|---|---|
| | 500 |
| $\Delta$ UAB | 82 |

$$\Delta B/\Delta C = \frac{82(P/A,10\%,10)}{500} = 1.01$$

DESIRABLE INCREMENT

Reject B

Select A
$\leqq$

## 9-27

| | A | B | C | D | E |
|---|---|---|---|---|---|
| cost | 100 | 200 | 300 | 400 | 500 |
| UA B | 37 | 69 | 83 | 126 | 150 |

PW of Benefits = UAB (P/A,15%,5)

| | | | | | |
|---|---|---|---|---|---|
| PW of Benefits | 124 | 231.3 | 278.2 | 422.4 | 502.8 |
| B/c ratio | 1.24 | 1.16 | 0.93 | 1.06 | 1.01 |

| | B-A | D-B | E-B |
|---|---|---|---|
| $\Delta$ cost | 100 | 200 | 300 |
| $\Delta$ UAB | 32 | 57 | 81 |
| PW of Benefits | 107.3 | 191.1 | 271.5 |
| $\Delta B/\Delta C$ | 1.07 | 0.96 | 0.91 |
| | Reject A | Reject D | Reject E |

Select B
$\leqq$

## 9-28

(a.)
$$Payback_A = 4 + \frac{150}{350} = YEAR\ 4.4$$

$$Payback_B = YEAR\ 4$$

$$Payback_C = 5 + \frac{100}{200} = YEAR\ 5.5$$

For shortest payback: alt B
$\leqq$

$$NFW_A = 200(F/A,12\%,5)+[50(P/G,12\%,5)-400](F/P,12\%,5)$$
$$-500(F/P,12\%,6)$$
$$= 200(6.353)+[50(6.397)-400](1.762)-500(1.974)=+142.38$$

$$NFW_B = 350(F/A,12\%,5)+[-50(P/G,12\%,5)-300](F/P,12\%,5)$$
$$-600(F/P,12\%,6)$$
$$= 350(6.353)+[-50(6.397)-300](1.762)-600(1.974)= -53.03$$

$$NFW_C = 200(F/A,12\%,5)-900(F/P,12\%,6)$$
$$= 200(6.353)-900(1.974) = -506.00$$

To max NFW, Select A

## 9-29

Costs = Benefits at end of year 8.
∴ Payback Period = 8 yrs

## 9-30

(a)
Increment

| B-A | |
|---|---|
| ΔCost | 300 |
| ΔUAB | 50 |

(a)
Incremental Payback $= \dfrac{Cost}{UAB} = \dfrac{300}{50} = 6$ yrs

(b)
$$\frac{\Delta B}{\Delta C} = \frac{50(P/A,12\%,8)}{300} = 0.83$$

Reject B, Select A

## 9-31

(a) B/c of alt. $X = \dfrac{25(P/A,10\%,4)}{100} = 0.79$

(b) Payback
$$X = 100/25 = 4 \text{ yrs}$$
$$Y = 50/16 = 3.1$$
$$Z = 50/21 = 2.4$$

To minimize payback select Z

(c) No computations are needed.  The problem may be solved by inspection.

Alternative $X$ has a 0% rate of return. (Total benefits = cost.)

Alternative $Z$ dominates Alternative $Y$. (Both cost 50, but Alternative $Y$ yields more benefits.)

Alternative $Z$ has a positive rate of return (actually 24.5%) and is obviously the best of the three mutually exclusive alternatives.

Choose Alternative $Z$

# 9-32

(a) <u>Future Worth Analysis at 6%</u>

$NFW_E = 20(F/A, 6\%, 6) - 90(F/P, 6\%, 6) = +11.79$

$NFW_F^* = 35(F/A, 6\%, 4)(F/P, 6\%, 2) - 110(F/P, 6\%, 6) = +16.02$

$NFW_G = [10(P/G, 6\%, 6) - 100](F/P, 6\%, 6) = +20.70$ ⟵

$NFW_H = 180 - 120(F/P, 6\%, 6) = +9.72$

To maximize NFW, <u>Select G</u>

(b) <u>Future Worth Analysis at 15%</u>

$NFW_E = 20(F/A, 15\%, 6) - 90(F/P, 15\%, 6) = -33.09$

$NFW_F^* = [35(P/A, 15\%, 4) - 110](F/P, 15\%, 6) = -23.30$ ⟵

$NFW_G = 10(P/G, 15\%, 6) - 100](F/P, 15\%, 6) = -47.72$

$NFW_H = 180 - 120(F/P, 15\%, 6) = -97.56$

\* Note: Two different equations that might be used.

To maximize NFW, <u>Select F</u>

(c) $Payback_E = 90/20 = 4.5\,yr$

$Payback_F = 110/35 = 3.1\,yr$ ⟵

$Payback_G = 5\,yr$

$Payback_H = 6\,yr$    To minimize Payback, <u>Select F</u>

(d) $B/C_G = \dfrac{PW\ of\ Benefits}{PW\ of\ Cost} = \dfrac{10(P/G, 7\%, 6)}{100} = \underline{1.10}$

# 9-33

(a)

$NFW_A = 18.8(F/A,10\%,5) - 75(F/P,10\%,5) = -6.06$

$NFW_B = 13.9(F/A,10\%,5) - 50(F/P,10\%,5) = +4.31$ ←

$NFW_C = 4.5(F/A,10\%,5) - 15(F/P,10\%,5) = +3.31$

$NFW_D = 23.8(F/A,10\%,5) - 90(F/P,10\%,5) = +0.31$

Select B

(b)

|  | C | B | A | D |
|---|---|---|---|---|
| Cost | 15.0 | 50.0 | 75.0 | 90.0 |
| Uniform annual Benefit (UAB) | 4.5 | 13.9 | 18.8 | 23.8 |
| computed Uniform annual Cost (UAC) | 3.96 | 13.19 | 19.78 | 23.74 |
| B/C | 1.14 ok | 1.05 ok | 0.95 Reject | 1.00 ok |

Incremental Analysis

|  | B-C | D-B |
|---|---|---|
| ΔUAB | 9.40 | 9.90 |
| ΔUAC | 9.23 | 10.55 |
| ΔB/ΔC | 1.02 Reject C | 0.94 Reject D |

SELECT B

(c)

$Payback_A = 75/18.8 = 4.0$

$Payback_B = 50/13.9 = 3.6$

$Payback_C = 15/4.5 = 3.3$ ←

$Payback_D = 90/23.8 = 3.8$

To minimize Payback, Select C

# 9-34

| | | | Part (a) | |
|---|---|---|---|---|
| YEAR | Conventional | Solar | Solar minus Conventional | Net Investment |
| 0 | -200 | -1400 | -1200 | -1200 |
| 1-4 | -230/yr | -60/yr | +170/yr | -520 |
| 4 | | -180 | -180 | -700 |
| 5-8 | -230/yr | -60/yr | +170/yr | -20 |
| 8 | | -180 | -180 | -200  ← Payback |
| 9-12 | -230/yr | -60/yr | +170/yr | +480 |
| 12 | | -180 | -180 | +300 |

Part (a)

$$\text{Payback} = 8\,\text{yrs} + \frac{200}{170} = 9.18\,\text{yrs}$$

Part (b)

The key to solving this part of the problem is selecting a suitable analysis method.   The Present Worth method requires a common analysis period, which is virtually impossible for this problem.   The problem is easy to solve by Annual Cash Flow Analysis.

$$\text{EUAC}_{\substack{\text{conventional} \\ \text{20 years}}} = 200\,(A/P, 10\%, 20) + 230 = \$253.50$$

$$\text{EUAC}_{\substack{\text{solar for} \\ N\,\text{yrs}}} = 1400\,(A/P, 10\%, N) + 60$$

$$\text{For Equal EUAC:}\quad (A/P, 10\%, N) = \frac{253.50 - 60}{1400} = 0.1382$$

From interest tables: N = 13.5 yrs

# 9-35

For A
$$(\text{EUAB} - \text{EUAC})_A = 230 - 800\,(A/P, 12\%, 5) = +8.08$$

Set $(\text{EUAB} - \text{EUAC})_B = +8.08$ and solve for $X$.

For B
$$(\text{EUAB} - \text{EUAC})_B = 230 - 1000\,(A/P, 12\%, X) = +8.08$$

$$\therefore (A/P, 12\%, X) = \frac{230 - 8.08}{1000} = 0.2219$$

From 12% compound interest table: X = 6.9 yrs.

**9-36**

$NPW_A = 40(P/A, 12\%, 6) + 100(P/F, 12\%, 6) - 150 = +65.10$

Set $NPW_B = NPW_A$

$\qquad = 65(P/A, 12\%, 6) + 200(P/F, 12\%, 6) - X = +65.10$

$\qquad\qquad\qquad\qquad 368.54 - X = 65.10$

$\qquad\qquad\qquad\qquad\qquad X = \underline{303.44}$

**9-37**

<u>NPW Solution</u>

$NPW_A = \dfrac{75}{0.10} - 500 = +250$

$NPW_B = 75(P/A, 10\%, N) - 300 = +250$

$\qquad (P/A, 10\%, N) = \dfrac{550}{75} = 7.33$

$\qquad\qquad\qquad$ From 10% table, $N = \underline{13.9 \text{ yrs}}$

**9-38**

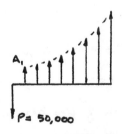

geometric gradient at a 10% uniform rate

$\qquad A_1 = 10,000 \qquad i = 10\% \qquad g = 10\% \qquad n = 8 \text{ yrs}$

where $i = g \qquad P = A_1 \, n \, (1+i)^{-1}$

$\dfrac{B}{C} = \dfrac{PW \text{ of Benefits}}{PW \text{ of Cost}} = \dfrac{10,000(8)(1+0.10)^{-1}}{50,000} = \underline{1.45}$

# 9-39

Difference between alternatives

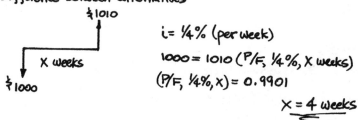

$i = \frac{1}{4}\%$ (per week)

$1000 = 1010 \, (P/F, \frac{1}{4}\%, X \text{ weeks})$

$(P/F, \frac{1}{4}\%, X) = 0.9901$

$X = 4 \text{ weeks}$

# 9-40

(a) Payback period

    at first glance Payback would appear to be

$$\frac{5240}{1000} = 5.24 \text{ years}$$

However, based on end-of-year benefits, as specified in the problem, the correct answer is

        Payback = 6 years.

(b) Breakeven point (in years)

Here interest is used in the computations

For continuous compounding:

$$P = A\left[\frac{e^{rn}-1}{e^{rn}(e^{r}-1)}\right]$$ where $P = 5240$ $r = 0.10$
$A = 1000$ $n = unknown$

$$5240 = 1000\left[\frac{e^{0.1(n)}-1}{e^{0.1(n)}(e^{0.1}-1)}\right] = 1000\left[\frac{e^{0.1n}-1}{0.1052\,e^{0.1n}}\right]$$

$$\left[e^{0.1n}-1\right] = 5.24\left[0.1052\,e^{0.1n}\right]$$

$$e^{0.1n}\left[1-0.5511\right] = 1$$

$$e^{0.1n} = \frac{1}{1-0.5511} = 2.23$$

Solving, $n = 8$ years

(c) Both (a) and (b) are "correct".

Since the breakeven analysis takes all eight years of benefits into account, as well as the interest rate, it is a better measure of long term economic efficiency.

**9-41**

geometric gradient: $g = 100\%$  $A_1 = 100$  $i = 10\%$

$$P = A_1\left[\frac{1-(1+g)^n(1+i)^{-n}}{i-g}\right] = 100\left[\frac{1-(1+1.0)^{10}(1+0.10)^{10}}{0.10-1.0}\right]$$

$$P = 100\left[\frac{1-1024(0.3855)}{-0.90}\right] = 43,755$$

Future Worth $= 43,755(F/P, 10\%, 10) = \$\,113,500.$
$\quad\quad\quad\quad\quad\quad\quad\quad 2.594$

# 9-42

untreated:   $EUAC = \$10.50 \overset{0.1627}{(A/P, 10\%, 10)} = \$1.71$

Treated:   $EUAC = (10.50 + treatment)(A/P, 10\%, 15) = 1.38 + 0.1315 (Treatment)$

Set $EUAC_{untreated} = EUAC_{treated}$

$1.71 = 1.38 + 0.1315 (Treatment)$   $Treatment = \dfrac{1.71 - 1.38}{0.1315} = \$2.51$

So— up to $2.51 could be paid for post treatment.

# 9-43

Since both motors have the same annual maintenance cost, it may be ignored in the computations. Here, however, we will include it.

graybar

$EUAC_G = 7000(A/P, 10\%, 20) + 300 + \dfrac{(200 hp)(0.746 Kw/hp)(\$0.072/Kwhr)}{0.89 \, eff} (Hrs)$

$= 7000(0.1175) + 300 + 12.07 (Hrs) = 1122.50 + 12.07 (Hrs)$

Blueball

$EUAC_B = 6000 \overset{0.1175}{(A/P, 10\%, 20)} + 300 + \dfrac{(200hp)(0.746 Kw/hp)(\$0.072/Kwhr)}{0.85 \, eff} (Hrs)$

$= 705 + 300 + 12.64 (Hrs)$

Set $EUAC_B = EUAC_G$

$1005 + 12.64 (Hrs) = 1122.50 + 12.07 (Hrs)$

The minimum number of hours the graybar, with its smaller power cost, must be used is $(12.64 - 12.07) Hrs = 1122.50 - 1005$

$Hours = \dfrac{117.50}{0.57} = \underline{206 \, hrs}$

# 9-44

By inspection one can see that A, with its smaller cost and identical benefits, is preferred to F in all situations, hence F may be immediately rejected. Similarly, D, with greater benefits and identical cost, is preferred over B. Hence B may be rejected. Based on the B/C ratio for the remaining four alternatives, three exceed 1.0 and only C is less than 1.0. On this basis C may be rejected. That leaves A, D, and E for incremental B/C analysis.   $(P/A, 15\%, 5) = 3.352$

|  | E - D | | A - E |
|---|---|---|---|
| $\Delta$ Cost | 25 | | 50 |
| $\Delta$ Benefits | 10 | | 16 |

$\Delta B/\Delta C = \dfrac{10(3.352)}{25} = 1.34$   Reject D

$\Delta B/\Delta C = \dfrac{16(3.352)}{50} = 1.07$   Reject E   $\therefore$ Do $\underline{A}$

**9-45**

The difference between the alternatives is that Plan A requires $20,000 extra now and Plan B requires $40,000 extra n years hence.

At breakeven

$$20,000 = 40,000 (P/F, 8\%, n)$$

$$(P/F, 8\%, n) = 0.5$$

From 8% interest table, $\underline{n = 9 \text{ years}}$

**9-46**

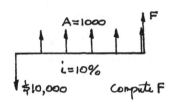

$$
\begin{aligned}
F &= 10,000 \,(F/P, 10\%, 5) - 1000 \,(F/A, 10\%, 5) \\
&= 10,000 \,(1.611) - 1000 \,(6.105) = \underline{\$10,000}
\end{aligned}
$$

**9-47**

$$i = \frac{0.0865}{12} = 0.007208 \qquad n = 24$$

$$F = P(1+i)^n = 2500 \,(1+0.007208)^{24} = \underline{\$2970.30}$$

**9-48**

| YEAR | Cash flow |
|------|-----------|
| 0 | $-X$ |
| 1 | $+8400$ |
| $\vdots$ | $\vdots$ |
| 11 | $+8400$ |
| 12 | $+8400$ |
|    | $+80\,000$ |

where $X$ = maximum purchase price

$$X = (14,400 - 6000)\overset{7.943}{(P/A, 7\%, 12)}$$

$$+ 80000 \underset{0.4440}{(P/F, 7\%, 12)}$$

$$\underline{X = 102,240}$$

# 9-49

The annual cost of the untreated part
$$350\,(A/P, 10\%, 6) = \$80.36$$
$$\phantom{350\,(A/P,}0.2296$$

The annual cost of the treated part must be at least this low

so $\$80.36 = 500\,(A/P, 10\%, n)$

$$(A/P, 10\%, n) = \frac{80.36}{500.} = 0.1607$$

From interest tables:

| $n$ | $(A/P, 10\%, n)$ |
|------|------|
| 10 yrs | 0.1627 |
| 11 yrs | 0.1540 |

So $n = 10\,\text{yrs} + (1)\left(\dfrac{0.1627 - 0.1607}{0.1627 - 0.1540}\right) = \underline{10.2\ \text{years}}$

# 9-50

Lease: $A = 5000/\text{yr}$

Purchase:

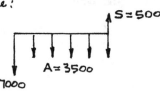

(a) Payback period

Cost = 7000    Benefit = 1500/year + 500 at any time

$$\text{Payback} = \frac{7000 - 500}{1500} = \underline{4.3\ \text{years}}$$

(b) Benefit-cost ratio

$$B/c = \frac{EUAB}{EUAC} = \frac{1500 + 500\,(A/P, 10\%, 6)}{7000\,(A/P, 10\%, 6)} = \underline{0.97}$$

with $0.1296$ over the numerator's $(A/P, 10\%, 6)$ term and $0.2296$ under the denominator's $(A/P, 10\%, 6)$ term.

# 9-51

(a) PW ₂ CostₐA $\qquad$ PW ₂ CostB

$55,000 + 16,200 (P/A, 10\%, n) = 75000 + 12,450 (P/A, 10\%, n)$

$$(P/A, 10\%, n) = \frac{75000 - 55000}{16200 - 12450} = \frac{20000}{3750} = 5.33$$

From 10% interest table

$\qquad (P/A, 10\%, 8) = 5.335$

$\qquad\qquad$ ∴ Machines equivalent at 8 years

(b) at 0% interest

$\qquad$ From (a) $(P/A, 0\%, n) = 5.33$

$\qquad\qquad\qquad$ which equals n

$\qquad\qquad$ ∴ Machines equivalent at 5⅓ years

# 9-52

$F_{56} = 25,000(F/P, 6\%, 35) + 1000(F/A, 6\%, 35) + 200(P/G, 6\%, 35)(F/P, 6\%, 35)$ *
$F = 25,000\ (8.147) + 1000(111.435) + 200(165.743)(7.686)$
$F = \$569.890$

* The factor we want is $(F/G, 6\%, 35)$ but it is not tabulated in the back of the book. Instead we can substitute
$(P/G, 6\%, 35)(F/P, 6\%, 35)$

# 9-53

Assuming no disruption, the expected end-of-year deposits are:
$$A_1 = 1,000,000\ (A/F, 7\%, 10)$$
$$A_1 = 1,000,000\ (0.0724) = \$72,400$$

Compute the future worth of $72,400 per year at the end of 7 years:
$$F_7 = 72,400\ (F/A, 7\%, 7) = \$626,550$$

Compute the future worth of $626,550 in 3 years i.e.at the end of year 10:
$$F_{10} = \$626,550(F/P, 7\%, 3) = \$767,524$$

Remaining two deposits $= (1,000,000 - 767,524)(A/F, 7\%, 2) = \$112,309$

# 9-54

$F = 2000(F/A, 10\%, 41) = 2000(487.852) = \$975,704$
Alternate solution using interest table values:
$F = 2000(F/A, 10\%, 40) + 2000(F/P, 10\%, 40)$
$= 2000(45.259) + 2000(442.593) = \$975,704$

# 9-55

*a.* Payback periods.

|        | Alternative A. |        | Alternative B. |        |
|--------|----------------|--------|----------------|--------|
| Period | Cash Flow      | Sum CF | Cash Flow      | Sum CF |
| -2     | -30            | -30    | -30            | -30    |
| -1     | -100           | -130   | -100           | -130   |
| 0      | -70            | -200   | -70            | -200   |
| 1      | 40             | -160   | 32.5           | -167.5 |
| 2      | 40             | -120   | 32.5           | -135   |
| 3      | 40             | -80    | 32.5           | -102.5 |
| 4      | 40             | -40    | 32.5           | -70    |
| 5      | 40             | 0      | 32.5           | -37.5  |
| 6      | 40             | 40     | 32.5           | -5     |
| 7      | 40             | 80     | 32.5           | 27.5   |

Payback$_A$ = 5.0 years
Payback$_B$ = 7 years (based on end of year cash flows)

*b.* Equivalent Investment Cost:

$$= 30(F/P,10\%,2) +100(F/P,10\%,1) + 70$$
$$= 30(1.210) +100(1.100) + 70$$
$$= \$216.3 \text{ million}$$

*c.* Equivalent Uniform Annual Worth = EUAB - EUAC

$$\text{EUAW}_A = 40 - 216.3(A/P,10\%,10) = \$4.81 \text{ million}$$
$$\text{EUAW}_B = 32.5 - 216.3(A/P,10\%,20) = \$7.08 \text{ million}$$

Since the EUAW for the Alternative *B* is higher, this alternative should be selected. Alternative *A* may be considered if the investor is very short of cash and the short payback period is importance to him.

# 9-56

FW of Costs = $150,000(F/P,10\%,10) +1500(F/A,10\%,10)$
$\qquad\qquad +500(P/G,10\%,7)(F/P,10\%,7) - (0.05)(150,000)$
$\qquad = 150,000(2.594) +1500(15.937) +500(12.763)(1.949) - 7500$
$\qquad = \$417,940$

# 9-57

FW of Costs (from problem 9-5)  = $417,940
Annual Savings $A$ = (0.05)(322,000) =$16,100
Set FW of Savings - FW of Costs = 0
Try $i$ = 20%
16,100($F/A$,20%,10) -417,940 =? 0
16,100(25,959) - 417,940 = 0
So the rate of return is exactly 20% and the machinery should be purchased.

# 9-58

Given:

$P$ = $325,000
$A_{1-120}$ = $1200
$A_{84-120}$ = $2000 - 1200 = $800
$F_{60}$ = $55,000 overhaul
$n$ = 12(10) = 120
$i = \dfrac{7.2}{12}$ = 0.60% per month

Find:  $F_{120}$ = ?

$F_P$ = ($F/P$, 0.60%, 120)(325,000) = $(1 + 0.006)^{120}$ (325,000) = 666,250

$F_{A1-120}$ = ($F/A$, 0.60%, 120)(1200)
= $\left(\dfrac{(1 + 0.006)^{120} - 1}{0.006}\right)$ (1,200) = 210,000

$F_{A84-120}$ = ($F/A$, 0.60%, 36)(800) = $\left(\dfrac{(1 + 0.006)^{36} - 1}{0.006}\right)$ (800) = 32,040

$F_{60}$ = ($F/P$, 0.60%, 60)(55,000) = $(1 + 0.006)^{60}$ (55,000) = 78,750

$F_{120}$ = 666,250 + 210,000 + 32,040 + 78,750 = $987,040

# 9-59

Find: $F$
$F$ = 150($F/A$, 9%,10) + 150($P/G$, 9%,10)($F/P$, 9%,10) = $10,933

**Alternate solution**
Remembering that G must equal zero at the end of period 1, adjust the time scale where
equation time zero = problem time -1.  Then
$F$ = 150($F/G$, 9%, 11) =150($P/G$,9%,11)($F/P$,9%,11)
= 150(28.248)(2.580) = $10,932

# 9-60

$$i_a = \left(1 + \frac{r}{m}\right)^m - 1$$

$$i_a = \left(1 + \frac{0.16}{48}\right)^{48} - 1 = 0.17320$$

$$F = P (1 + i_a)^5 = 50,000 (1 + 0.1732)^5 = \$ 111,130$$

# 9-61

$P_{\text{system 1}}$   $= A (P/A, 12\%, 10) = 15,000 ( 5.650) = 84,750$

$P_{\text{system 2}}$   $= G (P/G, 12\%, 10) = 1200 ( 20.254) = 24,305$

$P_{\text{total}}$   $= 84,750 + 24,305 = \$109,055$

$F_{\text{total}}$   $= P_{\text{total}} (F/P, 12\%, 10) = 109,055 ( 3.106) = \$338,725$

# 9-62

$$i_{\text{semiannual}} = \left[1 + \left(\frac{0.192}{12}\right)\right]^6 - 1 = 0.10 = 10\%$$

$F_{1/1/12} = F_A + F_G$
From the compound interest tables $(i = 10\%, \ n = 31 )$ :
$F_A = 5000 (F/A, 10\%, 31) = 5000 (181.944) = 909,720$
$F_G = -150 (P/G, 10\%, 31)(F/P, 10\%, 31) = -150 (78.640) (19.194) = -226,412$

$F_{1/1/12} = 909,720 - 226,412 = 683,308$
$F_{7/1/14} = 683,308 (F/P, 10\%, 5) = 683,308 (1.611) = \$1,100,809$

# 9-63

The monthly deposits to the savings account do not match the twice a month compounding period.  To use the standard formulas we must either
        (1) compute an equivalent twice a month savings account deposit, or
        (2) compute an equivalent monthly interest rate.

**Method (1)**

$n = 2$

$i = \dfrac{0.045}{24} = 0.001875$

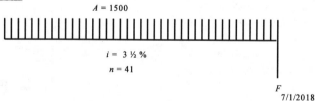

Equivalent twice a month deposit $(A) = 75 \, (A/F, \, i, \, n) = 75 \left[ \dfrac{0.001875}{\left(1+0.001875\right)^2 - 1} \right] = 37.4649$

Future Sum $F_{1/1/15} = A \, (F/A, \, i, \, 18 \times 24) = 37.4649 \left[ \dfrac{\left(1+0.001875\right)^{432} - 1}{0.001875} \right] = \$24{,}901$

**Method (2)**

Effective $i$ per month $(i_{month}) = \left(1 + \dfrac{0.045}{24}\right)^2 - 1 = 0.0037535$

Future Sum $F_{1/1/15} = A \, (F/A, \, i_{month}, \, 18 \times 12) = 75 \left[ \dfrac{\left(1+0.0037535\right)^{216} - 1}{0.0037535} \right] = \$24{,}901$

# 9-64

<u>Bob's Plan</u>

$A = 1500$

$i = 3\;\tfrac{1}{2}\;\%$

$n = 41$

$F$
7/1/2018

$F = 1500 \, (F/A, \, 3\;\tfrac{1}{2}\%, \, 41) = 1500 \, (86.437) = 129{,}650$

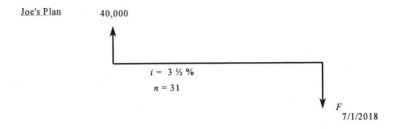

$F = 40,000 \ (F/P, \ 3 \ \tfrac{1}{2}\%, \ 31) \ = \ 40,000 \ (2.905) = 116,200$

Joe's deposit will be insufficient.  He should deposit $132,764(P/F, \ 3 \ \tfrac{1}{2}\%, \ 31) \ = 132,764$
$(0.3442) = \underline{\$45,701}$

**Solutions to Spreadsheet supplement problems are after Chapter 19.**

$P = 12,000 \quad S = 600 \quad N = 4 \text{ years}$

(a) <u>Straight Line Depreciation</u>

$$\text{SL depreciation in each year} = \frac{P-S}{N} = \frac{12000-600}{4} = \underline{\underline{2850}}$$

(b) <u>Sum-of-Years Digits Depreciation</u>

$$\text{SOYD in any year} = \frac{\substack{\text{Remaining Useful Life} \\ \text{at begin. of year}}}{\frac{N}{2}(N+1)} (P-S)$$

1st yr: $\text{SOYD} = \frac{4}{10}(12000-600) = 4560$

2nd yr: $\quad = \frac{3}{10}(12000-600) = 3420$

3rd yr: $\quad = \frac{2}{10}(12000-600) = 2280$

4th yr: $\quad = \frac{1}{10}(12000-600) = 1140 \qquad \Sigma = 11,400$

(c) <u>Double Declining Balance Depreciation</u>

$$\text{DDB in any year} = \frac{2}{N}(\text{Book Value})$$

1st Yr: $\text{DDB} = \frac{2}{4}(12000-0) = 6000$

2nd Yr: $\quad = \frac{2}{4}(12000-6000) = 3000$

3rd Yr: $\quad = \frac{2}{4}(12000-9000) = 1500$

4th Yr: $\quad = \frac{2}{4}(12000-10500) = 750 \qquad \Sigma = 11,250$

(d) <u>DDB Depreciation with conversion (is desirable) to Straight Line</u>

$$\text{SL Deprec for year} = \frac{\text{Book Value beginning of Yr} - \text{Salvage Value}}{\text{Remaining Useful Life beginning of Yr.}}$$

217

I's switch to Straight Line Depreciation

for 2$^{nd}$ year: $SL = \dfrac{12000 - 6000 - 600}{3} = 1800$

for 3$^{rd}$ year: $SL = \dfrac{12000 - 9000 - 600}{2} = 1200$

for 4$^{th}$ year: $SL = \dfrac{12000 - 10500 - 600}{1} = 900$

We will switch to Straight line Depreciation when it exceeds the computed Double Declining Balance Depreciation. This is not the situation until the beginning of the fourth year.

## Summary

| YEAR | Str. Line | SOYD | DDB | DDB/SL |
|------|-----------|------|------|--------|
| 1 | 2850 | 4560 | 6000 | 6000 |
| 2 | 2850 | 3420 | 3000 | 3000 |
| 3 | 2850 | 2280 | 1500 | 1500 |
| 4 | 2850 | 1140 | 750 | 900 |

# 10-2

The computations for the first three methods (SL, DDB, and SOYD) are similar to Problem 10-1.

## (d) Accelerated Cost Recovery System (MACRS)

Read the appropriate percentages from the 7-year class personal property table

| YEAR | Percentage | Year | Percentage |
|------|-----------|------|-----------|
| 1 | 14.29 | 5 | 8.93 |
| 2 | 24.49 | 6 | 8.92 |
| 3 | 17.49 | 7 | 8.93 |
| 4 | 12.49 | 8 | 4.46 |

Computed MACRS depreciation

| YEAR | MACRS | YEAR | MACRS |
|------|-------|------|-------|
| 1 | 14.29%(50,000) = 7145 | 5 | 8.93%(50000) = 4465 |
| 2 | 24.49%(50,000) = 12 245 | 6 | 8.92%(50000) = 4460 |
| 3 | 17.49%(50,000) = 8745 | 7 | 8.93% (50000) = 4465 |
| 4 | 12.49% (50,000) = 6245 | 8 | 4.46%(50,000) = 2230 |

$$\sum_1^8 = 50,000$$

| Year | SL | DDB | SOYD | MACRS |
|------|------|--------|--------|--------|
| 1 | 5000 | 10000 | 9091 | 7145 |
| 2 | 5000 | 8000 | 8182 | 12245 |
| 3 | 5000 | 6400 | 7273 | 8745 |
| 4 | 5000 | 5120 | 6364 | 6245 |
| 5 | 5000 | 4096 | 5455 | 4465 |
| 6 | 5000 | 3277 | 4545 | 4460 |
| 7 | 5000 | 2621 | 3636 | 4465 |
| 8 | 5000 | 2097 | 2727 | 2230 |
| 9 | 5000 | 1678 | 1818 | 0 |
| 10 | 5000 | 1342 | 909 | 0 |
| | 50,000 | 44,631 | 50,000 | 50,000 |

## 10-3

(a)

| Year | SL Deprec | SOYD Deprec | | DDB Deprec |
|------|-----------|-------------|---|-----------|
| 1 | 15 200 | 25 333 | $2/5 \,(76000 - 0) =$ | 30 400 |
| 2 | 15 200 | 20 267 | $2/5 \,(76000 - 30,400) =$ | 18 240 |
| 3 | 15 200 | 15 200 | $2/5 \,(76000 - 48,640) =$ | 10 944 |
| 4 | 15 200 | 10 133 | $2/5 \,(76000 - 59,584) =$ | 6 566 |
| 5 | 15 200 | 5067 | $2/5 \,(76000 - 66,150) =$ | 3 940 |
| | 76,000 | 76,000 | | 70,090 |

Part (b)

By looking at the data in Part (a), some students may jump to the
conclusion that one should switch from DDB to Straight Line
depreciation at the beginning of Year 3.  This mistaken view is
based on the fact that in the table above the Straight Line
depreciation for Year 3 is 15,200, while the DDB depreciation
is only 10,944.  This is not a correct analysis of the situation.

This may be illustrated by computing the Straight Line depreciation
for Year 3, if DDB depreciation had been used in the prior years.

With DDB depreciation for the first two years, the book value at
the beginning of Year 3 = 76,000 - 30,400 - 18,240 = 27,360.

SL depreciation for subsequent years = $\dfrac{27,360 - 0}{3}$ = 9,120

Thus, the choice for Year 3 is to use DDB = 10,944 or SL = 9,120.
One would naturally choose to continue with DDB depreciation.

For subsequent years:

| If Switch for Year | Beginning of Yr Book Value | Remaining Life | $SL = \dfrac{Book - Salvage}{Remaining\ Life}$ |
|---|---|---|---|
| 4 | $16,416 | 2 yrs | $8208 |
| 5 | 9,850 | 1 yr | 9850 |

When SL is compared to DDB in Part (a), it is apparent that the switch should take place at the beginning of Year 4. The resulting depreciation schedule is:

| Year | DDB with Conversion to Straight Line |
|---|---|
| 1 | $30,400 |
| 2 | 18,240 |
| 3 | 10,944 |
| 4 | 8,208 |
| 5 | 8,208 |
| | 76,000 |

# 10-4

DDB Depreciation

| Year | | DDB Deprec |
|---|---|---|
| 1 | 2/5(16,000 -      0) = | 6400 |
| 2 | 2/5(16,000 -   6400) = | 3840 |
| 3 | 2/5(16,000 - 10240) = | 2304 |
| 4 | 2/5(16,000 - 12544) = | 1382 |
| 5 | 2/5(16,000 - 13926) = | 830 |
| | | 14,756 |

Converting to Straight Line Depreciation

| If Switch for Year | Beginning of Yr Book Value | Remaining Life | $SL = \dfrac{Book - Salvage}{Remaining\ Life}$ | Decision |
|---|---|---|---|---|
| 2 | $9600 | 4 yr | $2400 | Do Not Switch |
| 3 | 5760 | 3 | 1920 | Do Not Switch |
| 4 | 3456 | 2 | 1728 | Switch to SL |
| 5 | 2074 | 1 | 2074 | |

Resulting Depreciation Schedule:

$6400
3840
2304
1728
1728
16,000

# 10-5

Part (a).  DDB Depreciation with conversion to SOYD Depreciation

There is no example in the text, hence this is a challenging problem.

DDB Depreciation

| Year | | DDB Deprec |
|------|--|------------|
| 1 | 2/5(1,500,000 -         0) = | $600,000 |
| 2 | 2/5(1,500,000 -   600,000) = | 360,000 |
| 3 | 2/5(1,500,000 -   960,000) = | 216,000 |
| 4 | 2/5(1,500,000 - 1,176,000) = | 129,600 |
| 5 | 2/4(1,500,000 - 1,305,600) = | 77,760 |

Converting to SOYD Depreciation

| If Switch for Year | Begin of Yr Book Value | Remaining Life | SOYD Sum | | SOYD Deprec | Sw? |
|------|------|------|------|------|------|------|
| 2 | $900,000 | 4 yr | 10 | 4/10(900,000) = | 360,000 | no |
| 3 | 540,000 | 3 | 6 | 3/6(540,000) = | 270,000 | Yes |
| After Switch | | | | | | |
| 4 | | 2 | | 2/6(540,000) = | 180,000 | |
| 5 | | 1 | | 1/6(540,000) = | 90,000 | |

Resulting composite depreciation schedule:

$$\begin{array}{r} \$600,000 \\ 360,000 \\ 270,000 \\ 180,000 \\ 90,000 \end{array}$$

Part (b).  MACRS Depreciation

| Year | | MACRS Deprec |
|------|--|------------|
| 1 | $20.00\%(1.5\times10^6)$ = | $300,000 |
| 2 | $32.00\%(1.5\times10^6)$ = | 480,000 |
| 3 | $19.20\%(1.5\times10^6)$ = | 288,000 |
| 4 | $11.52\%(1.5\times10^6)$ = | 172,800 |
| 5 | $11.52\%(1.5\times10^6)$ = | 172,800 |
| 6 | $5.76\%(1.5\times10^6)$ = | 86,400 |
| | $\Sigma$ = | $1,500,000 |

# 10-6

Gross income from sand and gravel

$$65 ¢/m^3 \times 45,000\, m^3 = 29,250$$
to Engineering Student $\quad \underline{-2,500}$
$\quad\quad\quad\quad\quad\quad \$\; 26,750$  taxable income excluding depletion

Percentage depletion $= 5\% \times 29,250 = \$1462.50$

$\therefore$ Allowable depletion $= \$1462.50$

# 10-7

mr. Salt's cost depletion $= \$45,000 \dfrac{1000\, Bbl}{15000\, Bbl} = \$3000.$

Percentage depletion $= 15\%(\$12,000) = \$1800$, but limited to 50% of taxable income before depletion
or $50\%(12,000-3000) = \$4500.$

$\therefore$ Allowable depletion $= \$3000.00$

# 10-8

(a) SOYD Depreciation

$N = 8$   SUM $= \dfrac{N}{2}(N+1) = 36$

First Year SOYD Depreciation
$= \dfrac{8}{36}(600,000 - 60,000)$
$= 120,000$

Subsequent years are a declining gradient

$G = \dfrac{1}{36}(600,000 - 60,000)$
$= 15,000$

| YEAR | SOYD |
|------|------|
| 1 | 120,000 |
| 2 | 105,000 |
| 3 | 90,000 |
| 4 | 75,000 |
| 5 | 60,000 |
| 6 | 45,000 |
| 7 | 30,000 |
| 8 | 15,000 |
| | 540,000 |

(b) Unit of Production (UOP) Depreciation

$$\text{Deprec/hour} = \frac{\$540,000}{21,600 \text{hrs}} = \$25/\text{hr}$$

| YEAR | utilization hrs/yr | UOP Depreciation |
|---|---|---|
| 1 | 6000 | 150,000 |
| 2 | 4000 | 100,000 |
| 3 | 4000 | 100,000 |
| 4 | 1600 | 40,000 |
| 5 | 800 | 20,000 |
| 6 | 800 | 20,000 |
| 7 | 2200 | 55,000 |
| 8 | 2200 | 55,000 |
| | 21,600 | 540,000 |

## 10-9

| YEAR | Possible UOP | SL | SOYD | 150% DB | DDB | DDB w/conv SL | MACRS |
|---|---|---|---|---|---|---|---|
| 1 | 35 | 27 | 45 | 43.50 | 58.00 | 58.00 | 29.00 |
| 2 | 20 | 27 | 36 | 30.45 | 34.80 | 34.80 | 46.40 |
| 3 | 30 | 27 | 27 | 21.32 | 20.88 | 20.88 | 27.84 |
| 4 | 30 | 27 | 18 | 14.92 | 12.53 | 12.53 | 16.70 |
| 5 | 20 | 27 | 9 | 10.44 | 7.52 | 8.79 | 16.70 |
| 6 | | | | | | | 8.36 |
| | 135 | 135 | 135 | 120.63 | 133.73 | 135 | 145.00 |
| ans: | B | | | E | D | A | C |

Based on Cost = 145 and Salvage value = 10

# 10-10

(a) 1st payment = $\$2$    Final payment = $132 \times \$2 = \$264$

$$\text{average payment} = \frac{264+2}{2} = \$133$$

Total amount = 132 payments × $\$133$ average payment = $\$17,556$

<u>Alternate Solution</u>

The payments are of the same form as Sum-of-Years digits.

$$\text{SUM} = \frac{n}{2}(n+1) = \frac{132}{2}(133) = 8778$$

Total amount = $\$2$ (SUM) = $\$2 \times 8778 = \$17,556$

(b) The bank will lend the present worth of the gradient series

$$\text{Loan} (P) = \$2 \,(P/G, 1\%, 133)$$    Note: $n-1 = 132$
$$\therefore \; n = 133$$

By interpolation

$$(P/G, 1\%, 133) = 3334.11 + \frac{13}{120}(6878.6 - 3334.1) = 3718.1$$

$$\text{Loan} (P) = \$2 \,(3718.1) = \$7436.20$$

# 10-11

| YEAR | SL | SOYD | DDB | UOP* | MACRS | YEAR |
|------|------|------|------|------|-------|------|
| 1 | 1060 | 1767 | 2600 | 707 | 1300 | 1 |
| 2 | 1060 | 1413 | 1560 | 1178 | 2080 | 2 |
| 3 | 1060 | 1060 | 936 | | 1248 | 3 |
| 4 | 1060 | 707 | 204 | | 749 | 4 |
| 5 | 1060 | 353 | 0 | | 749 | 5 |
| | 5300 | 5300 | 5300 | | 374 | 6 |
| | | | | | 6500 | |

* UOP deprec
is based on
<u>actual</u> production.

# 10-12

| YEAR | SOYD | DDB |
|------|------|------|
| 1 | 2400 | 3333 |
| 2 | 2000 | 2222 |
| 3 | 1600 | 1482 |
| 4 | 1200 | 988 |
| 5 | 800 | 375* |
| 6 | 400 | 0 |
| | 8400 | 8400 |

*computed 658 must be reduced to 375 to avoid depreciating the asset below its salvage value.

# 10-13

DDB with conversion to Straight Line depreciation.
One-half year depreciation in first and last years.

| YEAR | | | | | MACRS Deprec |
|------|---|---|---|---|------|

1   $\frac{1}{2}$yr   $\frac{1}{2}\left(\frac{2}{5}\right)(100 - 0 ) = 20.00$

2   $\left(\frac{2}{5}\right)(100 - 20.00) = 32.00$

3   $\left(\frac{2}{5}\right)(100 - 52.00 ) = 19.20$

4   $\left(\frac{2}{5}\right)(100 - 71.20) = 11.52$

check for conversion to SL in Yr 4

$SL = \dfrac{100 - 71.20}{2.5} = 11.52$

Yes - convert to Straight Line

5   = 11.52

6   $\frac{1}{2}$ yr SL   = 5.76

100.00

These computed values are the same as Table 10-4.

# 10-14

computations:

SL   deprec in any year = $\frac{45000-0}{5}$ = 9000

SOYD   sum = $\frac{n}{2}(n+1) = \frac{5}{2}(6) = 15$

YEAR 1 = $\frac{5}{15}(45000-0) = 15000$

gradient = $\frac{1}{15}(45000-0) = -3000$

### DDB

YEAR

1   $\frac{2}{5}(45,000-0)$    = 18,000

2   $\frac{2}{5}(45000-18000) = 10800$

3   $\frac{2}{5}(45000-28800) = 6480$

4   $\frac{2}{5}(45000-35280) = 3888$

5   $\frac{2}{5}(45000-39168) = 2333$

### If Convert to SOYD

SOYD = $\frac{\text{Remaining Life}}{\text{Sum Yrs digits}}$ (Book Value)

YR     of remaining life

2   $\frac{4}{4+3+2+1}(45000-18000) = 10,800$   DO NOT SWITCH

3   $\frac{3}{3+2+1}(45000-28800) = 8,100$   switch

4   $\frac{2}{2+1}(45000-36900) = 5400$*

5   $\frac{1}{1}(45000-42300) = 2700$*

*An alternate computation of SOYD for the 2 years after the switch (Yrs 4 and 5):

YEAR 4: $\frac{2}{3+2+1}(45000-28800) = 5400$

YEAR 5: $\frac{1}{3+2+1}(45000-28800) = 2700$

### MACRS

Depreciation Percentages:   20%, 32%  19.20%
                            11.52%  11.52%  5.76%

## DEPRECIATION SCHEDULES

| YEAR | SL | SOYD | DDB | DDB with Conv to SOYD | MACRS | YEAR |
|---|---|---|---|---|---|---|
| 1 | 9000 | 15000 | 18000 | 18000 | 9000 | 1 |
| 2 | 9000 | 12000 | 10800 | 10800 | 14400 | 2 |
| 3 | 9000 | 9000 | 6480 | 8100 | 8640 | 3 |
| 4 | 9000 | 6000 | 3888 | 5400 | 5184 | 4 |
| 5 | 9000 | 3000 | 2333 | 2700 | 5184 | 5 |
|  | 45,000 | 45,000 | 41,501 | 45,000 | 2592 | 6 |
|  |  |  |  |  | 45,000 |  |

**10-15**

YEAR

1  $\frac{1}{2} \text{ yr} \times \frac{2}{10} (\text{Cost} - 0) = 10.00\%$

2  $\frac{2}{10} (\text{Cost} - 0.10 \text{ Cost}) = 18.00$

3  $\frac{2}{10} (\text{Cost} - 0.28 \text{ Cost}) = 14.40$

4  $\frac{2}{10} (\text{Cost} - 0.424 \text{ Cost}) = 11.52$

5  $\frac{2}{10} (\text{Cost} - 0.5392 \text{ Cost}) = 9.22$

6  $\frac{2}{10} (\text{Cost} - 0.6314 \text{ Cost}) = 7.37$

7  $\frac{2}{10} (\text{Cost} - 0.7051 \text{ Cost}) = 5.89$ DDB

OR is switch to Str. Line:

7  $\dfrac{100 - 0.7051}{4.5} = 6.55$ SL  (actually 6.5533)

Since SL deprec > DDB deprec, use SL for year 7
and subsequent years: 8, 9, 10

Year 11:  $\dfrac{1.00 - 0.7051}{4.5} \times 0.5 = 3.28$  But check to see if total
equals 100%.

Therefore the MACRS depreciation for 10-year personal property
is

| YEAR | MACRS |
|------|-------|
| 1 | 10.00% |
| 2 | 18.00 |
| 3 | 14.40 |
| 4 | 11.52 |
| 5 | 9.22 |
| 6 | 7.37 |
| 7 | 6.55 |
| 8 | 6.55 |
| 9 | 6.56 |
| 10 | 6.55 |
| 11 | 3.28 |

This is the same as table 10-4.

# 10-16

Ratio $S/P = \dfrac{75000}{1,000,000} = 0.075$

From Table 10-2 : $S/P = 0.05$    DDB w/conv to SL for year 5

$S/P = 0.10$    DDB    Conversion not needed

So in this problem there are three possibilities

1. DDB w/conv to SL for year 5

2. DDB w/conv to SL for year 6

3. DDB    Conversion not needed

| YEAR | | DDB Deprec |
|---|---|---|
| 1 | $2/6 \,(1,000,000 - 0\ \ \ )=$ | 333,333 |
| 2 | $2/6 \,(1,000,000 - 333,333)=$ | 222,222 |
| 3 | $2/6 \,(1,000,000 - 555,555)=$ | 148,148 |
| 4 | $2/6 \,(1,000,000 - 703,703)=$ | 98,766 |
| 5 | $2/6 \,(1,000,000 - 802,469)=$ | 65,844 |
| 6 | $2/6 \,(1,000,000 - 868,313)=$ | 43,896 |
| | | 912,209 |

If switch to SL for year 5:

$SL = \dfrac{1,000,000 - 802,469 - 75,000}{2} = 61,266$    Do Not Switch

If switch to SL for year 6:

$SL = \dfrac{1,000,000 - 868,313 - 75000}{1} = 56,687$    Switch

Preferred Depreciation Schedule:

| Year | |
|---|---|
| 1 | 333,333 |
| 2 | 222,222 |
| 3 | 148,148 |
| 4 | 98,766 |
| 5 | 65,844 |
| 6 | 56,687 |
| | 925,000 |

# 10-17

| YEAR | DDB | If Conv to SL |
|---|---|---|
| 1 | $2/5 (1000 - 0) = 400$ | |
| 2 | $2/5 (1000 - 400) = 240$ | |
| 3 | $2/5 (1000 - 640) = 144$ | |
| 4 | $2/5 (1000 - 784) = 86.40$ | $\frac{1000-784-50}{2} = 83.$ Don't switch |
| 5 | $2/5 (1000 - 870.4) = 51.84$ | $\frac{1000-870.4-50}{1} = 79.6$  switch |

| YEAR | SOYD | PW at Yr1 at 10% | OR | PW at Yr0 at 10% |
|---|---|---|---|---|
| 1 | $5/15 (1000-50) = 316.67$ | 316.67 | | 287.88 |
| 2 | $4/15 (1000-50) = 253.33$ | 230.30 | | 209.35 |
| 3 | $3/15 (1000-50) = 190.00$ | 157.02 | | 142.15 |
| 4 | $2/15 (1000-50) = 126.67$ | 95.17 | | 86.52 |
| 5 | $1/15 (1000-50) = 63.33$ | 43.25 | | 39.32 |
| | 950.00 | 842.41 | | 765.82 |

| YEAR | DDB w/conv to SL | PW at Yr1 at 10% | OR alternately compute at Yr0 | PW at Yr0 at 10% |
|---|---|---|---|---|
| 1 | 400.00 | 400.00 | | 363.64 |
| 2 | 240.00 | 218.18 | | 198.34 |
| 3 | 144.00 | 119.00 | | 108.19 |
| 4 | 86.40 | 64.91 | | 59.01 |
| 5 | 79.60 | 54.37 | | 49.42 |
| | 950.00 | 856.46 | | 778.60 |

To maximize the Present Worth (at either Yr 0 or Yr 1)
Choose Double Declining Balance with
   Conversion to Straight Line Depreciation

# 10-18

The depreciation schedules are
  A  150% Declining Balance with conversion to Straight Line
  B  Accelerated Cost Recovery System (MACRS)
  C  Double Declining Balance
  D  Straight Line
  E  Unit of Production

# 10-19

Since the building is a leasehold improvement, which reverts to the landowner at the end of the lease, it may be depreciated over the period of the lease. Below MACRS is based on straight line depreciation using the mid-month convention and 15 years.

Recovery
Year                                      MACRS

1     $\frac{11.5 \text{ mo}}{12 \text{ mo}} \times \frac{250,000}{15 \text{ yr}} = 15,972$

2-15        $\frac{250,000}{15 \text{ yr}} = 16,666$

16    $\frac{0.5 \text{ mo}}{12 \text{ mo}} \times \frac{250,000}{15 \text{ yr}} = 704$    calculation gives 694, but increased to 704 to total depreciation = 250,000

| Year | MACRS Deprec | PW at Yr 0 at 10% | SOYD Deprec | PW at Yr 0 at 10% |
|------|-------------|-------------------|-------------|-------------------|
| 1 | $15,972 | $14,520 | $31,250 | $28,409 |
| 2 | 16,666 | 13,773 | 29,167 | 24,104 |
| 3 | 16,666 | 12,521 | 27,083 | 20,347 |
| 4 | 16,666 | 11,383 | 25,000 | 17,075 |
| 5 | 16,666 | 10,348 | 22,917 | 14,229 |
| 6 | 16,666 | 9,408 | 20,833 | 11,760 |
| 7 | 16,666 | 8,553 | 18,750 | 9,622 |
| 8 | 16,666 | 7,775 | 16,667 | 7,775 |
| 9 | 16,666 | 7,068 | 14,583 | 6,185 |
| 10 | 16,666 | 6,425 | 12,500 | 4,819 |
| 11 | 16,666 | 5,841 | 10,417 | 3,651 |
| 12 | 16,666 | 5,310 | 8,333 | 2,655 |
| 13 | 16,666 | 4,828 | 6,250 | 1,811 |
| 14 | 16,666 | 4,388 | 4,167 | 1,097 |
| 15 | 16,666 | 3,990 | 2,083 | 499 |
| 16 | 704 | 153 | | |
| | $250,000 | $126,284 | $250,000 | $154,038 |

To maximize PW, choose SOYD depreciation.

# 10-20

From Table 10-2 (Choosing Between SOYD and DDB Depreciation) we see the preferred depreciation is DDB with conversion to SL depreciation at either four or five years.  The proper conversion point must be calculated.

| YEAR | DDB | | DDB w/conv to Straight Line |
|---|---|---|---|
| 1 | $\frac{2}{5}(12000 - 0) = 4800$ | | 4800 |
| 2 | $\frac{2}{5}(12000 - 4800) = 2880$ | Is convert for | 2880 |
| 3 | $\frac{2}{5}(12000 - 7680) = 1728$ | Year four: | 1728 |
| 4 | $\frac{2}{5}(12000 - 9408) = 1036.8$ | $\frac{12000 - 9408 - 400}{2} = 1096$ | 1096 |
| 5 | $\frac{2}{5}(12000 - 10444.8) = \underline{622.1}$ | | $\underline{1096}$ |
| | 11066.9* | | 11600 |

*Since this amount is less than P - S = 12,000 - 400 = 11,600 we see that conversion to straight line is required as is specified in Table 10-2.

Preferred Depreciation Schedule

# 10-21

(a) DDB with conversion (is appropriate) to SL depreciation

YEAR
1  $\frac{2}{4}(10,000 - 0) = 5000$
2  $\frac{2}{4}(10,000 - 5000) = 2500$

Is switch to SL for Year 2:

$SL = \frac{10000 - 5000}{3} = 1667$ ∴ Don't Switch

$2^{nd}$ year depreciation = 2500

(b) SOYD

2nd year SOYD = $\frac{3}{10}(10,000 - 0) = 3000$

(c) MACRS

Special Tools with 4-year life are in the 3-year property class

$2^{nd}$ year MACRS = 44.45% (10,000) = 4445

# 10-22

YEAR                    MACRS DEprec

| | | |
|---|---|---|
| 1 | $1.177\%$ (600,000) = 7062 | 5½ months |
| 2-4 | $2.564\%$ (600,000) = 15,384 | |
| 5 | $1.391\%$ (600,000) = 8,346 | 6½ months |

Note that Year 1 + Year 5 ≠ 15,384.
This is caused by rounding in the MACRS table.

# 10-23

## SOYD Depreciation

$$\text{SUM} = \frac{5}{2}(5+1) = 15$$

| YEAR | SOYD Deprec | PW at Yr0 at 8% |
|---|---|---|
| 1 | $5/15$ ( 120,000) = 40,000 | 37,036 |
| 2 | $4/15$ ( 120,000 ) = 32,000 | 27,434 |
| 3 | $3/15$ ( 120,000 ) = 24,000 | 19,051 |
| 4 | $2/15$ (120,000) = 16,000 | 11,760 |
| 5 | $1/15$ (120,000) = 8,000 | 5,445 |
| | 120,000 | 100,726 |

## Unit Of Production Depreciation

| YEAR | UOP Deprec | PW at Yr0 at 8% |
|---|---|---|
| 1 | $\frac{15000}{40000}$ (120,000) = 45,000 | 41,666 |
| 2 | $\frac{11000}{40000}$ (120,000) = 33,000 | 28,291 |
| 3 | $\frac{4000}{40000}$ (120,000) = 12,000 | 9,526 |
| 4 | $\frac{6000}{40000}$ (120,000) = 18,000 | 13,230 |
| 5 | $\frac{4000}{40000}$ (120,000) = 12,000 | 8,167 |
| | 120,000 | 100,880 |

choose UOP depreciation

# 10-24

150% DB depreciation with conversion to straight line

| YEAR | | 150% DB |
|---|---|---|
| 1 | $\frac{1.5}{5}(2,000,000 - 0)$ = | 600,000 |
| 2 | $\frac{1.5}{5}(2,000,000 - 600,000)$ = | 420,000 |
| 3 | $\frac{1.5}{5}(2,000,000 - 1,020,000)$ = | 294,000 |
| 4 | $\frac{1.5}{5}(2,000,000 - 1,314,000)$ = | 205,800 |
| 5 | $\frac{1.5}{5}(2,000,000 - 1,519,800)$ = | 144,060 |
| | | 1,663,860 |

Is switch to straight line depreciation
for

Year 3:  SL deprec = $\frac{2,000,000 - 1,020,000 - 250,000}{3}$ = 243,333

This is < 294,000. Don't switch.

Year 4:  SL deprec = $\frac{2,000,000 - 1,314,000 - 250,000}{2}$ = 218,000

This is > 205,800. ∴ Switch.

Resulting Depreciation Schedule

> 600,000
> 420,000
> 294,000
> 218,000
> 218,000
> 1,750,000

# 10-25

The depreciation schedules

    A   Sum-Of-Years digits
    B   150% Declining Balance
    C   MACRS
    D   DDB with conversion to SL

It is very helpful, as a first step, to compute the sum of the depreciation schedule.

# 10-26

Straight Line depreciation is never preferred so long as the firm is profitable and prefers to depreciate its assets as rapidly as possible.

No, the same depreciable life might not be applicable. The MACRS property classes almost always assume lives shorter than the Asset Depreciation Range (ADR) midpoint lives. Thus office furniture, that would be depreciated over 10 years using SOYD depreciation, is in the 7-year MACRS property class.

# 10-27

A hotel is nonresidential real property with a 39-year useful life. Using Table 10-5, with the midmonth convention, the MACRS depreciation is:

    Calendar Year 1 (purchased in June*)
        1.391% x $850,000 = $11,823.50
    Calendar Years 2 & 3
        2.564% x $850,000 = $21,794.00
    Calendar Year 4 (sold in June*)
        1.177% x $850,000 = $10,004.50

*The mid-month convention means we assume June 15th for property placed in service in June. Thus there are 6½ months (June 15 to Dec 31) of depreciation in the first calendar year. In the fourth calendar year the June sale is taken as June 15th also. This time there would be just 5½ months (Jan 1 - June 15) of depreciation.

# 10-28

At higher salvage values, the book value will reach the salvage value (S) prior to the end of the depreciable life (N). Since the depreciation must be stopped when the salvage value is reached, there is no conversion. This situation is shown in Fig. 10-5(a).

# 10-29

Computers are in the 5-year property class. Year 1 will be double declining balance, with the computer assumed to be put in service February 15th (the mid-quarter).

For full year:
$$DDB = \frac{2}{5}(70,000) = \$28,000.$$

For the mid-first quarter installation:
$$MACRS\ depreciation = \frac{10½\ months}{12\ months}(28,000) = \$24,500$$

# 10-30

(a)

$$EUAC_I = (P-S)(A/P, i, n) + Si + \text{Annual operating cost}$$

$$= (80000 - 20000)(A/P, 10\%, 20) + 20000(0.10) + 18000$$

with $0.1175$ above $(A/P, 10\%, 20)$

$$= 27,050$$

$$EUAC_{II} = (100000 - 25000)(A/P, 10\%, 25) + 25000(0.10) + 20000$$

with $0.1102$ above $(A/P, 10\%, 25)$

$$- 5000(P/A, 10\%, 10)(A/P, 10\%, 25)$$

$$= 75000(0.1102) + 2500 + 20000$$

$$- 5000(6.145)(0.1102)$$

$$= 27,380$$

To minimize EUAC, select machine II

(b)

Capitalized cost of machine I
= PW of an infinite life = $\dfrac{EUAC}{i}$

In Part(a) EUAC = 27050

So Capitalized Cost = $\dfrac{EUAC}{i} = \dfrac{27050}{0.10} = \$270,500.$

(c)

Fund to replace machine I

Required future sum F = 80,000 - 20,000 = 60,000

Annual deposit A = 60,000 (A/F, 10%, 20)

$$= 60,000(0.0175) = \$1050$$

(d)

| Year | Cash flow |
|------|-----------|
| 0 | -80,000 |
| 1-20 | $\begin{cases} +28000 \\ -18000 \end{cases}$ |
| 20 | +20,000 |

$$80,000 = (28000 - 18000)(P/A, i\%, 20) + 20000(P/F, i\%, 20)$$

Solve by trial and error

Try $i = 10\%$

$$80,000 \overset{?}{=} (10,000)(8.514) + 20000(0.1486) = 88,112.$$

Try $i = 12\%$

$$80000 \overset{?}{=} (10000)(7.469) + 20000(0.1037) = 76,764.$$

$$\text{Rate of Return} = 10\% + (2\%)\left(\frac{88112 - 80000}{88112 - 76764}\right) = \underline{\underline{11.4\%}}$$

(e)

SOYD depreciation

Book value of Machine I after two periods

$$\frac{\text{Depreciation charge}}{\text{in any year}} = \frac{\begin{array}{c}\text{Remaining useful life}\\\text{at beginning of year}\end{array}}{\begin{array}{c}\text{SOYD for total useful}\\\text{life}\end{array}} (P-S)$$

Sum of years digits $= \frac{n}{2}(n+1) = \frac{20}{2}(20+1) = 210$

1st yr depreciation $= \frac{20}{210}(80000 - 20000) = 5714$

2nd yr depreciation $= \frac{19}{210}(80000 - 20000) = \underline{5429}$

$\Sigma = 11,143$

Book value = Cost − deprec to date $= 80,000 - 11,143 = \underline{\underline{68,857}}$

(f)

DDB depreciation

Book value of Machine II after three years

$$\frac{\text{Depreciation Charge}}{\text{in any year}} = \frac{2}{n}(P - \text{deprec charges to date})$$

$$\text{1st yr deprec} = \frac{2}{25}(100,000 - \quad 0) = 8000$$

$$\text{2nd yr deprec} = \frac{2}{25}(100,000 - 8000) = 7360$$

$$\text{3rd yr deprec} = \frac{2}{25}(100,000 - 15360) = \underline{6771}$$

$$\Sigma = 22,131$$

Book value = Cost - deprec to date
$$= 100,000 - 22,131 = \underline{77,869.}$$

(g)

MACRS depreciation   7 yr Class

Machine II  third year

From table 10-4 read:  17.49%

$$\text{MACRS depreciation} = 0.1749(100,000) = \underline{17,490}$$

# 10-31

**a.** Straight Line Method

| Year | SL Depr | PW of Deprec |
|------|---------|--------------|
| 1 | $\dfrac{100,000-20,000}{5}=16,000$ | 14,546 |
| 2 | = 16,000 | 13,222 |
| 3 | = 16,000 | 12,021 |
| 4 | = 16,000 | 10,928 |
| 5 | = 16,000 | 9,934 |
|   | 80,000 | 60,651 |

**b.** Double Declining Balance Method

| Year | Depreciation | DDB Depr | PW of Depr |
|------|--------------|----------|------------|
| 1 | 2/5 (100,000 - 0) = 40,000 | 40,000 | 36,364 |
| 2 | 2/5 (100,000-40,000) = 24,000 | 24,000 | 19,834 |
| 3 | 2/5 (100,000-64,000) = 14,400 | 14,400 | 10.819 |
| 4 | 2/5 (100,000-78,400) = 8,640 | 1,600* | 1,093 |
| 5 | 2/5 (100,000- 87,040) = 5,184 | 0 | 0 |
|   |   | 80,000 | 68,110 |

* DDB depreciation must stop when it reaches the salvage value.

**c.** MACRS Method

| Year | MACRS Depreciation | PW of Depr |
|------|--------------------|------------|
| 1 | 20.00% (100,000) = 20,000 | 18,182 |
| 2 | 32.00% (100,000) = 32,000 | 26,445 |
| 3 | 19.20% (100,000) = 19,200 | 14,425 |
| 4 | 11.52% (100,000) = 11,520 | 7,868 |
| 5 | 11.52% (100,000) = 11,520 | 7,153 |
| 6 | 5.76% (100,000) = 5,760 | 3,252 |
|   | 100,000 | 77,325 |

**Conclusion:** Select the depreciation method that has the largest PW of depreciation. Choose MACRS.

# 10-32

Initial investment = $100,000 ; $n$ = 6 years; SV = $10,000
Straight Line depreciation:
Annual Depreciation = ($100,000 - $10,000)/6 years = $15,000/yr.

| Year | SL Deprec | Book Value |
|------|-----------|------------|
| 1 | $15,000 | 85,000 |
| 2 | $15,000 | 70,000 |
| 3 | $15,000 | 55,000 |
| 4 | $15,000 | 40,000 |
| 5 | $15,000 | 25,000 |
| 6 | $15,000 | 10,000 |

Sum-of-years digits (SOYD):  SOYD = $n/2(n + 1)$ = $6/2(6 + 1)$ = 21

| Year | Depreciation Calculation | SOYD Deprec | Book Value |
|------|--------------------------|-------------|------------|
| 1 | 6/21($100,000 - $10,000) | $25,714 | 74,286 |
| 2 | 5/21($90,000.00) | $21,429 | 52,857 |
| 3 | 4/21($90,000.00) | $17,143 | 35,714 |
| 4 | 3/21($90,000.00) | $12,857 | 22,857 |
| 5 | 2/21($90,000.00) | $ 8,571 | 14,286 |
| 6 | 1/21($90,000.00) | $ 4,286 | 10,000 |
| | | $90,000 | |

MACRS depreciation
Office equipment is in the MACRS seven-year property class

| Year | | MACRS Deprec | Book Value |
|------|--|--------------|------------|
| 1 | 14.29%($100,000) | $14,290 | 85,710 |
| 2 | 24.49%($100,000) | $24,490 | 61,220 |
| 3 | 17.49%($100,000) | $17,490 | 43,730 |
| 4 | 12.49%($100,000) | $12,490 | 31,240 |
| 5 | 8.93%($100,000) | $ 8,930 | 22,310 |
| 6 | 8.92% ($100,000) | $ 8,920 | 13,390 |

MACRS depreciation continues to year 8.

# 10-33

Office furniture, fixtures and equipment are in the seven year MACRS property class.

The depreciation schedule

| Year | MACRS depreciation | | | | |
|------|------|------|------|------|------|
| 1 | 14.29 % | x | 1,750,000 | = | 250,075 |
| 2 | 24.49 % | x | "    " | = | 428,575 |
| 3 | 17.49 % | x | "    " | = | 306,075 |
| 4 | 12.49 % | x | "    " | = | 218,575 |
| 5 | 8.93 % | x | "    " | = | 156,275 |
| 6 | 8.92 % | x | "    " | = | 156,100 |
| 7 | 8.93 % | x | "    " | = | 156,275 |
| 8 | 4.46 % | x | "    " | = | 78,050 |
| | | | | | $1,750,000 |

Solutions to Spreadsheet supplement problems are after Chapter 19 .

# Income Taxes

## 11-1

(a) Adjusted gross income – itemized or standard deduction – exemptions = taxable Income
48,000 – 2650 – 4150 = 41,200 taxable income
Federal Taxes = 3697.50 + (41,200 – 24,650)(0.28) = 8,331.50
(b) Adjusted Gross Income = 48,000 + 16,000 = 64,000 – 2650 – 4150 = 57,200 taxable income
Federal Taxes = 3697.5 + (57,200 – 24,650)(0.28) = 12,811.50
Difference = 12,811.50 – 8,331.50 = $4480.
Or 16,000(0.28) = $4480. This is valid since the incremental 16,000 is taxed at 28%.

## 11-2

|  | John | Mary | Joint |
|---|---|---|---|
| Adjusted Gross Income | 50,000 | 45,000 | 95,000 |
| Exemptions | – 2650 | – 2650 | – 5300 |
| Deductions(itemized or Std) | – 5000 | – 4160 | – 7000 |
| Taxable Income | 42,350 | 38,200 | 82,700 |

Federal Taxes as Individuals
John = 3697.5 + (42,350 – 24,650)(0.28) = 8653.50
Mary = 3697.50 + (38,200 – 24,650)(0.28) = 7491.50
Total = 16,145.

Federal Taxes filed as Joint Income
John + Mary = 6180 + (82700 – 41,200)(0.28) = 17,800
Penalty for Joint filing = 17,800 – 16,145 = $1655.

## 11-3

Without the extra work: Taxable Income = $1800   Tax = $270
With the extra work: Taxable Income =  3400   Tax =  510
Additional income = 1600 – 240 = $1360.

# 11-4

Ann Arbor Municipal Bonds

| Year | Before-Tax Cash Flow | Taxable Income | 28%* Income Taxes | After-Tax Cash Flow |
|------|------|------|------|------|
| 0 | −800 | | | −800 |
| 1-15 | +60 | | | +60 |
| 15 | +1000 | 200** | −56 | +944 |

*Incremental tax rate based on $40,000 of other taxable income.
** capital gain

Compute the after-tax rate of return

$$800 = 60 (P/A, i, 15) + 944 (P/F, i, 15)$$

Try i=8%
$$800 \stackrel{?}{=} 60(8.559) + 944 (0.3152) = 811 \quad i \text{ too low}$$
Try i= 9%
$$800 \stackrel{?}{=} 60(8.061) + 944 (0.2745) = 743 \quad i \text{ too high}$$

$$\text{Rate of Return} = 8\% + \left(\frac{11}{11+57}\right)(1\%) = \underline{\underline{8.16\%}}$$

Southern Coal Corporation Bonds

| Year | Before-tax Cash flow | Taxable Income | 28% Income Taxes | After-tax Cash flow |
|------|------|------|------|------|
| 0 | −1000 | | | −1000 |
| 1-20 | +100 | +100 | −28 | +72 |
| 20 | +1000 | | | +1000 |

By inspection: $\underline{\underline{i = 7.2\%}}$

# 11-5

Income = $800/month.   Expenses = $600/year    Net = $9000/year
SOYD Depreciation

$$N = 20 \quad \text{SUM} = N/2 * (N + 1) = 210$$

First year depreciation $= \dfrac{20}{210}(93,000 - 9000) = \$8000$

Declining Gradient $= \dfrac{1}{210} (93,000 - 9000) = \$400$

| YEAR | Before-Tax Cash Flow | SOYD Deprec. | Taxable Income | 38% Income Taxes | After-Tax Cash Flow |
|------|------|------|------|------|------|
| 0 | -93,000 | | | | -93,000 |
| 1 | +9,000 | 8000 | 1000 | -380 | +8,620 |
| 2 | +9,000 | 7600 | 1400 | -532 | +8,468 |
| 3 | +9,000 | 7200 | 1800 | -684 | +8316 |
| ⋮ | ⋮ | ⋮ | ⋮ | ⋮ | $G = -152$ |

assumption (a)

| 20 | $\{$ +9000 | 400 | 8600 | -3268 | +5732 $\}$ |
|----|------|------|------|------|------|
| | +9000 Lot + Bldg | | 0 | | +9000 |

assumption (b)

| 20 | $\{$ +9000 | 400 | 8600 | -3268 | +5732 $\}$ |
|----|------|------|------|------|------|
| | +100,000 Lot + Bldg | | 91,000* Cap gain | -25,480*** | +74,520 |

*Capital gain = Selling Price - (Cost - depreciation)
      = 100,000 - (93,000 - 84,000)  = 91,000

** Capital gain
   taxed at 28%


After-Tax Rate of Return, based on assumption (a)
   PW of Benefits - PW of Cost = 0
   $8620(P/A, i\%, 20) - 152(P/G, i\%, 20) + 9000(P/F, i\%, 20) - 93000 = 0$
Try i = 4½%
   $8620(13.008) - 152(104.78) + 9000(0.4146) - 93000 = +6934$
Try i = 6%
   $8620(11.470) - 152(87.23) + 9000(0.3118) - 93000 = -4581$

   $i^* = 4\frac{1}{2}\% + 1\frac{1}{2}\%\left(\dfrac{6934}{4581 + 6934}\right) = \underset{\sim}{5.4\%}$

After-Tax Rate of Return, based on assumption (b)
PW of Benefits - PW of Cost = 0

$8620 (P/A, i\%, 20) - 152 (P/G, i\%, 20) + 74,520 (P/F, i\%, 20) - 93000 = 0$

$i = 7\%$

$8620(10.594) - 152(77.509) + 74,520(0.2584) - 93000 = +5795$

$i = 8\%$

$8620(9.818) - 152(69.090) + 74,520(0.2145) - 93000 = -2886$

$\therefore$ Rate of Return $= 7\% + (1\%) \dfrac{5795}{5795 - (-2886)} = 7.67\%$

# 11-6

| Year | Before Tax Cash Flow | MACRS* Deprec | Taxable Income | Income Taxes ** | After-Tax Cash Flow | A.T. Present Worth @ 10% |
|------|----------------------|---------------|----------------|-----------------|---------------------|--------------------------|
| 0 | -82,000 (bld) | | | | | |
| | -30,000 (land) | | | | -112,000 | -112,000 |
| 1 | 9,000 | 2,018 | 6,982 | -1955 | 7,045 | 6,405 |
| 2 | 9,000 | 2,012 | 6,898 | -1931 | 7,069 | 5,842 |
| 3 | 9,000 | 2,012 | 6,898 | -1931 | 7,069 | 5,311 |
| 4 | 9,000 | 2,012 | 6,898 | -1931 | 7,069 | 4,828 |
| 5 | 9,000 | 2,012 | 6,898 | -1931 | 7,069 | 4,389 |
| 5 | 125,000 | - | 53,066*** | -10,613 | 14,387 | 71,023 |
| | | | | AFTER-TAX PW = | | -14,202 |

* MACRS Depr. (39 yrs)

| Year | Depreciation |
|------|--------------|
| 1 | 2.461%(82,000) = 2,018 |
| 2-5 | 2.564%(82,000) = 2,102 |

** 28% on up to (99,600-63,900) = $35,100 additional taxable income
20% on capital gains and losses held more than 18 months

*** Cap G/L = 125,000 - [82,000-2,018-(4)(2,012)]= $53,066

# 11-7

| YEAR | Before-Tax Cash Flow | Depreciation | $\Delta$ Taxable Income | 40% Income Taxes | After-Tax Cash Flow |
|------|----------|--------------|---------|---------|---------|
| 0 | $-X-5500$ | | $-3000$ | $+1200$ | $-X-4300$ |
| 1 | $+7000$ | None | $7000$ | $-2800$ | $+4200$ |
| 2 | $+7000$ | | $7000$ | $-2800$ | $+4200$ |
| $\vdots$ | $\vdots$ | | $\vdots$ | $\vdots$ | $\vdots$ |
| 9 | $+7000$ | | $7000$ | $-2800$ | $+4200$ |
| 10 | $\left\{\begin{array}{l} +7000 \\ +X+2500 \end{array}\right.$ | | $\begin{array}{l} 7000 \\ 0 \end{array}$ | $\begin{array}{l} -2800 \\ 0 \end{array}$ | $\left.\begin{array}{l} +4200 \\ +X+2500 \end{array}\right\}$ |

where  $X$ = maximum purchase price for old building and lot.

PW of Benefits - PW of Cost = 0

$$4200(P/A, i\%, 10) + (X+2500)(P/F, i\%, 10) - X - 4300 = 0$$

At the desired $i = 15\%$

$$4200(5.019) + (X+2500)(0.2472) - X - 4300 = 0$$

$$21,080 + 0.2472X + 618 - X - 4300 = 0$$

$$X = \frac{21,080 + 618 - 4300}{0.7528} = \$23,100$$

# 11-8

SOYD Depreciation

$N = 8$   SUM $= \frac{N}{2}(N+1) = 36$

1st year depreciation $= \frac{8}{36}(120,000 - 12,000) = 24,000$

annual decline $= \frac{1}{36}(120,000 - 12,000) = 3000$.

| YEAR | Before-Tax CASH FLOW | SOYD Deprec. | TAXABLE INCOME | 46% INCOME TAXES | AFTER-TAX CASH FLOW |
|---|---|---|---|---|---|
| 0 | −120,000 | | | | −120,000 |
| 1 | +29,000 | 24,000 | 5,000 | −2300 | +26,700 |
| 2 | +26,000 | 21,000 | | | +23,700 |
| 3 | +23,000 | 18,000 | | | +20,700 |
| 4 | +20,000 | 15,000 | | | G=−3000 |
| 5 | +17,000 | 12,000 | | | |
| 6 | +14,000 | 9,000 | | | |
| 7 | +11,000 | 6,000 | | | + 8700 |
| 8 | { +8000 | 3000 | | | + 5700 |
|   | { +12000 | | 0 | 0 | +12,000 |
| | Σ = 108,000 | | | | |

Will the firm obtain a 6% after tax rate of return?
    PW of Cost = PW of Benefits

$$120,000 = 26,700(P/A, i\%, 8) - 3000(P/G, i\%, 8) + 12000(P/F, i\%, 8)$$

at i=6%

$$= 26,700(6.210) - 3000(19.842) + 12000(0.6274)$$

$$= 113,810 \quad i \text{ too high.}$$

        Firm will __not__ obtain a 6% after tax rate of return

Further calculations show actual rate of return ~ 4.5%

# 11-9

| YEAR | Before-Tax CASH FLOW | SOYD Deprec | TAXABLE INCOME | 20% INCOME TAXES | AFTER-TAX CASH FLOW |
|---|---|---|---|---|---|
| 0 | −50 000 | | | | −50 000 |
| 1 | +20 000 | 15000 | 5000 | 1000 | 19 000 |
| 2 | +17 000 | 12000 | 5000 | 1000 | 16 000 |
| 3 | +14 000 | 9 000 | 5000 | 1000 | |
| 4 | +11 000 | 6000 | 5000 | 1000 | G=−3000 |
| 5 | { +8 000 | 3000 | 5000 | 1000 | 7000 } |
|   | { +5000 Salvage Value | | 0 | 0 | 5000 } |
| | | Σ = 45,000 | | | |

PW of Benefits - PW of Cost = 0

$19000(P/A, i\%, 5) - 3000(P/G, i\%, 5) + 5000(P/F, i\%, 5) - 50000 = 0$

Try $i = 15\%$

$19000(3.352) - 3000(5.775) + 5000(0.4972) - 50000 = -1151$

Try $i = 12\%$

$19000(3.605) - 3000(6.397) + 5000(0.5674) - 50000 = +2141$

$$\therefore i^* = 14\%$$

# 11-10

Parts (a) & (b)

| YEAR | Before-Tax Cash Flow | Str Line Deprec | Taxable Income | 40% Income Taxes | After-Tax Cash Flow |
|---|---|---|---|---|---|
| 0 | -20000 | | | | -20000 |
| 1-8 | +5000 | 2500 | 2500 | -1000 | +4000 |
| Totals: | | 20,000 | 20,000 | -8,000 | |

(a) Before Tax Rate of Return

$20,000 = 5000(P/A, i\%, 8)$

$(P/A, i\%, 8) = \dfrac{20000}{5000} = 4$ $i^* = 18.6\%$

(b) After Tax Rate of Return

$20,000 = 4000(P/A, i\%, 8)$

$(P/A, i\%, 8) = \dfrac{20000}{4000} = 5.00$ $i^* = 11.8\%$

Part (c)

| YEAR | Before-Tax Cash Flow | Str Line Deprec | Taxable Income | 40% Income Taxes | After-Tax Cash Flow |
|---|---|---|---|---|---|
| 0 | -20,000 | | | | -20,000 |
| 1-8 | +5000 | 1000 | 4000 | -1600 | +3,400 |
| 9-20 | 0 | 1000 | -1000 | +400 | +400 |
| Totals: | | 20,000 | 20,000 | -8,000 | |

Note that the changed depreciable life does not change
Total Depreciation, Total Taxable Income, or Total Income Taxes.
It does change the timing of these items.

(c) After Tax Rate of Return

PW of Benefits - PW of Cost = 0

$$400 (P/A, i, 20) + 3000 (P/A, i, 8) - 20,000 = 0$$

$i = 9\%$    $400 (9.129) + 3000 (5.535) - 20,000 = + 256.60$

$i = 10\%$    $400 (8.514) + 3000 (5.335) - 20,000 = - 589.40$

$$\overset{*}{i} \approx 9.3\%$$

$$(HP\text{-}12c \rightarrow 9.29\%)$$

# 11-11

MACRS Depreciation (27½ yrs)

Year

| | | |
|---|---|---|
| 1 (11½ months) | 3.485% (90000) = | 3136 |
| 2-4 | 3.636% (90000) = | 3276 |
| 5 (½ month) | 0.152% (90000) = | 137 |

$$\sum_{}^{5} = \$13,089$$

Book value of house and lot after four years = 99,700 - 13,089 = 86,611

| YEAR | Before-Tax Cash flow | MACRS DEPREC | Taxable Income | 24% Income Taxes | After-tax Cash flow |
|---|---|---|---|---|---|
| 0 | -99 700 | | | | -99700 |
| 1 | + 5500 | 3136 | 2364 | - 567 | +4933 |
| 2 | + 6000 | 3276 | 2724 | -654 | +5346 |
| 3 | + 6000 | 3276 | 2724 | -654 | +5346 |
| 4 | + 6000 | 3276 | 2724 | -654 | +5346 ⎫ |
| 5 { | + 500 +105,000 | 137 | 363 18,389* | - 87 -4413 ⎬ | +101,000 ⎭ *** |

*Capital gain = 105,000 - 86,611 = 18,389

The Year 4 - Year 5 timing is a little confusing due to the MACRS "mid-month" convention.

*** all assumed to be Year 4 as the sales receipts closer to end of Year 4 than end of Year 5.

PW of Benefits = PW of Cost

$$4933 (P/F, i, 1) + 5346 (P/A, i, 3)(P/F, i, 1) + 101,000 (P/F, i, 4) = 99,700$$

HP-12c:    after-tax rate of return = 5.55%

# 11-12

| YEAR | Before-Tax Cash Flow | Str line Deprec | Taxable Income | 40% INCOME TAXES |
|------|------|------|------|------|
| 0 | -P | | | |
| 1 | +87500 - 0.065P | 0.0667P | +87500 - 0.1317P | -35000 + 0.0527P |
| 2 | | | | |
| ⋮ | | | | |
| 15 | | | | |

| YEAR | After-Tax Cash Flow |
|------|------|
| 0 | -P |
| 1 | +52,500 - 0.0123P |
| 2 | |
| ⋮ | |
| 15 | |

$P$ = maximum expenditure for new equipment

Solve the after-tax cash flows for $P$
PW of Cost = PW of Benefits

$$P = (52,500 - 0.0123P)(P/A, 8\%, 15)$$
$$= (52,500 - 0.0123P(8.559) = 449,348 - 0.1053P$$
$$= \frac{449,348}{1.1053} = \$406,500.$$

# 11-13

Let $X$ = Number of days/year truck used
Annual Benefit of truck ownership = ($83-$35)X - 1100 = 48X - 1100

| YEAR | Before-Tax Cash Flow | SL Deprec | TAXABLE INCOME | 50% INCOME TAXES | AFTER-TAX CASH FLOW |
|------|------|------|------|------|------|
| 0 | -13,000 | | | | -13,000 |
| 1 | 48X-1100 | 1429 | 48X-2529 | -24X+1264 | 24X+164 |
| ⋮ | ⋮ | ⋮ | ⋮ | ⋮ | ⋮ |
| 7 { | 48X-1100 +3000 | 1429 | 48X-2529 0 | -24X+1264 0 | 24X+164 3000 } |

Set PW of Cost = PW of Benefits

$$13000 = (24x + 164)(P/A, 10\%, 7) + 3000(P/F, 10\%, 7)$$
$$= (24x + 164)(4.868) + 3000(0.5132)$$
$$= 116.8x + 798 + 1540$$
$$x = \frac{13000 - 798 - 1540}{116.8} \doteq 91\frac{1}{2} \text{ days}$$

ALTERNATE ANALYSIS

An alternate approach is to compute the after-tax cash flow of owning the truck.        From this the after-tax EUAC may be calculated (= 2189 + 17.5X).

In a separate calculation the after-tax EUAC of hiring a truck is determined (= 41.5X).  By equating the EUAC for the alternatives, we get:

$$2189 + 17.5X = 41.5X \quad X = 91.2 \text{ days}, \quad \text{say} \quad 91\frac{1}{2} \text{ days}$$

# 11-14

SOYD Depreciation

$N = 5 \quad$ SUM $= \frac{N}{2}(N+1) = \frac{5}{2}(6) = 15$

1st year depreciation $= \frac{5}{15}(20,000 - 5000) = 5000$

annual decline $= \frac{1}{15}(20,000 - 5000) = 1000$

| YEAR | Before-Tax CASH FLOW | SOYD Deprec. | TAXABLE INCOME | 50% INCOME TAXES | AFTER-TAX CASH FLOW |
|------|------|------|------|------|------|
| 0 | -20 000 | | | | -20,000 |
| 1 | + A | 5000 | A-5000 | -0.5A+2500 | 0.5A + 2500 |
| 2 | + A | 4000 | A-4000 | -0.5A+2000 | 0.5A + 2000 |
| 3 | + A | 3000 | A-3000 | -0.5A+1500 | 0.5A + 1500 |
| 4 | + A | 2000 | A-2000 | -0.5A+1000 | 0.5A + 1000 |
| 5 { | + A | 1000 | A-1000 | -0.5A+500 | 0.5A + 500 |
|  { | +5000 | | 0 | 0 | +5000 |

A = Before-tax annual benefit

After-tax cash flow computation:

$$20,000 = (0.5A + 2500)(P/A, 8\%, 5) - 500(P/G, 8\%, 5) + 5000(P/F, 8\%, 5)$$
$$20,000 = (0.5A + 2500)(3.993) - 500(7.372) + 5000(0.6806)$$
$$A = \frac{20,000 - 9983 + 3686 - 3403}{2} = \$5150$$

Required Before Tax Annual Benefit = $5150

# 11-15

This multiple alternative after-tax rate of return problem is one where neither input nor output is fixed. From the given data, compute the after-tax cash flow for each alternative. From this the after-tax rate of return may be computed.

**Alternative B**

| YEAR | Before-Tax Cash Flow | Deprec | Taxable Income | 20% Taxes | After-Tax Cash Flow | |
|---|---|---|---|---|---|---|
| 0 | −25 | | | | −25 | Rate of Return = 12.4% |
| 1-5 | +7.5 | 5 | 2.5 | −0.5 | +7 | |

**Alternative C**

| YEAR | Before-Tax Cash Flow | Deprec | Taxable Income | 20% Taxes | After-Tax Cash Flow | |
|---|---|---|---|---|---|---|
| 0 | −10 | | | | −10 | Rate of Return = 12.4% |
| 1-5 | +3 | 2 | 1.0 | −0.2 | +2.8 | |

**Alternative D**

| YEAR | Before-Tax Cash Flow | Deprec | Taxable Income | 20% Taxes | After-Tax Cash Flow | |
|---|---|---|---|---|---|---|
| 0 | −5 | | | | −5 | Rate of Return = 16.9% |
| 1-5 | +1.7 | 1 | 0.7 | −0.14 | +1.56 | |

**Alternative E**

| YEAR | Before-Tax Cash Flow | Deprec | Taxable Income | 20% Taxes | After-Tax Cash Flow | |
|---|---|---|---|---|---|---|
| 0 | −15 | | | | −15 | Rate of Return = 16.2% |
| 1-5 | +5 | 3 | 2.0 | −0.4 | +4.6 | |

**Alternative F**

| YEAR | Before-Tax Cash Flow | Deprec | Taxable Income | 20% Taxes | After-Tax Cash Flow | |
|---|---|---|---|---|---|---|
| 0 | −30 | | | | −30 | Rate of Return = 11.2% |
| 1-5 | +8.7 | 6 | 2.7 | −0.54 | +8.16 | |

Alternatives B through F each meet the 10% after-tax rate of return criterion. The do-nothing alternative therefore may be discarded. Proceed with incremental analysis, starting with the least cost remaining alternative.

Ranked by increasing cost:

| Alternative | Cost | Alternative | Cost |
|---|---|---|---|
| D | 5 | B | 25 |
| C | 10 | F | 30 |
| E | 15 | | |

Alt. C – Alt. D

| YEAR | After-Tax Cash Flow |
|---|---|
| 0 | −5 |
| 1–5 | +1.24 |

Incremental Rate of Return = 7.6%.   Reject Alt. C

Alt. E – Alt. D

| YEAR | After-Tax Cash Flow |
|---|---|
| 0 | −10 |
| 1–5 | +3.04 |

Incremental Rate of Return = 15.8%   Reject Alt. D

Alt. B – Alt. E

| YEAR | After-Tax Cash Flow |
|---|---|
| 0 | −10 |
| 1–5 | +2.40 |

Incremental Rate of Return = 6.4%   Reject Alt. B

Alt. F – Alt. E

| YEAR | After-Tax Cash Flow |
|---|---|
| 0 | −15 |
| 1–5 | +3.56 |

Incremental Rate of Return = 6%   Reject Alt. F

CONCLUSION: Select Alternative E

# 11-16

| Year | Before-Tax Cash Flow | DDB Deprec | Taxable Income | 34% Income Taxes | After-Tax Cash Flow | NPW at 10% |
|---|---|---|---|---|---|---|
| 0 | −1000 | | | | −1000 | −1000 |
| 1 | +500 | 400 | 100 | −34 | +466 | 423.6 |
| 2 | +340 | 240 | 100 | −34 | +306 | 252.9 |
| 3 | +244 | 144 | 100 | −34 | +210 | 157.8 |
| 4 | +100 | 86.4 | 13.6 | −4.6 | +95.4 | 65.2 |
| 5 | +100 / +125 | 4.6* | 95.4 | −32.4 } | +192.6 | 119.6 |
| | | 875 | | | | +19.1 |

\* Reduced to 4.60 so book value not less than salvage value.

At 10% NPW = +19.1
Thus the rate of return exceeds 10%.
(HP 12C says 10.94%)
The project should be undertaken.

# 11-17

| | |
|---|---|
| Adjusted Gross Income | = $75,000 |
| Exemptions | = -(2)(2,650) |
| Deductions | = -6,900 |
| Taxable Income | $62,000 |

Federal Taxes = 41,200(15%) + (62,800-41,200)(28%) = $12,228

# 11-18

State tax = 9.6% (150,000) = 14,400

Federal taxable income = 150,000 - 14,400 = 135,600

Federal tax = 22,250 + 39%(135,600 - 100,000) = 36,134.

   Total state plus Federal tax = $50,534

Combined incremental state and federal income tax rate:

   0.096 + 0.39(1 - 0.096) = 0.4486 = 44.86%

# 11-19

Proprietorship
                            Exemption  Std deduction
Taxable Income = 65000 - 2500  - 3900  = 58,600
      Tax = 12,798.50 + 0.31(58600 - 56,550) = $13,434

Corporation
  Jane's tax on $22,000:    Exemption  Std deduct
  Taxable Income = 22,000 - 2500  - 3900  = 15,600
         Tax = 0.15(15600) = $2340
  Corporate tax on $43,000 taxable income:
         Tax = 0.15(43,000) = $6450
      Total tax = 2340 + 6450 = $8790

# 11-20

| YEAR | Before-Tax CASH FLOW | SL Deprec | Taxable Income | 28% Income Taxes | After-Tax Cash Flow |
|------|------|------|------|------|------|
| 0 | -155,000 | | | | -155,000 |
| 1-10 | +12 000 | 4000 | 8000 | -2240 | +9760 |
| 10 | + X | | (X-115000) | -.28(X- 115000) | $\left\{ \begin{array}{c} +0.72X \\ +32200 \end{array} \right\}$ |

$$\Sigma = \overline{40,000}$$

Book value at end of 10 yrs

$$= 155,000 - 10(4000) = 115,000$$

Taxable income $= X - 115,000$    where X = Selling Price

For 10% after-tax rate of return:

$$155,000 = 9760 (P/A, 10\%, 10) + (0.72X + 32,200)(P/F, 10\%, 10)$$

$$155,000 = 9760(6.145) + (0.72X + 32,200)(0.3855)$$

$$= 59,975 + 0.2776X + 12413$$

$$X = \frac{155,000 - 59975 - 12413}{0.2776} = 297,590.$$

# 11-21

Let $x$ = the number of months that Valerie will work in the year

| | |
|---|---|
| Adjusted Gross Income | = $36,000 + 2,000x$ |
| Exemptions | = -(2)(2,650) |
| Deductions | = -6,900 |

Taxable Income    $36,000 - 2000x - 5,300 - 6,900 = 2000x + 23,800$

For $6,900 in tax they are in the 28% tax bracket

From Table 11-2

Tax = 6,180 + (28%)(taxable income above $41,200)

Break-Even Point is:

$6,900 = 6,180 + (28\%)[(2000x + 23,800) - 41,2000]$

thus,    $x = 10$ months

# 11-22

Part(a)  Bonds plus Loan

| YEAR | Before-Tax Cash Flow | Taxable Income | Income Taxes | After-Tax Cash Flow |
|------|----------------------|----------------|--------------|---------------------|
| 0 | $\begin{cases} -75\,000 \\ +50\,000 \end{cases}$ | | | -25000 |
| 1-5 | $\begin{cases} +5000 \\ -5000 \end{cases}$ | 0 | 0 | 0 |
| 5 | $\begin{cases} +100\,000 \\ -50\,000 \end{cases}$ | 25000* Capital gain | -7000* | +43000 |

* taxed at 28% max capital gain rate

After-tax rate of return

$$25000 = 43,000(P/F, i, 5)$$

$$(P/F, i, 5) = 0.5814 \qquad \text{Rate of return} = 11.46\%$$

Note:  The Tax Reform Act of 1986 permits interest paid on loans
to finance investments to continue to be deductible, but
only up to the taxpayer's investment income.

## Part (b) Bonds but no loan

| YEAR | Before-Tax Cash Flow | Taxable Income | Income Taxes | After-Tax Cash Flow |
|------|---------------------|----------------|--------------|---------------------|
| 0 | -75,000 | | | -75,000 |
| 1-5 | +5,000 | 5000 | -2500 | +2500 |
| 5 | +100,000 | 25000* Capital gain | -7000* | +93000 |

\* Taxed at 28%

After-tax rate of return

$$75000 = 2500(P/A, i, 5) + 93000(P/F, i, 5)$$

$i=7\%$   $75000 \overset{?}{=} 2500(4.100) + 93000(0.7130) = 76559$

$i=8\%$   $75000 \overset{?}{=} 2500(3.993) + 93000(0.6806) = 73278$

Rate of Return = 7.46%

# 11-23

| YEAR | Before-Tax Cash Flow | 5-Yr Class MACRS Deprec | Taxable Income | 34% Income Taxes | After-Tax Cash Flow |
|------|---------------------|-------------------------|----------------|------------------|---------------------|
| 0 | -50,000 | | | | -50,000 |
| 1 | 2000 | 10000 | (8000) | +2720 | +4720 |
| 2 | 8000 | 16000 | (8000) | +2720 | +10,720 |
| 3 | 17600 | 9600 | 8000 | -2720 | +14,880 |
| 4 | 13760 | 5760 | 8000 | -2720 | +11,040 |
| 5 | 5760 | 5760 | 0 | 0 | +5760 |
| 6 | 2880 | 2880 | 0 | 0 | +2880 |
| | 0 | 50,000 | 0 | 0 | 0 |

(a) The sum of the After-Tax Cash Flow equals zero, indicating the after-tax rate of return equals 0% ≲

(b) Similarly, the before-tax rate of return equals 0% ≲

# 11-24

## ALTERNATIVE 1

| YEAR | Before Tax Cash Flow | SL Deprec | Taxable Income | 34% Income Taxes | after Tax Cash Flow | PW at 10% | EUAB -EUAC |
|------|------|------|------|------|------|------|------|
| 0 | -10,000 | | | | -10000 | -10000 | - 1175 |
| 1-10 | 4500 | 1000 | 3500 | -1190 | 3310 | +20,340 | + 2390 |
| 11-20 | 0 | 0 | | | 0 | 0 | 0 |
| | | | | | | +10,340 | +1215 |

| YEAR | After Tax Cash Flow | FW Yr20 at 10% |
|------|------|------|
| 0 | -10000 | - 67,270 |
| 1-10 | + 3310 | + 136,836 |
| 11-20 | 0 | 0 |
| | | +69,566 |

Part(a)
Max NPW
choose
Alt. 1

Part(b)
max
(EUAB
-EUAC)
choose
Alt. 1

## ALTERNATIVE 2

| YEAR | Before Tax Cash Flow | SL Deprec | Taxable Income | 34% Income Taxes | After Tax Cash Flow | PW at 10% | EUAB -EUAC |
|------|------|------|------|------|------|------|------|
| 0 | -20000 | | | | -20000 | -20,000 | - 2350 |
| 1-10 | 4500 | 2000 | 2500 | -850 | 3650 | +22,429 | +2635 |
| 11-20 | 4500 | 0 | 4500 | -1530 | 2970 | + 7,036 | + 827 |
| | | | | | | + 9,465 | +1112 |

| YEAR | After-Tax Cash Flow | FW Yr20 at 10% |
|------|------|------|
| 0 | -20000 | - 134,540 |
| 1-10 | 3650 | +150,902 |
| 11-20 | 2970 | + 47,338 |
| | | + 63,700 |

Part(d)  max   choose
NFW   Alt. 1

## ALTERNATIVE 2-1: After-Tax Cash Flow

| YEAR | Alt. 1 | Alt. 2 | Alt 2-Alt 1 |
|------|------|------|------|
| 0 | -10000 | -20000 | -10000 |
| 1-10 | +3310 | +3650 | + 340 |
| 11-20 | 0 | +2970 | +2970 |
| Rate of Return | 30.9% | 10% | 9.2% |
| B/c ratio | 2.03 | 1.47 | 0.91 |

Part(c) Reject   Choose
Increment  Alt. 1

Part(e) Reject   Choose
Increment  Alt. 1

# 11-25

| YEAR | Before Tax Cash Flow | MACRS Deprec | Taxable Income | 34% Income Taxes | After Tax Cash Flow | Cumulative After-Tax Cash Flow |
|---|---|---|---|---|---|---|
| 0 | -100,000 | | | | -100,000 | -100,000 |
| 1 | 35,000 | 20 000 | 15000 | -5100 | 29,900 | -70,100 |
| 2 | 35,000 | 32 000 | 3000 | -1020 | 33,980 | -36,120 |
| 3 | 35,000 | 19 200 | 15 800 | -5372 | 29,628 | -6 492 |
| 4 | 35,000 | 11 520 | 23480 | -7983 | 27,017 | +20,525 |
| 5 | 35,000 | 11 520 | 23 480 | -7983 | 27,017 | +47,542 |
| 6 | 35,000 | 5760 / 100 000 | 29 240 | -9942 | 25,058 | +72,600 |

$$\text{After-tax payback period} = 3\,\text{yrs} + \frac{6492}{6492 + 20\,525} = 3.24\ \text{yrs}$$

# 11-26

| YEAR | Before Tax Cash Flow | MACRS Deprec | Taxable Income | 34% Income Taxes | After-Tax Cash Flow |
|---|---|---|---|---|---|
| 0 | -400 | | | | -400 |
| 1 | +200* | 133 | 67 | -23 | 177 |
| 2 | +200 | 178 | 22 | -7 | 193 |
| 3 | +200 | 59 | 141 | -48 | 152 |
| 4 | +200 | 30 | 170 | -58 | 142 |

*For 2-year payback, annual benefits must be ½(400) = 200

Part (a) Before Tax Rate of Return

$$400 = 200\ (P/A, i\%, 4);\quad (P/A, i\%, 4) = 2$$

Before Tax Rate of Return = 34.9%

Part (b) After Tax Rate of Return

$$400 = 177\ (P/F, i\%, 1) + 193(P/F, i\%, 2) + 152(P/F, i\%, 3) + 142(P/F, i\%, 4)$$

After Tax Rate of Return = 25.2%

# 11-27

Double Declining Balance with conversion to straight line

YEAR

1   $\frac{2}{10}(100,000 - 0) = 20,000$

2   $\frac{2}{10}(100,000 - 20000) = 16,000$

3   $\frac{2}{10}(100,000 - 36,000) = 12,800$

4   $\frac{2}{10}(100,000 - 48,800) = 10,240$

5   $\frac{2}{10}(100,000 - 59,040) = 8,192$

There is no switch to straight line in the first five years.

| YEAR | Before Tax Cash Flow | DDB/SL Deprec | Taxable Income | 34% Income Taxes | After Tax Cash Flow |
|---|---|---|---|---|---|
| 0 | -100,000 | | | | -100,000 |
| 1 | 30,000 | 20,000 | 10000 | -3400 | 26,600 |
| 2 | 30,000 | 16,000 | 14000 | -4760 | 25,240 |
| 3 | 30,000 | 12,800 | 17200 | -5848 | 24,152 |
| 4 | 30,000 | 10,240 | 19760 | -6718 | 23,282 |
| 5 | $\begin{cases} 30,000 \\ 35,000 = S \end{cases}$ | 8,192 ———— 67,232 | $\begin{cases} 21808 \\ 2232^* \end{cases}$ | $\begin{cases} -7415 \\ -759 \end{cases}$ | $\begin{cases} 22,585 \\ 34,241 \end{cases}$ |

$^*$Capital gain = 35000 - (100,000 - 67,232)
= 2232

After-tax Rate of Return = 14.9%

# 11-28

MACRS Depreciation

Year
1   $20.00\%(14000) = 2800$
2   $32.00\%(14000) = 4480$
3   $19.20\%(14000) = 2688$

YEAR
4   $11.52\%(14000) = 1613$
5   $11.52\%(14000) = 1613$
6   $5.76\%(14000) = 806$

| Year | Before Tax Cash Flow | MACRS Deprec | Taxable Income | 45% Income Taxes | After-Tax Cash Flow |
|---|---|---|---|---|---|
| 0 | −14,000 | | | | −14,000 |
| 1 | 5000 | 2800 | 2200 | −990 | +4010 |
| 2 | 5000 | 4480 | 520 | −234 | +4766 |
| 3 | 5000 | 2688 | 2312 | −1040 | +3960 |
| 4 | {5000 / 3000 | 1613 | 3387 / 581* | −1524 / −261 } | +6,215 |
| | | 11,581 | | | |

* End of Yr 4
Book Value = 14000 − 11,581 = 2419
Capital gain = 3000 − 2419 = 581

after-tax
Rate of Return = 12.5%

# 11-29

| Year | Before Tax Cash Flow | Bldg MACRS Deprec* | Machinery MACRS Deprec* | Taxable Income | 34% Income Taxes | After-Tax Cash Flow |
|---|---|---|---|---|---|---|
| 0 | −400,000 | | | | | −400,000 |
| 1 | 17,500 | 1070 | 21 435 | −5005 | +1701 | +19,201 |
| 2 | 70 000 | 5128 | 36735 | 28 137 | −9567 | +60,433 |
| 3 | 70 000 | 5128 | 26 235 | 38637 | −13,137 | +56,863 |
| 4 | 70000 | 5128 | 18 735 | 46 137 | −15687 | +54,313 |
| 5 | 70000 | 5128 | 13 395 | 51,477 | −17,502 | +52,498 |
| 6 | {52,500 / 328,000 = S | 4066 | 6705 | 41,729 / 76888** | −14,188 / −26,142 { | +38,312 / +301,858 } |
| | | 25,648 | 123,240 | | | |

End of 5 yrs (in Yr 6) Book value = 400,000 − 25,648 − 123,240 = 251,112
** capital gain = 328,000 − 251,112 = 76,888

* MACRS Depreciation:

| YEAR | Bldg. | machinery |
|---|---|---|
| 1 | 0.535% | 14.29 % |
| 2 | 2.564% | 24.49% |
| 3 | | 17.49 % |
| 4 | | 12.49% |
| 5 | | 8.93% |
| 6 | 2.033% | 4.47% |

After-tax
Rate of Return = 8.27%

The project fails to meet
the corporation's criterion.

# 11-30

| YEAR | Before-Tax CASH FLOW | MACRS Deprec | Taxable Income | 34% Income Taxes | After-Tax CASH FLOW |
|------|------|------|------|------|------|
| 0 | -55,000 | | | | -55,000 |
| 1 | 10,000 | 5500 | 4500 | -1530 | 8470 |
| 2 | 10 000 | 9900 | 100 | -34 | 9966 |
| 3 | 10 000 | 7920 | 2080 | -707 | 9293 |
| 4 | 10 000 | 6336 | 3664 | -1246 | 8754 |
| 5 | 10 000 | 5071 | 4929 | -1676 | 8324 |
| 6 { | 10 000 | 2030 | 7970 | -2710 | 7290 } |
| | 35 000 | | 16 757* | -5697 | 29303 } |

$$\overline{36,757}$$

*End Yr 6 Book Value = 55000 - 36757 = 18243
Capital gain = 35000 - 18243 = 16,757.

after tax
Rate of Return = $\underline{9.86\%}$

# 11-31

Problem similar to 11-12.

| YEAR | Before Tax Cash Flow | SOYD Deprec* | Taxable Income | 50% Income Taxes | After Tax Cash Flow |
|------|------|------|------|------|------|
| 0 | -P | | | | -P |
| 1 | 110,000 | $\frac{6}{21}P$ | $110,000 - \frac{6}{21}P$ | $-(55000 - \frac{3}{21}P)$ | $+55000 + \frac{3}{21}P$ |
| 2 | 110,000 | $\frac{5}{21}P$ | $110,000 - \frac{5}{21}P$ | $-(55000 - \frac{2.5}{21}P)$ | $+55000 + \frac{2.5}{21}P$ |
| 3 | 110,000 | $\frac{4}{21}P$ | $110,000 - \frac{4}{21}P$ | $-(55000 - \frac{2}{21}P)$ | $+55000 + \frac{2}{21}P$ |
| 4 | 110,000 | $\frac{3}{21}P$ | $110,000 - \frac{3}{21}P$ | $-(55000 - \frac{1.5}{21}P)$ | $+55000 + \frac{1.5}{21}P$ |
| 5 | 110,000 | $\frac{2}{21}P$ | $110,000 - \frac{2}{21}P$ | $-(55000 - \frac{1}{21}P)$ | $+55000 + \frac{1}{21}P$ |
| 6 | 110,000 | $\frac{1}{21}P$ | $110,000 - \frac{1}{21}P$ | $-(55000 - \frac{0.5}{21}P)$ | $+55000 + \frac{0.5}{21}P$ |

$$*Sum = \frac{N}{2}(N+1) = \frac{6}{2}(7) = 21$$

write an equation for the after-tax cash flow.

$$P = \left(55000 + \frac{3}{21}P\right)(P/A,15\%,6) - \frac{0.5}{21}P(P/G,15\%,6)$$

$$\phantom{P = (55000 + \frac{3}{21}P)}\underset{3.784}{} \phantom{(P/A,15\%,6) - \frac{0.5}{21}P}\underset{7.937}{}$$

$$P = 208,120 + 0.541P - 0.189P$$

$$P = \frac{208,120}{0.648} = \$321,173$$

# 11-32

SOYD Depreciation

$$\frac{n}{2}(n+1) = \frac{5}{2}(6) = 15$$

Year

$$1 \quad \frac{5}{15}(120,000 - 0) = 40,000$$

$$\text{gradient} = \frac{-1}{15}(120,000 - 0) = -8,000$$

| YEAR | Before Tax Cash Flow | SOYD Deprec | Taxable Income | 34% Income Taxes | After Tax Cash Flow |
|------|------|------|------|------|------|
| 0 | -120,000 | | | | -120,000 |
| 1 | 32,000 | 40000 | (8000) | +2720 | +34 720 |
| 2 | 32,000 | 32000 | 0 | 0 | +32 000 |
| 3 | 32,000 | 24000 | 8000 | -2720 | +29 280 |
| 4 | 32000 | 16000 | 16000 | -5440 | +26 560 |
| 5 | $\begin{cases} 32000 \\ 40,000 = S \end{cases}$ | 8000 | $\begin{matrix} 24000 \\ 40000 \end{matrix}$ | $\begin{Bmatrix} -8160 \\ -13600 \end{Bmatrix}$ | +50 240 |
| | | $\overline{120000}$ | | | |

after tax rate of return:

try i = 12%

NPW = 34,720 (P/A,12%,4) - 2720 (P/G,12%,4) + 50 240 (P/F,12%,5) - 120,000

$\phantom{NPW}$ = 105 445 - 11 225 + 28 506 - 120 000 = +2726

(HP12-C: ROR = 12.88%)                    ∴ Investment was satisfactory

# 11-33

ALTERNATIVE A

| YEAR | Before-Tax CASH FLOW | SOYD Deprec | Taxable Income | 34% Income Taxes | After-Tax Cash Flow |
|---|---|---|---|---|---|
| 0 | -3000 | | | | -3000 |
| 1 | 1000 | 1000 | 0 | 0 | 1000 |
| 2 | 1000 | 800 | 200 | -68 | 932 |
| 3 | 1000 | 600 | 400 | -136 | 864 |
| 4 | 1000 | 400 | 600 | -204 | 796 |
| 5 | 1000 | 200 | 800 | -272 | 728 |

ALTERNATIVE B

| YEAR | Before-Tax CASH FLOW | SL Deprec | Taxable Income | 34% Income Taxes | After-Tax Cash Flow |
|---|---|---|---|---|---|
| 0 | -5000 | | | | -5000 |
| 1 | 1000 | 1000 | 0 | 0 | 1000 |
| 2 | 1200 | 1000 | 200 | -68 | 1132 |
| 3 | 1400 | 1000 | 400 | -136 | 1264 |
| 4 | 2600 | 1000 | 1600 | -544 | 2056 |
| 5 | 2800 | 1000 | 1800 | -612 | 2188 |

ALTERNATIVE B - ALTERNATIVE A

| YEAR | B-A After-Tax CASH FLOW | PW at 15% | PW at 12% |
|---|---|---|---|
| 0 | -2000 | -2000 | -2000 |
| 1 | 0 | 0 | 0 |
| 2 | 200 | 151 | 159 |
| 3 | 400 | 263 | 285 |
| 4 | 1260 | 720 | 801 |
| 5 | 1460 | 726 | 828 |
| | | -140 | +73 |

The B-A increment has a desirable 13% rate of return.

Choose B

# 11-34

| YEAR | Before Tax CASH FLOW | MACRS Deprec | Taxable Income | 34% tx (income) | After-Tax Cash Flow | PW at 10% |
|---|---|---|---|---|---|---|
| 0 | -1 800 000 | | | | -1 800 000 | -1 800 000 |
| 1 | 450 000 | 360 000 | 90000 | -30 600 | 419 400 | 381 277 |
| 2 | 450 000 | 576 000 | -126 000 | +42 840 | 492 840 | 407 283 |
| 3 | 450 000 | 345 600 | 104 400 | -35 496 | 414 504 | 311 417 |
| 4 | 450 000 | 207 360 | 242 640 | -82 498 | 367 502 | 251 004 |
| 5 | 450 000 | 207 360 | 242 640 | -82 498 | 367 502 | 228 182 |
| 6 | 450 000 | 103 680 | 346 320 | -117 749 | 332 251 | 187 556 |
| 7 | 450 000 | 0 | 450 000 | -153 000 | 297 000 | 152 420 |
| 8 | 450 000 | 0 | 450 000 | -153 000 | 297 000 | 138 550 |

$$NPW_{10\%} = +257\ 689$$

After-tax rate of return = 14.2%     ∴ Investment is satisfactory

# 11-35

| YEAR | Before Tax Cash Flow | DDB Deprec | Taxable Income | 46% Income Taxes | after Tax Cash Flow |
|---|---|---|---|---|---|
| 0 | -100,000 | | | | -100,000 |
| 1 | 30,000 | 50000 | -20000 | +9,200 | 39,200 |
| 2 | 30,000 | 25000 | 5000 | -2,300 | 27,700 |
| 3 | 35,000 | 12500 | 22500 | -10,350 | 24,650 |
| 4 | 40,000 | 6250 | 33750 | -15,525 | 24,475 |
| 5 | 10,000 | 0 | 10 000 | -4,600 | 5,400 |
| 6 | 10,000 / 6,250=S | 0 | 10000 / 0* | -4,600 | 11,650 |

93,750

\* Sold for book value.

After-tax Rate of Return = 11.6%

# 11-36

| Year | Before Tax Cash Flow | DDB Deprec | $25,240^*$ Loan Payment Principal | Interest | Taxable Income^** | 46% Income Taxes | After Tax Cash Flow |
|------|------|------|------|------|------|------|------|
| 0 | -20000 | | | | | | -20,000 |
| 1 | 30 000 | 50000 | 17240 | 8000 | -28000 | +12880 | 17,640 |
| 2 | 30000 | 25000 | 18964 | 6276 | -1276 | +587 | 5347 |
| 3 | 35000 | 12500 | 20 860 | 4380 | 18120 | -8335 | 1425 |
| 4 | 40000 | 6250 | 22936$^†$ | 2294 | 31456 | -14,470 | 290 |
| 5 | 10 000 | 0 | | | 10 000 | -4600 | 5400 |
| 6 | { 10000 | 0 | | | 10 000 | -4600 | } 11,650 |
|   | { 6250 =S | | | | 0 | | |
|   |  | 93 750 | 80,000 | | | | |

$*$ Loan payment = $80,000 (A/P, 10\%, 4) = 25,240$

$†$ to adjustment. If the loan payment had been exactly computed, it is 25,237.66

$**$ Taxable Income = $\dfrac{\text{Before Tax}}{\text{Cash Flow}}$ − $\dfrac{\text{DDB}}{\text{Deprec}}$ − $\dfrac{\text{Interest}}{\text{payment}}$

(a)   After-tax Rate of
Return = 34.3%

## Part (b)

The purchase of the special tools for $20,000 cash plus an $80,000 loan represents a leveraged situation.

Under the tax laws all the interest paid is deductible when computing taxable income, so the after-tax cost of the loan is not 10%, but 5.4%. The resulting rate of return on the $20,000 cash is therefore much higher in this situation.

Note, however, that the investment now is not just $20,000, but really $20,000 plus the obligation to repay the $80,000 loan.

# 11-37

| YEAR | Before-Tax CASH FLOW | SOYD Deprec | Taxable Income | 34% Income Taxes | After-Tax CASH FLOW | PW at 15% |
|------|------|------|------|------|------|------|
| 0 | $\begin{cases} -108,000 \\ -25,000 \end{cases}$ | | | | -133,000 | -133 000 |
| 1 | 24 000 | 24000 | 0 | 0 | 24 000 | 20 870 |
| 2 | 24 000 | 21000 | 3000 | -1020 | 22 980 | 17 315 |
| 3 | 24000 | 18000 | 6000 | -2040 | 21 960 | 14 439 |
| 4 | 24000 | 15000 | 9000 | -3060 | 20 940 | 11 973 |
| 5 | 24000 | 12000 | 12000 | -4080 | 19 920 | 9 904 |
| 6 | 24000 | 9000 | 15000 | -5100 | 18 900 | 8 170 |
| 7 | 24000 | 6000 | 18000 | -6120 | 17 880 | 6 721 |
| 8 | $\begin{cases} 24000 \\ 25000 \end{cases}$ | 3000 | $\begin{matrix} 21000 \\ 0 \end{matrix}$ | $\begin{matrix} -7140 \\ 0 \end{matrix} \Big\}$ | 41 860 | 13 684 |
| | | 108,000 | | | | -29 864 |

SOYD Deprec

$$\frac{n}{2}(n+1) = \frac{8}{2}(9) = 36$$

1st yr: $\frac{8}{36}(108,000-0) = 24,000$

$g = -\frac{1}{36}(108,000-0) = -3,000$

NPW at 15% is
negative, therefore
project should not
be undertaken.

(HP12C → $i = 8.05\%$)

# 11-38

## ALTERNATIVE A

| YEAR | Before Tax CASH FLOW | SL DEPREC | Taxable INCOME | 34% Income Taxes | After-Tax Cash Flow |
|---|---|---|---|---|---|
| 0 | -11,000 | | | | -11000 |
| 1 | 3000 | 3000 | 0 | 0 | 3000 |
| 2 | 3000 | 3000 | 0 | 0 | 3000 |
| 3 | 3000 | 3000 | 0 | 0 | 3000 |
| 4 | 3000 | 0 | 3000 | -1020 | 1980 |
| 5 | { 3000 / 2000=S | 0 | 3000 / 0 | -1020 } | 3980 |

$$NPW_{12\%} = -278$$

## ALTERNATIVE B

| YEAR | Before Tax CASH FLOW | SOYD Deprec | Taxable Income | 34% Income Taxes | After-Tax Cash Flow |
|---|---|---|---|---|---|
| 0 | -33,000 | | | | -33,000 |
| 1 | 9000 | 12000 | -3000 | +1020 | 10020 |
| 2 | 9000 | 9000 | 0 | 0 | 9000 |
| 3 | 9000 | 6000 | 3000 | -1020 | 7980 |
| 4 | 9000 | 3000 | 6000 | -2040 | 6960 |
| 5 | { 9000 / 5000=S | 0 | 9000 / 2000 Cap gain | -3060 / -680 } | 10260 |

$$NPW_{12\%} = -953$$

Neither A nor B meet the 12% criterion. By NPW one can see that A is the better of the two undesirable alternatives.

Select A

# 11-39

DEPRECIATION SCHEDULE

| YEAR | | | DDB | | Is convert to Straight line |
|------|------|------|------|------|------|

YEAR                            DDB        Is convert to Straight line
 1   ⅔(12000 −   0) = 4000
 2   ⅔(12000 − 4000) = 2667                              convert
 3   ⅔(12000 − 6667) = 1778     For Year                   ?
 4   ⅔(12000 − 8445) = 1185      4  $\frac{12000-8445-700}{3}$ = 952  No
 5   ⅔(12000 − 9630) = ~~792~~ 835  5  $\frac{12000-9630-700}{2}$ = 835  YES
 6                          835
                    Σ = 11,300

| YEAR | Before Tax Cash Flow | DDB w/Conv to SL | Taxable Income | 34% Income Taxes | after-Tax Cash Flow |
|------|------|------|------|------|------|
| 0 | −12000 | | | | −12000 |
| 1 | 1727 | 4000 | −2273 | +773 | 2500 |
| 2 | 2414 | 2667 | −253 | +86 | 2500 |
| 3 | 2872 | 1778 | 1094 | −372 | 2500 |
| 4 | 3177 | 1185 | 1992 | −677 | 2500 |
| 5 | 3358 | 835 | 2523 | −858 | 2500 |
| 6 | { 1997 / 1000 | 835 | 1162 / 300 cap gain | −395 / −102 } | 2500 |

Annual Cash Flow Analysis
  EUAC = 12,000 (A/P, 9%, 6) = 12000 (0.2229) = 2675
  EUAB = 2500
Since EUAC > EUAB, Investment is not desirable.

# 11-40

(a)   $\text{Payback} = \dfrac{500,000}{12,000,000 \times (0.05 - 0.03)} = \underline{2.08 \text{ years}}$

(b)   after-tax Payback

| YEAR | Before-Tax Cash flow | Str Line Deprec | Taxable Income | 40% Income Taxes | After tax Cash Flow |
|------|------|------|------|------|------|
| 0 | -500000 | | | | -500 000 |
| 1-5 | 240 000 | 100000 | 140000 | -56000 | 184 000 |

$\text{after-tax payback} = \dfrac{500,000}{184,000} = \underline{2.72 \text{ years}}$

after-Tax Rate of Return

$500,000 = 184000 \, (P/A, i, 5)$

$(P/A, i, 5) = \dfrac{500\,000}{184\,000} = 2.7174$    Rate of Return $= \underline{24.5\%}$

# 11-41

MACRS Depreciation: Special tools-plastic products = 3 year property class.

| YEAR | | MACRS Deprec |
|------|------|------|
| 1 (½ Year depruc) | $33.33\% \times 300\,000 =$ | 99,990 |
| 2 | $44.45\% \times 300\,000 =$ | 133,350 |
| 3 | $14.81\% \times 300\,000 =$ | 44,430 |
| 4 | $7.41\% \times 300\,000 =$ | 22,230 |
| | | 300,000 |

| Yr | Before tax Cash Flow | MACRS Deprec | Taxable Income | 39% Income Taxes | After tax Cash flow | Unrecovered Investment | PW at 12% |
|------|------|------|------|------|------|------|------|
| 0 | -300 000 | | | | -300 000 | 300 000 | -300 000 |
| 1 | 150 000 | 99 990 | 50010 | 19504 | 130 496 | 169 504 | 116 520 |
| 2 | 150 000 | 133 350 | 16650 | 6493 | 143 507 | 25 997 | 114 404 |
| 3 | 150 000 | 44 430 | 105570 | 41 172 | 108 828 | 0 | 77 464 |
| 4 | 150 000 | 22 230 | 127770 | 49 830 | 100 170 | | 63 658 |
| 5 | 150 000 | 0 | 150 000 | 58 500 | 91 500 | | 51 917 |
| | | | | | | | +123,963 |

(a) after tax payback
   - assuming end of period benefits = 3 yrs
   - assuming benefits throughout year = 2.24 yrs

(b) This is desirable investment.  (PW at 12% > 0 ;  After tax ROR = 29%)

# 11-42

Combined incremental tax rate

$$= \Delta \text{State tax rate} + (\Delta \text{Fed tax rate})(1 - \Delta \text{State tax rate})$$

$$= 0.093 + (0.31)(1 - 0.093) = 0.3742 = 37.4\%$$

# 11-43

Generally all depreciation methods allocate the cost of the equipment (less salvage value) over some assigned useful life. While the depreciation charges in any year may be different for different methods, the <u>sum</u> of the depreciation charges will be the same. This will affect the amount of taxes paid in any year, but with a stable income tax rate, <u>the total taxes paid will be the same.</u> (The difference is not the amount of the taxes, but their timing.)

# 11-44

MACRS Depreciation. Pickup in 5-year property class

Year
1   20% (14000) = 2800
2   32% (14000) = 4480

Year
3   19.2% (14000) = 2688
4   11.52% (14000) = 1613

(a)

| Year | Before Tax Cash Flow Truck | Loan | MACRS Deprec | Taxable Income | 45% Income Taxes | After-tax Cash Flow |
|------|------|------|------|------|------|------|
| 0 | -14000 | +10000 | | | | -4000 |
| 1 | +5000 | -2500 -1000 | 2800 | 1200 | -540 | +960 |
| 2 | +5000 | -2500 -750 | 4480 | (230) | +103 | +1853 |
| 3 | +5000 | -2500 -500 | 2688 | 1812 | -815 | +1185 |
| 4 | +5000 | -2500 -250 | 1613 | 3137 | -1412 | +3577 |
|   | +3000 | | | 581* | -261 | |

11581

Book value = 14000 - 11581 = 2419

*Capital gain = 3000 - 2419 = 581

Computed after-tax rate of return = 25.3%

(b)  This problem illustrates the leverage that a loan can produce. The cash investment is greatly reduced. Since the truck rate of return (12.5% in Problem 11-28) exceeds the loan interest rate (10%), combining the two increased the overall rate of return.

Two items worth noting:
1.  The truck and the loan are independent decisions and probably should be examined separately.
2.  There is increased risk when investments are leveraged.

**11-45**

SOYD Depreciation   $\frac{n}{2}(n+1) = \frac{7}{2}(8) = 28$

1st Yr SOYD $= \frac{7}{28}(14000 - 0) = 3500$   $\Delta = \frac{1}{28}(14000 - 0) = 500$

| YEAR | Before Tax Cash Flow | SOYD Deprec | Taxable Income | 47% Income Taxes | After-tax Cash flow |
|------|------|------|------|------|------|
| 0 | -14000 | | | | -14000 |
| 1 | +3600 | 3500 | 100 | -47 | 3553 |
| 2 | +3600 | 3000 | 600 | -282 | 3318 |
| 3 | +3600 | 2500 | 1100 | -517 | 3083 |
| 4 | +3600 | 2000 | 1600 | -752 | 2848 |
| 5 | +3600 | 1500 | 2100 | -987 | 2613 |
| 6 | +3600 | 1000 | 2600 | -1222 | 2378 |
| 7 | +3600 | 500 | 3100 | -1457 | 2143 |
| | | 14,000 | | $\Delta = 235$ | $\Delta = -235$ |

Solve for rate of return

NPW = PW of Benefits - PW of Costs = 0

$\qquad 3553(P/A, i, 7) - 235(P/G, i, 7) - 14000 = 0$

Try i = 10%

$\qquad 3553(4.868) - 235(12.763) - 14000 = +296.7$

Try i = 12%

$\qquad 3553(4.564) - 235(11.644) - 14000 = -520.4$

After-tax rate of return $= 10\% + (2\%)\left(\dfrac{296.7}{296.7 + 520.4}\right) = \underline{10.73\%}$

# 11-46

Let X = number of days car used per year. Automobiles are in the MACRS 5-year property class.

| Year | Before Tax Cash Flow | MACRS Depreciation | Taxable Income | Income Tax 50% | ATCF |
|------|----------------------|--------------------|----------------|----------------|------|
| 0 | +14,500 | | | | -14,500 |
| 1 | 80X - 1000 - 50X = 30X - 1000 | .20 (14,500) = 2900 | 30X - 3900 | -15X+1950 | 15X+950 |
| 2 | 30X - 1500 | 0.32(14,500) = 4640 | 30X - 6140 | -15X+3070 | 15X+1570 |
| 3 | 30X-2000 +5,000* | 0.192 (14,500) = 2784 | 30X - 4784+ 824 | -15X+2392-412 | 15X+4980 |

* Salvage value of which $824 subject to capital gain tax.
NPW = -14,500 + 15X(P/A,12%,3) +950(P/F,12%,1) +1570(P/F,12%,2) + 4980(P/F,12%,3) = 0
-14,500 +15X(2.402) +950(0.8929) +1570(0.7972) +4980(0.7118) = 0
36.03X = 14,500 - 848 - 1252 -3545
X = 8855/36.03 = 246 days

# 11-47 *a.*

| Year | Gross Income | Expense | BTCF | MACRS Deprec | ΔTax. Income | 40% ΔTax | ATCF |
|------|-------------|---------|-------|--------------|--------------|----------|------|
| 0 | | | -10,000 | | | | -10,000 |
| 1 | 2000 | 400 | 1800 | 1429 | 371 | -148 | 1652 |
| 2 | 2200 | 400 | 1800 | 2449 | -649 | +260 | 2060 |
| 3 | 2400 | 600 | 1800 | 1749 | 51 | -20 | 1780 |
| 4 | 2600 | 800 | 1800 | 1249 | 551 | -220 | 1580 |
| 5 | 2800 | 1000 | 1800 | 893 | 907 | -363 | 1437 |
| 6 | 3000 | 1200 | 1800 | 892 | 908 | -363 | 1437 |
| 7 | 3200 | 1400 | 1800 | 893 | 907 | -363 | 1437 |
| 8 | 3400 | 1600 | 1800 | 446 | 1354 | -542 | 1258 |
| 9 | 3600 | 1800 | 1800 | 0 | 1800 | -720 | 1080 |
| 10 | 3800 | 2000 | 1800 | 0 | 1800 | -720 | 1080 |

*b.* Solving the ATCF for the rate of return

Try $i = 8\%$

NPW = -10,000 + 1652(*P/F*,8%,1) +2060(*P/F*,8%,2) +1780(*P/F*,8%,3) +1580(*P/F*,8%,4)
+1437(*P/F*,8%,3)(*P/F*,8%,4) +1258(*P/F*,8%,8) +1080(*P/F*,8%,9) +1080(*P/F*,8%,10) = +312

interest rate too low

Try i = 9%

NPW = -10,000 + 1652(*P/F*,9%,1) +2060(*P/F*,9%,2) +1780(*P/F*,9%,3) +1580(*P/F*,9%,4)
+1437(*P/F*,9%,3)(*P/F*,9%,4) +1258(*P/F*,9%,8) +1080(*P/F*,9%,9) +1080(*P/F*,9%,10) = -95

So Rate of Return = 8% + (1%)[312/(312+95)] = 8.8%

*c.* **Add** to year 5 in table for part *a.*

| Year | BTCF | DEPR | ΔTI | ΔT | ATCF |
|------|------|------|------|------|------|
| 5 | 7000 | | 4769 | -1908 | 5092 |

End of Yr 5 Book Value = 10,000 - 7769 = 2331

Capital gain = 7000 -2331 = 4769

At 40%, additional tax = 1908

Compute NPW at 9% for sale of gas generator ar the end of Yr 5.

NPW = -14

At 9% the 10yr life gives NPW = -95 and the sale of the generator at the end of 5 years give a NPW = -14. The two situations are almost identical, but the sale of the generator at the end of 5 years is slightly preferred.

# 11-48

| Year | BTCF | MACRS Deprec | Taxable Income | 40% Taxes | ATCF |
|------|------|------|------|------|------|
| 0 | -25,000 | | | | -25,000 |
| 1 | 8000 | 8332 | -332 | +133 | 8133 |
| 2 | 8000 | 11,113 | -3113 | +1245 | 9245 |
| 3 | 8000 | 3702 | 4298 | -1719 | 6281 |
| 4 | 8000 5000 | 1853 | 6147 5000* | -2459 | 8688 |

* Capital Gain

Compute the NPW of the ATCF at 10%
NPW = -25,000 + 8133(P/F,10%,1) + 9245(P.F,10%,2) + 6281(P/F,10%,3) + 8688(P/F,10%,4) = +25,933
Since the NPW is positive at 10%, the after tax rate of return exceeds 10% (the after tax rate of return is about 11.3%). So, Granny should buy the churn!

# 11-49

MACRS Depreciation
**a.** 1st Recovery year: 11 ½ months depreciation = 3.485%(60,000) = 2091
2-4 Recovery years: 3.636%(60,000) = 2182
5th Recovery year: 11 ½ months deprec = 3.485%(60,000) = 2091
Total MACRS depreciation = 10,728
**b.** Book Value when sold = 60,000 - 10,728 + 10,000 land = 59,272
Capital gain = 80,000 - 59,272 = 20,728
**c.** Required uniform after tax cash flow to produce a 15% after tax ROR.
NPW = 0
   -70,000 + A(P/A,15%,5) + 74,196(P/F,15%,5) = 0
   -70,000 + 3.352 A + 74,196(0.4972) = 0
   A = 9,878

**d.**

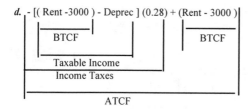

Years 1,5
-0.28 (Rent -3000) + 2091(0.28) + (Rent -3000) = ATCF = 9878
(Rent -3000) = (9878-585) / 0.72 = 12,907
Rent = $15,907
Years 2-4
-0.28(Rent -3000) + 2182(0.28) + (Rent-3000) = ATCF = 9878
(Rent -3000) = (9878 -611) / 0.72 = 12,871
Rent = $15,871

| Year | Income (rent) | Expense | Before tax cash flow | MACRS Deprec | Taxable income | 28% Income tax | After tax cash flow |
|------|---------------|---------|----------------------|--------------|----------------|----------------|---------------------|
| 0 | | | -$70,000 | | | | -$70,000 |
| 1 | $15,907 | -$3000 | 12,907 | $2091 | $10,816 | $3029 | 9,878 |
| 2 | 15,871 | -3000 | 12,871 | 2182 | 10,689 | 2993 | 9,878 |
| 3 | 15,871 | -3000 | 12,871 | 2182 | 10,689 | 2993 | 9,878 |
| 4 | 15,871 | -3000 | 12,871 | 2182 | 10,689 | 2993 | 9,878 |
| 5 | 15,907 | -3000 | 12,907 | 2091 | 10,816 | 3029 | 9,878 |
| | | | $80,000 | $10,728 | 20,728 | $5,804 | $74,196 |

# 11-50

| Year | Before tax cash flow | MACRS* depreciation | Taxable income | Income tax (45%) | After tax cash flow | Present worth (12%) |
|------|----------------------|---------------------|----------------|------------------|---------------------|---------------------|
| 0 | -20,000 | | | | - $20,000 | -$20,000 |
| 1 | +8,000 | $4,000 | $4,000 | $1,800 | $6,200 | $5,536 |
| 2 | +8,000 | $6,400 | $1,600 | $720 | $7,280 | $5,804 |
| 3 | +8,000 | $3840 | $4160 | $1872 | $6128 | $4362 |
| | +10,000 | | $4240** | $1908 | $8090 | $5760 |
| | | | | Net present worth = | | $1,462 |

\* Computers are in the 5-year property class.
\*\* Book Value = 5760.  Capital gain = 10,000 -5760 = 4240

# 11-51

**Purchase Option:**

| Year | Before Tax Cash Flow | MACRS Depreciation | Taxable Income | 40% Income Taxes | After Tax Cash Flow | PW of Cost |
|---|---|---|---|---|---|---|
| 1 (6mo-1995) | -5838 | 2950 | -2950 | 1180 | -4658 | 4159 |
| 2 (1996) | -11,676 | 4700 | -4700 | 1880 | -9796 | 7809 |
| 3 (1997) | -11,676 | 2850 | -2850 | 1140 | -10,536 | 7500 |
| 4 (6 mo-1998) | 0 | 838 | -838 | +335 | +335 | |
| 4 | +15,200 | 2650 | -2650* | +1060 | +16,260 | -10,546 |
| | | | | | | $8922 |

\* Book Value = Cost - Deprec = 17,850
Capital loss on disposal = 17,850 - 15,200 = 2650

**Lease Option**

| Year | Before Tax Cash Flow | Taxable Income | 40% Income Taxes | After Tax Cash Flow | PW of Cost |
|---|---|---|---|---|---|
| 1 (6mo-1995) | -4464 | -4464 | 1786 | -2678 | 2391 |
| 2 (1996) | -4428 | -4428 | 1771 | -2657 | 2118 |
| 3 (1997) | -4428 | -4428 | 1771 | -2657 | 1891 |
| 4 (6 mo-1998) | -2214 | -2214 | +886 | -1328 | 844 |
| | | | | | $7244 |

The lease option, with its smaller PW of Cost is preferred.

# 11-52

Let $i_a$ = annual effective after-tax cost of capital
Sole Brother is paying (100%)/(100% - 3%) -1 = 0.030928 = 3.0928% for
use of the money for 45 - 5 = 40 days.
Number of 40 day periods in 1 year = 365/40 = 9.125
$i_a = [1 + (0.030928)(1 - 0.4)]^{9.125} -1 = 0.1827$
$i_a$ = 18.27%

# 11-53

$A = \$5000(A/P,15\%,4) = 5000(0.3503) = \$1751.50$

| | $n = 0$ | 1 | 2 | 3 | 4 |
|---|---|---|---|---|---|
| Loan Balance | 5000 | | | | |
| Interest Payment | | 750.00 | 599.80 | 427.02 | 228.35 |
| Principal Payment | | 1001.50 | 1151.70 | 1324.48 | 1522.32 |
| Loan Balance | | 3998.50 | 2846.80 | 1522.32 | 0 |
| Sum of Payments | | 1751.50 | 1751.50 | 1751.50 | 1751.50 |
| Additional "Point" Interest | | 75.00 | 75.00 | 75.00 | 75.00 |
| Before Tax Cash Flow | +4700 | -1751.50 | -1751.50 | -1751.50 | -1751.50 |
| Tax Benefit - Interest Deduction | | | | | |
| Interest | | 825.00 | 674.80 | 502.02 | 303.35 |
| Tax Saving (Interest x 0.40) | | +330.00 | +269.90 | +200.80 | +121.30 |
| After Tax Cash Flow | +4700 | -1421.50 | -1481.60 | -1550.70 | -1630.20 |

Solving the After Tax Cash Flow, the after tax interest rate is 10.9%

# 11-54

NOTE: All yield benefits are in thousands of dollars.

| Year | 0 | 1 | 2 | 3 | 4 |
|---|---|---|---|---|---|
| Purchase/Sale | -P | | | | 0.2P |
| Benefits | | 10 | 15 | 20 | 20 |
| Depreciation/Book Value | | 0.20P | 0.32P | 0.192P | 0.115P |
| Taxable Income | | 10-0.20P | 15-0.32P | 20-0.192P | 20+0.115P |
| 40% Income Taxes | | -4+0.08P | -6+0.128P | -8+0.077P | -8+0.046P |
| After Tax Cash Flow | | 6+0.08P | 9+0.128P | 12 + 0.077P | 12+0.046P |
| (P/F,10%,n) | | 0.9091 | 0.8264 | 0.7513 | 0.6830 |
| Discounted NPW | - P | 5.4546+0.073P | 4.9584+0.106P | 9.0156+.058P | 8.1960+.031 P |

NPW = 27,625 - 0.732 P = 0    P= \$37,740 maximum purchase price

# 11-55

*a.* **Purchase**

SL Depreciation = $(P-L)/n$ = (1,000,000 -400,000)/10= 60,000

Taxes =  (800,000 -200,000)(0.40) = 216,000

ATCF = (800,000 - 60,000 - 200,000 = 384,000/year + Year0 Purchase + Year 10 Resale

EUAB -EUAC  = 384,000 + 400,000(A/F,10%,10) - 1,000,000(A/P,10%,10)

$\qquad$ = 384,000 + 400,000(0.0627) - 1,000,000(0.1627)

$\qquad$ = +246,380

**Lease**

Taxes = (800,000 -200,000 -200,000)(0.40) = 160,000

EUAB -EUAC = 800,000 -200,000 -200,000 -160,000 = +240,000

So Purchasing the plant is preferred.

*b.* Breakeven Rate of Return

Set the $(EUAB - EUAC)_{purchase}$ - $(EUAB-EUAC)_{lease}$ = 0 and solve for the breakeven rate of return.

384,000 + 400,000$(A/F,i,10)$ - 1,000,000$(A/P,i,10)$ -240,000 = 0

From part *a.*, we know that at 10%

$\qquad$ $(EUAB - EUAC)_{purchase}$ - $(EUAB-EUAC)_{lease}$ = 246,380 -240,000 = +6380

Now try $i = 12\%$

384,000 + 400,000(0.0570) - 1,000,000(0.1770) -240,000 = -10,200.

So Breakeven Rate of Return

$\qquad$ = 10% +(2%)[6380/(6380 + 10,200)] = 10.8%

# 11-56

Taxable Income = Adjustable Gross Income - Allowable Deductions

    = (500,000 - 300,000) - 30,000

    = $170,000

Tax Bill    = 0.15(50,000) + 0.25(25,000) + 0.34(25,000) + 0.39(70,000) - tax credits

    = 49,550 - 8000

    = $41,550

# 11-57

GIVEN:    First Cost = 18,600
          Annual Cost = 16,000
          Salvage Value = 3,600
          Deprecation = S/L w/ N=10, S=3,600
          Savings/bag = $ 0.030
          Cartons/Year = 200,000
          Savings bags/carton = 3.5
          Thus Annual Savings = (0.03)(3.5)(200,000) = $21,000

| Year | Before Tax Cash Flow | S/L Deprec | Taxable Income | Income Taxes | After-Tax Cash Flow |
|------|----------------------|------------|----------------|--------------|---------------------|
| 0 | -18,600 | - | - | +1,860* | -16,740 |
| 1-10 | 5,000 | 1,500** | 3,500 | -1,750 | 3,250 |
| 10 | 3,600 | - | 0*** | 0 | 3,600 |

* S/L Depreciation = (18,600-3,600)/10 = $1,500 /year
** 10% ITC on 18,600,  18,600(.10) = $1,860
*** Cap G/L = 3,600 - [18,600-(10)(1,500)]= $0

*a.*  PW = -16,740 + 3,250(P/A, 20%,10) + 3,600(P/F,20%,10) = $-2,535

*b.*  set PW=0  @ i*, solve for i*
          0= -16,740 + 3,250(P/A, i*%,10) + 3,600(P/F,i*%,10)
          by trial and error method  i* = 16% per year

c.

| Year (n) | Cash Flow in (n) | Net Cash Flow from time 1-to-n |
|---|---|---|
| 0 | -16,740 | -16,740 |
| 1 | 3,250 | -10,240 |
| 2 | 3,250 | -6,990 |
| 3 | 3,250 | -3,740 |
| 4 | 3,250 | -490 |
| 5 | 3,250 | 2,760 |
| 6 | 3,250 | 6,010 |

**Simple Payback between 5 & 6 yrs**

By interpolation, Simple Payback = 5 + 490/3250 = <u>5.15 years</u>

<u>Alt. Solution:</u>
Simple Payback =  First Cost/Equivalent Net Cash Flow per Year
= 16,740/3,250 = <u>5.15 years</u>

Solutions to Spreadsheet supplement problems are after Chapter 19 .

# Replacement Analysis

## 12-1

Per the Replacement Analysis Decision Map, the appropriate analysis method is a function of the cash flows and assumptions made regarding the defender and challenger assets. Thus, the answer would be (d).

## 12-2

The replacement decision is a function of both the defender and the challenger.

> The statement is *false*.

## 12-3

The book value of the equipment describes past actions or a *sunk cost* situation. It should be ignored in this *before-tax* analysis.

> Answer is (c)

## 12-4

With no resale value, and maintenance costs that are expected to be higher in the future, EUAC would be a minimum for one year. (This is such a common situation that the early versions of the MAPI replacement analysis model were based on a one year remaining life for the defender.)

> Answer: One Year

## 12-5

The EUAC of installed cost will decline as the service life increases. The EUAC of maintenance is constant. Thus total EUAC is declining over time.

> Answer: For minimum EUAC, keep the bottling machine indefinitely.

# 12-6

The value to use is the present market value of the defender equipment. (The book indicates that trade-in value may be purposely inflated as a selling strategy, hence it may or may not represent market value.)

Answer is (b)

# 12-7

In a before-tax computation the data about depreciation is unneeded.

Before-Tax Cash Flow

| Year | Reconditioned Equipment | New Equipment | New rather than Reconditioned | PW at 12% | PW at 15% |
|------|------------------------|---------------|-------------------------------|-----------|-----------|
| 0 | -$35,000<br>-10,000 | -$85,000 | -$40,000 | -$40,000 | -$40,000 |
| 1-10 | | +7000 | +7,000 | +39,555 | +35,133 |
| 10 | +10,000 | +15,000 | +5,000 | +1,610 | +1,236 |
| | | | | +1,165 | -3,631 |

By interpolation the incremental before-tax rate of return is 12.7%

The 12.7% rate of return on the increment is unsatisfactory, so reject the increment and recondition the old tank car.

# 12-8

EUAC of Capital Recovery

In this situation $P = S = 15,000$

So EUAC of Capital Recovery = $15,000 (0.15) = \$2250$ for all useful lives.

EUAC of Maintenance

For a 1 year useful life

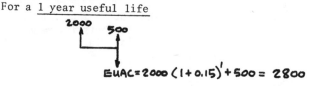

$$EUAC = 2000 (1 + 0.15)^1 + 500 = 2800$$

For a <u>2 year useful life</u>

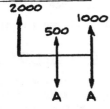

$$FW_{yr2} = 2000(F/P,15\%,2)$$
$$+ 500(F/P,15\%,1) + 1000$$
$$= 4220$$

$$A = 4220(A/F,15\%,2) = 1963$$

$$EUAC = A = 1963$$

For a <u>3 year useful life</u>

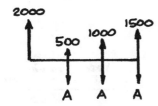

$$FW_{yr3} = 2000(F/P,15\%,3) + 500(F/P,15\%,2) + 1000(F/P,15\%,1)$$
$$+ 1500$$
$$= 6353$$
$$A = 6353(A/F,15\%,3) = 1829$$

$$EUAC = A = 1829$$

For a <u>4 year useful life</u>

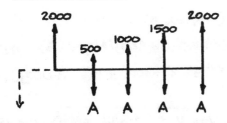

$$FW_{yr4} = 2000(F/P,15\%,4) + 500(P/G,15\%,5)(F/P,15\%,5) = 9305$$

$$A = 9305 (A/F,15\%,4) = 1864 \qquad EUAC = A = 1864$$

Alternate computation of maintenance in any year N:

$$EUAC_N = A = 2000(A/P,15\%,N) + 500 + 500(A/G,15\%,N)$$

(a)    Total EUAC = $2250 + EUAC of Maintenance

Therefore, to minimize Total EUAC, choose the alternative with minimum EUAC of Maintenance.

Economical Life = 3 years

(b)    The stainless steel tank will always be compared with the best available replacement (the challenger). If the challenger is superior, then the defender tank probably will be replaced.

It will cost a substantial amount of money to remove the existing tank from the plant, sell it to someone else, and then buy and install another one. As a practical matter, it seems unlikely that this will be economical.

# 12-9

| Year N | Salvage value S | maintenance |
|--------|--------|-------------|
| 0 | P=10000 | |
| 1 | 3000 | 300 |
| 2 | 3500 | 300 |
| 3 | 4000 | 300 |

| Year N | Salvage value S | maintenance |
|--------|--------|-------------|
| 4 | 4500 | 600 |
| 5 | 5000 | 1200 |
| 6 | 5500 | 2400 |
| 7 | 6000 | 4800 |

## EUAC of Maintenance

$EUAC_1 = EUAC_2 = EUAC_3 = 300$

$EUAC_4 = 300 + 300 \,(A/F, 15\%, 4) = 360$

$EUAC_5 = 300 + [300(F/P, 15\%, 1) + 900](A/F, 15\%, 5) = 485$

$EUAC_6 = 300 + [300(F/P, 15\%, 2) + 900(F/P, 15\%, 1) + 2100](A/F, 15\%, 6)$
$\qquad = 703$

$EUAC_7 = 300 + [300(F/P, 15\%, 3) + 900(F/P, 15\%, 2) + 2100(F/P, 15\%, 1)$
$\qquad + 4500](A/F, 15\%, 7) = 1074$

EUAC of Installed Cost

| YEAR | $(P-S)(A/P,i\%,n)+Si$ |
|------|------------------------|
| 1 | $(10,000-3000)(A/P,15\%,1)+ 3000(0.15) = 8500$ |
| 2 | $(10,000-3500)(A/P,15\%,2)+ 3500(0.15) = 4523$ |
| 3 | $(10,000-4000)(A/P,15\%,3)+ 4000(0.15) = 3228$ |
| 4 | $(10,000-4500)(A/P,15\%,4)+ 4500(0.15) = 2602$ |
| 5 | $(10,000-5000)(A/P,15\%,5)+ 5000(0.15) = 2242$ |
| 6 | $(10,000-5500)(A/P,15\%,6)+ 5500(0.15) = 2014$ |
| 7 | $(10,000-6000)(A/P,15\%,7)+ 6000(0.15) = 1862$ |

| YEAR | EUAC of Installed Cost | + | EUAC of Maintenance | = | Total EUAC |
|------|------------------------|---|---------------------|---|-----------|
| 1 | 8500 | | 300 | | 8800 |
| 2 | 4523 | | 300 | | 4823 |
| 3 | 3228 | | 300 | | 3528 |
| 4 | 2602 | | 360 | | 2962 |
| 5 | 2242 | | 485 | | 2727 |
| 6 | 2014 | | 703 | | 2717 ← Economical Life = 6 yrs |
| 7 | 1862 | | 1074 | | 2936 |

# 12-10

(a) Before Tax Analysis

| YEAR | New Machine Before-Tax CASH FLOW | Existing Machine Before-Tax Cash FLOW | New Machine rather than Existing Machine Before-Tax Cash Flow |
|------|------|------|------|
| 0 | -3700 | -1000 | -2700 |
| 1 | +900 | 0 | +900 |
| 2 | +900 | 0 | +900 |
| 3 | +900 | 0 | +900 |
| 4 | +900 | 0 | +900 |

Compute Rate of Return
  PW of Cost = PW of Benefits

$$2700 = 900(P/A, i\%, 4) \; ; \; (P/A, i\%, 4) = \frac{2700}{900} = 3.0$$

Rate of Return $i = 12.6\%$

(b) After Tax Analysis

| YEAR | NEW MACHINE Before-Tax Cash Flow | SOYD Deprec | TAXABLE INCOME | 40% INCOME TAXES | AFTER-TAX CASH FLOW |
|------|------|------|------|------|------|
| 0 | -3700 | | | | -3700 |
| 1 | +900 | 1480 | -580 | +232 | +1132 |
| 2 | +900 | 1110 | -210 | +84 | +984 |
| 3 | +900 | 740 | +160 | -64 | +836 |
| 4 | +900 | 370 | +530 | -212 | +688 |

SOYD Deprec.    SUM = $\frac{4}{2}(5) = 10$

1st yr. SOYD = $\frac{4}{10}(3700-0)$ = 1480

Annual decline = $\frac{1}{10}(3700-0)$ = 370

EXISTING MACHINE

| YEAR | Before-Tax Cash Flow | SL Deprec | TAXABLE INCOME | 40% INCOME TAXES | After-TAX Cash Flow |
|------|------|------|------|------|------|
| 0 | −1000 | | 1000* | −400** | −1400 |
| 1 | 0 | 500 | −500 | +200 | +200 |
| 2 | 0 | 500 | −500 | +200 | +200 |
| 3 | 0 | 500 | −500 | +200 | +200 |
| 4 | 0 | 500 | −500 | +200 | +200 |

*Long term capital loss foregone by keeping machine:
   = $2000 Book Value - $1000 Selling Price = $1000 capital loss

**The $1000 long term capital loss foregone would have offset $1000
   of long term capital gains elsewhere in the firm.  The result
   is a tax saving of $40\%(1000) = 400$ is foregone.

NEW MACHINE RATHER THAN EXISTING ONE

| YEAR | NEW TOOL AFTER-TAX CASH FLOW | EXISTING TOOL AFTER-TAX CASH FLOW | NEW−EXISTING AFTER-TAX CASH FLOW | PW @ 10% | PW @ 12% |
|------|------|------|------|------|------|
| 0 | −3700 | −1400 | −2300 | −2300 | −2300 |
| 1 | +1132 | +200 | 932 | 847 | 832 |
| 2 | +984 | +200 | 784 | 648 | 625 |
| 3 | +836 | +200 | 636 | 478 | 453 |
| 4 | +688 | +200 | 488 | 333 | 310 |
| | | | +540 | +6 | −80 |

$\Delta$ after-tax rate of return = 10.14%

## 12-11

Alternative I   Retire the 4 old machines and buy 6
   new ones.

   Initial Cost:
      6 new machines at $32,000 each       $192,000
      Training Program  6 x 700             + 4,200
                                           $ 196,200

   Annual labor saving = 12,000
      less: maintenance = 3600
      Net Annual Benefit  $8,400

Compute Equivalent Uniform Annual Cost (EUAC)

Initial Cost: $196,200 (A/P,9%,8)=196,200(0.1807)= 35,453
Less Salvage Value
        6x 750(A/F,9%,8)= 4500(0.0907)        =    - 408
Less Net annual Benefit                        =  -8,400
                                EUAC    = $26,645

Alternative II    Keep 4 old machines and buy 3 new ones.
    Initial Cost: Value of 4 old machines  4 * 2000 =  8000
                    3 new machines      3 * 32000 = 96 000
                    Training Program    3 * 700 =  2100
                                                    106,100

Annual maintenance
        4 old @ 1500 + 3 new @ 600 = 7800 per year
Salvage Value - 8 years hence
        4 old @ 500 + 3 new @ 750 = 4250
Compute EUAC
    Initial Cost  106,100(A/P,9%,8)=106,100(0.1807)= 19,172
    Less Salvage Value
            4250(A/F,9%,8)= 4250(0.0907)=   -385
    add Annual Maintenance                        7800
                                EUAC  = $ 26,587

            Decision: Choose Alternative II

# 12-12

From the facts stated, we see that if the old forklift is retained the EUAC is minimum for a one year useful life.  The problem says the challenger economic life is 10 years.  (Using the data provided this fact could be verified, but that is not part of the problem.)

Annual Cash Flow Analysis:

Keep Old Forklift Another Year:

| YEAR | Before Tax Cash Flow | Deprec | Taxable Income | 40% INCOME Taxes | After-tax Cash Flow |
|------|------|------|------|------|------|
| 0 | 0 | | | | 0 |
| 1 | 400 | 0 | -400 | +160 | -240 |

EUAC for one more year with old forklift = $240

Buy New Forklift

| YEAR | Before-Tax Cash Flow | Str Line Deprec | Taxable Income | 40% Income Taxes | After-Tax Cash Flow |
|------|------|------|------|------|------|
| 0 | -6500 | | | | -6500 |
| 1-10 | -50 | 650 | -700 | +280 | +230 |

$$EUAC = 6500 \,(A/P, 8\%, 10) - 230$$
$$= 6500 \,(0.1490) - 230 = \$738.50$$

Decision: Choose the alternative with
minimum EUAC.
Keep the old forklift another year.

# 12-13

The problem, with a 7-year analysis period, may be solved in a variety of ways.  A first step is to compute an after-tax cash flow for each alternative.

Alternative A

| YR | Before-Tax Cash Flow | Deprec | Taxable Income | 40% Income Taxes | After-Tax Cash Flow |
|------|------|------|------|------|------|
| 0 | -44,000 | | -44,000 | +17,600 | -26,400 |
| 1-7 | 0 | | 0 | | 0 |

**Alternative B**
This alternative is less desirable than Alternative D and may be immediately rejected.

**Alternative C**

| Yr | Before-Tax Cash Flow | SOYD Deprec | Taxable Income | 40% Income Taxes | After-Tax Cash Flow |
|---|---|---|---|---|---|
| 0 | -56,000 | | | | -56,000 |
| 1 | 12,000 | 14,000 | -2000 | +800 | +12,800 |
| 2 | 12,000 | 12,000 | 0 | 0 | +12,000 |
| 3 | 12,000 | 10,000 | 2000 | -800 | +11,200 |
| 4 | 12,000 | 8000 | 4000 | -1600 | +10,400 |
| 5 | 12,000 | 6000 | 6000 | -2400 | +9600 |
| 6 | 12,000 | 4000 | 8000 | -3200 | +8800 |
| 7 | 12,000 | 2000 | 10000 | -4000 | +8000 |

**Alternative D**

| Yr | Before-Tax Cash Flow | Deprec | Taxable Income | 40% Income Taxes | After-Tax Cash Flow |
|---|---|---|---|---|---|
| 0 | -49,000 | | | | -49,000 |
| 1-7 | 7000 | 7000 | 0 | 0 | +7000 |

**Alternative E (Do nothing)**

| Yr | Before-Tax Cash Flow | Deprec | Taxable Income | 40% Income Taxes | After-Tax Cash Flow |
|---|---|---|---|---|---|
| 0 | 0 | | | | 0 |
| 1-7 | -8000 | 0 | -8000 | +3200 | -4800 |

A NPW solution probably is easiest to compute.

Alt. A   $NPW = -26400$

Alt. C   $NPW = -56000 + 12,800 (P/A, 10\%, 7) - 800 (P/G, 10\%, 7)$
$= -56000 + 12,800 (4.868) - 800 (12.763)$
$= -3900$

Alt. D   $NPW = -49,000 + 7000 (P/A, 10\%, 7)$
$= -49,000 + 7000 (4.868) = -14,924$

Alt. E   $NPW = -4800 (P/A, 10\%, 7) = -4800 (4.868) = -23,366$

Choose the alternative that maximizes NPW - Choose Alt. C.
Alternate solution on next page.

## Rate of Return Solution - Incremental Analysis

**Alt. A rather than Alt. E (Do nothing)**

After-Tax Cash Flow

| YR | Alt. A | Alt. E | A-E |
|----|--------|--------|-----|
| 0 | -26,400 | 0 | -26,400 |
| 1-7 | 0 | -4800 | +4800 |

$\Delta ROR = 6.4\%$
∴ Reject alt. A

**Alt. D rather than Alt. E**

After-Tax Cash Flow

| YR | Alt. D | Alt. E | D-E |
|----|--------|--------|-----|
| 0 | -49000 | 0 | -49,000 |
| 1-7 | +7000 | -4000 | +11,000 |

$\Delta ROR = 12.8\%$
∴ Reject Alt. E

**Alt. C rather than Alt. D**

After-Tax Cash Flow

| YR | Alt. C | Alt. D | C-D |
|----|--------|--------|-----|
| 0 | -56 000 | -49000 | -7000 |
| 1 | 12 800 | 7000 | 5800 |
| 2 | 12 000 | 7000 | 5000 |
| 3 | 11 200 | 7000 | 4200 |
| 4 | 10 400 | 7000 | 3400 |
| 5 | 9 600 | 7000 | 2600 |
| 6 | 8 800 | 7000 | 1800 |
| 7 | 8 000 | 7000 | 1000 |

$7000 = 5800(P/A, i, 7)$
$\quad -800(P/G, i, 7)$
$\Delta ROR > 60\%$
(HP-12C = 65.9%)
∴ Reject D

Choose Alt. C

# 12-14

For various lives, determine the EUAC for the challenger assuming it is retired at the end of period. The best useful life will be the one whose EUAC is a minimum.

Useful Life = 1 year

$EUAC = 12000(F/P, 10\%, 1) = 13,200$

Useful Life = 2 years

$EUAC = 12000(A/P, 10\%, 2) = 6914$

Useful Life = 3 years

$$EUAC = 12,000(A/P, 10\%, 3) = 12000(0.4021)$$
$$= 4825$$

Useful Life = 4 years

$$EUAC = 12000(A/P, 10\%, 4) + 2000(A/F, 10\%, 4)$$
$$= 12000(0.3155) + 2000(0.2155)$$
$$= 4217$$

Useful Life = 5 years

$$EUAC = 12000(A/P, 10\%, 5) + [2000(1+1(F/P, 10\%, 1))]$$
$$\times (A/F, 10\%, 5)$$
$$= 12000(0.2638) + [2000 + 2000(1.100)]$$
$$\times 0.1638$$
$$= 3854$$

Useful Life = 6 years

$$EUAC = [12,000(F/P, 10\%, 6) + 2000(F/A, 10\%, 3)$$
$$+ 2500](A/F, 10\%, 6)$$
$$= [12000(1.772) + 2000(3.310)$$
$$+ 2500](0.1296)$$
$$= 3938$$

Summary:

| Useful Life | EUAC |
|---|---|
| 1 yr | 13200 |
| 2 | 6914 |
| 3 | 4825 |
| 4 | 4217 |
| 5 | 3854 ← minimum EUAC |
| 6 | 3938 |

Best Useful Life = 5 yrs

# 12-15

Book value of Machine A now

$= Cost - depreciation$ to date $= 54000 - \frac{9}{12}(54000 - 0) = 13,500$

Long term capital gain if sold now $= 30,000 - 13,500 = 16,500$

Machine A annual depreciation $= \frac{P-S}{n} = \frac{54000-0}{12} = 4500$

Machine B annual depreciation $= \frac{P-S}{n} = \frac{42000-0}{12} = 3500$

<u>Alternate 1</u> : Keep A for 12 more years

| YEAR | Before Tax Cash flow | Str Line Deprec | Taxable Income | 40% Income Taxes | After Tax Cash flow |
|---|---|---|---|---|---|
| 0 | -30 000* | | -16 500 | +6600 | -23,400 |
| 1 | 0 | 4500 | -4500 | +1800 | +1800 |
| 2 | 0 | 4500 | -4500 | +1800 | +1800 |
| 3 | 0 | 4500 | -4500 | +1800 | +1800 |
| 4-12 | 0 | 0 | 0 | 0 | 0 |

\* If A were sold the Year 0 entries
would be: +30,000   16500   -6600   +23 400.
If A is kept, the entries are just the reverse.

After tax annual cost

$= \left[ 23400 - 1800(P/A, 10\%, 3) \right] \left[ (A/P, 10\%, 12) \right]$

$= \left[ 23400 - 1800(2.487) \right] \left[ 0.1468 \right] = \underline{\underline{2778}}$

Solution continued on next page.

The cash flow in Year 0 reflects the loss of income after capital gains tax from _not_ selling machine A. This is the preferred way to handle the current market value of the "defender".

Alternate 2: Buy machine B

| YEAR | Before Tax Cash Flow | Str Line Deprec | Taxable Income | 40% Income Taxes | After Tax Cash flow |
|------|------|------|------|------|------|
| 0 | -42 000 | | | | -42 000 |
| 1-12 | +2 500 | 3500 | -1000 | +400 | +2 900 |

After tax annual cost

$$= 42,000 \underset{0.1468}{(A/P, 10\%, 12)} - 2900 = \underline{\underline{3266}}$$

Choose the alternative with the smaller annual cost

$$\underline{\underline{\text{Keep A}}}$$

# 12-16

*a.* **SONAR**

SOYD = 8(9)/2 = 36      $\Delta D/yr = (18,000-3600)/36 = 400$

| | Orig.<br>Year j | SOYD<br>Deprec | Book<br>Value | |
|---|---|---|---|---|
| | 1 | 3200 | 14800 | |
| | 2 | 2800 | 12000 | |
| | 3 | 2400 | 9600 | |
| | 4 | 2000 | 7600 | |
| NOW→ | 5 | 1600 | 6000 | $-BV_s$ |
| | 6 | 1200 | 4800 | |
| | 7 | 800 | 4000 | |
| | 8 | 400 | 3600 | |

| Orig.<br>Year | Analysis<br>Year | BTCF | SOYD<br>Deprec | $\Delta$Tax.<br>Income | $\Delta$Tax | ATCF |
|---|---|---|---|---|---|---|
| 5 | 0 | -7000 | | -1000* | +400 | -6600 |
| 6 | 1 | | 1200 | -1200 | +480 | 480 |
| 7 | 2 | | 800 | -800 | +320 | 320 |
| 8 | 3 | 1600 | 400 | -400 -<br>2000** | +160<br>+800 | 2560 |

\* Foregone Capital Gain is about 7000 - $BV_s$ = $1000
\*\* Capital Loss is about 1600-$BV_8$ = -2000

**b. SHSS**

| Year | BTCF | MACRS Deprec | ∆Tax Income | ∆Tax | ATCF |
|------|------|------|------|------|------|
| 0 | -10,000 | | | | -10,000 |
| 1 | 500 | 2000 | -1500 | 600 | 1100 |
| 2 | 500 | 3200 | -2700 | 1080 | 1580 |
| 3 | 500 4000 | 1920 | -1420 1120* | 568 -448 | 1068 3552 |

\* Capital Gain = 4000 - $BV_3$

$$BV_3 = 10,000 - \sum_{j=1}^{3} D_j = 2880$$

**c. Difference between Alternatives**

| Yr | ∆ATCF=$ATCF_{SHSS}$ -$ATCF_{Sonar}$ |
|------|------|
| 0 | -3400 |
| 1 | 620 |
| 2 | 1260 |
| 3 | 2060 |

**d.** Compute the NPW on the difference between the alternatives at 20%
   $NPW_\triangle$ = -3400 + 620(P/F,20%,1) + 1260(P/F,20%,2) + 2060(P/F,20%,3)
                     0.8333              0.6944              0.5787
                   = -816.29
Since NPW is Negative, then the incremental rate of return is < 20%.
Stay with the sonar device.

# 12-17

*a.* Expected good performance, productivity, energy efficiency, safety, long service life. Retraining in operation and maintenance may be required. High comfort of operation. High purchase price. May not be immediately available. Sales taxes to be paid. Can be depreciated. Supplier warranty and spare parts backup available.

*b.* All as in *a.* except for lower price and probably faster delivery.

*c.* All as in *a.* except for  still lower cost, lost production during the rebuild period, and that the rebuild costs can be expensed, at least partially.  No sales tax applies.

*d.* Performance and productivity may not be as good as in option *c.*  Retraining in operation and maintenance is not required.  Production will be lost during the rebuilding period.  Cost may be substantially lower than in the previous options.  The rebuild costs can be expensed.  No sales tax applies.

*e.* Performance, productivity, service life, energy efficiency, safety, reliability may be significantly lower than in the other options.  Retraining in operation and maintenance may be required if the new unit is different from the present one.  Cost may be only 20-50% of the new equipment.  Immediate delivery is a possibility.  The sales tax applies.  Equipment can be depreciated,

# 12-18

Find: $NPW_{overhaul}$ and $NPW_{replace}$

**NOTE:** All costs which occur before today are **SUNK COSTS** and are relevant.

$$NPW_{overhaul} = -1800 - 800(P/A, 5\%, 2)$$
$$= -1800 - 800(1.859)$$
$$= -\$3287$$

$$NPW_{replace} = +1500 - (2500 + 300)\,(P/A, 5\%, 2)$$
$$= +1500 - (2800)\,(1.859)$$
$$= -\$3705$$

Since the PW of Cost of the overhaul is less than the PW of Cost of the replacement car, the decision is to overhaul the 1988 auto.

# 12-19

First cost = 1,050,000
Salvage value = 225,000
Maintenance & operating cost = 235,000
Maintenance & operating gradient = 75,000
MARR = 10 %
EUAB - EUAC = -1,050,000 $(A/P, 10\%, n)$ + 225,000 $(A/F, 10\%, n)$
$\qquad\qquad$ -235,000 - 75,000 $(A/G, 10\%, n)$

Try $n = 4$ yrs
$\quad$ EUAB - EUAC = -331,275 + 48,488 - 235,000 - 103,575 = -621,362

Try $n = 5$ yrs
$\quad$ EUAB - EUAC = -276,990 + 36,855 - 235,000 - 135,750 = -610,885

Try $n = 6$ yrs
$\quad$ EUAB - EUAC = -241,080 + 29,160 - 235,000 - 166,800 = -613,720

Year 5 has the minimum EUAB - EUAC, hence the most economic life is 5 years.

# 12-20

*a.*
$\qquad$ The minimum cost life is where the EAUC of ownership is minimized for
$\qquad$ the number of years held. This would occur at
$\qquad$ <u>4 years</u> for the defender, where EAUC = $4,400

*b.*
$\qquad$ The minimum cost life of the challenger is <u>5 years</u> where the
$\qquad$ EAUC = $6,200.

*c.*
$\qquad$ Using Replacement Analysis Technique #3:
$\qquad$ Assuming that the defender and challenger costs do not change over the
$\qquad$ next 4 years we should keep the defender for four years and then reevaluate
$\qquad$ the costs with challengers at that time. Here we are comparing the min.
$\qquad$ EUAC (def) vs. min. EUAC(challenger), and $4,400 < $6,200 thus we keep
$\qquad$ the defender.

# 12-21

*a.*     The minimum cost life is where the EAUC of ownership is minimized for
the number of years held. This would occur at
1 year for the defender, where EAUC = $4,000

*b.*     The minimum cost life of the challenger is 4 years where the
EAUC = $3,300.

*c.*     Using Replacement Analysis Technique #3:
Given these costs for the defender and challenger we should replace the
defender with the challenger asset now.  This is because the min. EUAC
(def) > min. EUAC(challenger), $4,000 > $3,300.

# 12-22

For this problem we have marginal cost data for the defender, so we will check to see if that data is strictly increasing.

Defender:
Current market value = $25,000(.90)(.90)(.90)(.90)(.90) = $14,762

This table is used to tabulate the total marginal cost:

| Yr(n) | Time Line | Market Value (n) | Loss in MV (n) | Annual Costs (n) | Lost Interest in (n) | Total Marg Cost |
|---|---|---|---|---|---|---|
| 0 | | 25000 | | | | |
| 1 | -5 | 22500 | 2500 | 1,250 | 2000 | 5750 |
| 2 | -4 | 20250 | 2250 | 1,750 | 1800 | 5800 |
| 3 | -3 | 18225 | 2025 | 2,250 | 1620 | 5895 |
| 4 | -2 | 16403 | 1823 | 2,750 | 1458 | 6031 |
| 5 | -1 | 14762 | 1640 | 3,250 | 1312 | 6202 |
| 6 | 1 | 13286 | 1476 | 3,750 | 1181 | 6407 |
| 7 | 2 | 11957 | 1329 | 4,250 | 1063 | 6641 |
| 8 | 3 | 10762 | 1196 | 4,750 | 957 | 6902 |
| 9 | 4 | 9686 | 1076 | 5,250 | 861 | 7187 |
| 10 | 5 | 8717 | 969 | 5,750 | 775 | 7493 |

We see that this data is strictly increasing from the Time Line of today --> onward (year 6 of the original life). Thus we use Replacement Analysis Technique #1 and compare the marginal cost data of the defender against the min. EAUC of the challenger. Let's find the Challenger's min. EAUC at its 5 year life.

Challenger: Challenger's min. cost life is given at 5 years in the problem.

EAUC = $27,900 (A/P,8%,5) = $ 6,989

From this we would recommend that we keep the Defender for three more years and then replace it with the Challenger. This is because after three years the marginal costs of the Defender become greater than the min. EUAC of the Challenger.

# 12-23

For this problem we have marginal cost data for the defender, so we will check to see if that data is strictly increasing.

<u>Defender:</u>
Current market value = $25,000(.70)(.70)(.70)(.70)(.70) = $4,202

This table is used to tabulate the total marginal cost:

| Yr(n) | Time Line | Market Value (n) | Loss in MV (n) | Annual Costs (n) | Lost Interest in (n) | Total Marg Cost |
|-------|-----------|------------------|----------------|------------------|----------------------|-----------------|
| 0     |           | 25000            |                |                  |                      |                 |
| 1     | -5        | 17500            | 7500           | 3,000            | 2000                 | 12500           |
| 2     | -4        | 12250            | 5250           | 3,300            | 1400                 | 9950            |
| 3     | -3        | 8575             | 3675           | 3,630            | 980                  | 8285            |
| 4     | -2        | 6003             | 2573           | 3,993            | 686                  | 7252            |
| 5     | -1        | 4202             | 1801           | 4,392            | 480                  | 6673            |
| 6     | 1         | 2941             | 1261           | 4,832            | 336                  | 6428            |
| 7     | 2         | 2059             | 882            | 5,315            | 235                  | 6432            |
| 8     | 3         | 1441             | 618            | 5,846            | 165                  | 6629            |
| 9     | 4         | 1009             | 432            | 6,431            | 115                  | 6978            |
| 10    | 5         | 706              | 303            | 7,074            | 81                   | 7457            |

Again here the marginals cost of the Defender are strictly increasing from the Time Line of today --> onward (year 6 of the original life). Thus, we Replacement Analysis Technique #1 and compare the marginal cost data of the defender against the min. EAUC of the challenger. From the previous problem the Challenger's min. EAUC at its 5 year life is:

EAUC = $27,900 (A/P,8%,5) = <u>$ 6,989</u>

From this we would recommend that we <u>keep the Defender for four more</u> years and then replace it with the Challenger. This is because after three years the marginal costs of the Defender become greater than the min. EUAC of the Challenger.

# 12-24

Here we Replacement Analysis Technique #3. Because the remaining life of the defender and the life of the challenger are both 10 years we can use <u>either</u> the "opportunity cost' or "cash flow" approach to setting the first cost of each option (Keep defender, or Replace with challenger). Let's show each solution:

<u>Opportunity Cost Approach:</u>

$$EUAC(def) = (4)(600)(A/P,25\%,10) = \underline{\$672}$$

$$EUAC(chal) = 5000(A/P,25\%,10) - 10,000(0.075) = \underline{\$650}$$

<u>Cash Flow Cost Approach:</u>

$$EUAC(def) = \underline{\$0.00}$$

$$EUAC(chal) = (5000-2400)(A/P,25\%,10) - 10,000(0.075) = \underline{\$-22}$$

In either case we recommend that the new high efficiency machine be implemented today.

# 12-25

1st Cost = 15,000      ADRlig =12    ESTSa = 10,000 Atmarr= 0.25
Maint = 1000    Main Gr =1000 Oper = 4000 Tax % = 0.35

| Year (n) | (a/p,30,n) | Salv. | Maint | MACRS Depr. | MACRS Cap G/L | Tax Savings | AT SALV | EUAC CRCost | PW O&M(n) | SUMPW (1-n) | EUAC O&M | Total EUAC |
|---|---|---|---|---|---|---|---|---|---|---|---|---|
| 1 | 1.3 | 10000 | 1000 | 0.2 | -2000 | 700 | 10700 | 8265 | 520 | 520 | 676 | 8941 |
| 2 | 0.7348 | 9,000 | 2000 | 0.32 | 1800 | -630 | 8370 | 6964 | 832 | 1352 | 993 | 7958 |
| 3 | 0.5506 | 8,000 | 3000 | 0.192 | 3680 | -1288 | 6712 | 6241 | 998 | 2350 | 1294 | 7536 |
| 4 | 0.4616 | 7,000 | 4000 | 0.1152 | 4408 | -1543 | 5457 | 5769 | 1065 | 3415 | 1577 | 7346 |
| 5 | 0.4106 | 6,000 | 5000 | 0.1152 | 5136 | -1798 | 4202 | 5484 | 1065 | 4480 | 1840 | 7324 |
| 6 | 0.3784 | 5,000 | 6000 | 0.0576 | 5000 | -1750 | 3250 | 5259 | 1022 | 5503 | 2082 | 7341 |
| 7 | 0.3569 | 4,000 | 7000 | 0 | 4000 | -1400 | 2600 | 5076 | 954 | 6457 | 2304 | 7380 |
| 8 | 0.3419 | 3,000 | 8000 | 0 | 3000 | -1050 | 1950 | 4949 | 872 | 7329 | 2506 | 7455 |
| 9 | 0.3312 | 2,000 | 9000 | 0 | 2000 | -700 | 1300 | 4862 | 785 | 8114 | 2688 | 7550 |
| 10 | 0.3235 | 1,000 | 10000 | 0 | 1000 | -350 | 650 | 4805 | 698 | 8812 | 2851 | 7656 |

Here we see that the minimum after-tax EUAC  is at <u>five years</u> at a value of $7,324

# 12-26

1st Cost - 125,000   G/L Rate = 0.28   Est Salv = 80,000 Atmarr = 0.25   Maint = 5000   MainGR = 5000   Oper = 16,000 Tax % = 35

| Yr(n) | (a/p,30,n) | Salv | Insur | Maint | Oper | MACRS Depr. | MACRS Cap G/L | TAX Savings | AT SALV | EUAC CRCost | PW O&M(n) | SUMPW (1-n) | EUAC O&M | Total E• |
|---|---|---|---|---|---|---|---|---|---|---|---|---|---|---|
| 1 | 1.3 | 80,000 | 17,000 | 5000 | 16000 | 0.1429 | -27138 | 7599 | 87599 | 70522 | 19760 | 19760 | 25688 | 96• |
| 2 | 0.7348 | 78,000 | 16,000 | 10000 | 20000 | 0.2449 | 1475 | -413 | 77587 | 54236 | 19136 | 38896 | 28581 | 82• |
| 3 | 0.5506 | 76,000 | 15,000 | 15000 | 24000 | 0.1749 | 21338 | -5975 | 70026 | 47775 | 17971 | 56867 | 31311 | 79• |
| 4 | 0.4616 | 74,000 | 14,000 | 20000 | 28000 | 0.1249 | 34950 | -9786 | 64214 | 44112 | 16507 | 73374 | 33869 | 77• |
| 5 | 0.4106 | 72,000 | 13,000 | 25000 | 32000 | 0.0893 | 44113 | -12352 | 59649 | 41745 | 14909 | 88284 | 36249 | 77• |
| 6 | 0.3784 | 70,000 | 12,000 | 30000 | 36000 | 0.0892 | 53263 | -14914 | 55087 | 40227 | 13291 | 101574 | 38436 | 78 |
| 7 | 0.3569 | 68,000 | 11,000 | 35000 | 40000 | 0.0893 | 51263 | -14354 | 53647 | 38878 | 11723 | 113297 | 40436 | 79• |
| 8 | 0.3419 | 66,000 | 10,000 | 40000 | 44000 | 0.0446 | 49263 | -13794 | 52207 | 37940 | 10251 | 123548 | 42241 | 80• |
| 9 | 0.3312 | 64,000 | 10,000 | 45000 | 48000 | 0 | 47263 | -13234 | 50767 | 37278 | 8986 | 132534 | 43895 | 81 |
| 10 | 0.3235 | 62,000 | 10,000 | 50000 | 52000 | 0 | 45263 | -12674 | 49327 | 36812 | 7817 | 140351 | 45404 | 82 |

Here we see that the minimum after-tax EUAC is at <u>four years</u> at a value of $77,982

# 12-27

| Yr(n) | Time (n) | Salv | Oper | Insur | Maint | Lost Interest | Lost MV | Total Marg |
|---|---|---|---|---|---|---|---|---|
| 1 | -5 | 80,000 | 16000 | 17,000 | 5000 | 31250 | 45,000 | 114250 |
| 2 | -4 | 78,000 | 20000 | 16,000 | 10000 | 20000 | 2,000 | 68000 |
| 3 | -3 | 76,000 | 24000 | 15,000 | 15000 | 19500 | 2,000 | 75500 |
| 4 | -2 | 74,000 | 28000 | 14,000 | 20000 | 19000 | 2,000 | 83000 |
| 5 | -1 | 72,000 | 32000 | 13,000 | 25000 | 18500 | 2,000 | 90500 |
| 6 | 1 | 70,000 | 36000 | 12,000 | 30000 | 18000 | 2,000 | 98000 |
| 7 | 2 | 68,000 | 40000 | 11,000 | 35000 | 17500 | 2,000 | 105500 |
| 8 | 3 | 66,000 | 44000 | 10,000 | 40000 | 17000 | 2,000 | 113000 |
| 9 | 4 | 64,000 | 48000 | 10,000 | 45000 | 16500 | 2,000 | 121500 |
| 10 | 5 | 62,000 | 52000 | 10,000 | 50000 | 16000 | 2,000 | 130000 |

*a.*  Total marginal cost for this previously implemented asset is given above.

*b.*  In looking at the table above one can see that the marginal cost data of the defender is strictly increasing over the next five year period. Thus the Replacement Decision Analysis Map would suggest that we use Replacement Analysis Technique #1. We compare the defender marginal cost data against the challenger's minimum EUAC.

We would keep the defender asset for two more years and then replace it with the new automated shearing equipment. After two years the MC(def) > Min.EUAC(chal): $113,000 > $110,000.

*c.*  Here we calculate the marginal costs of defender ownership on an after-tax basis. These cost items include: opportunity capital gains (losses) foregone; AT operating, insurance and maintenance costs; foregone AT interest, and change in AT value.

FOREGONE CAPITAL GAINS (LOSSES) A.T.

| Life | (n) | Asset Yr begin of (n) | Book Value Cap G/L if sold in (n) | Foregone Cap G/L |
|------|-----|------|------|------|
| 6 | 1 | 27,888 | 72,000-27888=44,112 x .28 | 12,351 |
| 7 | 2 | 16,738 | 70,000-18738=53,262 x .28 | 14,913 |
| 8 | 3 | 5,575 | 68,000-5575 = 62,425 x .28 | 17,479 |
| 9 | 4 | 0 | 66,000-0 =66,000 x .28 | 18,480 |
| 10 | 5 | 0 | 64,000-0 =64,000 x .28 | 17,920 |

A.T. MARGINAL COSTS (Operating, Insurance & Maintenance)

| Yr (n) | Oper Cost | Insur Cost | Maint Cost | TOTAL Marginal | | AT Marg Cost |
|------|------|------|------|------|------|------|
| 1 | 36,000 | 12,000 | 30,000 | 78,000 | x (1-.35) | = 50,700 |
| 2 | 40,000 | 11,000 | 35,000 | 86,000 | x (1-.35) | = 55,900 |
| 3 | 44,000 | 10,000 | 40,000 | 94,000 | x (1-.35) | = 60,100 |
| 4 | 48,000 | 10,000 | 45,000 | 103,000 | x (1-.35) | = 66,950 |
| 5 | 52,000 | 10,000 | 50,000 | 112,,000 | x (1-.35) | = 72,800 |

FOREGONE A.T. INTEREST

| Yr(n) | Market Value Begin of (n) | | | Foregone AT Interest |
|------|------|------|------|------|
| 1 | 70,000 | x .28 | x (1-.35) | = 11,375 |
| 2 | 68,000 | x .28 | x (1-.35) | = 11,050 |
| 3 | 66,000 | x .28 | x (1-.35) | = 10,725 |
| 4 | 64,000 | x .28 | x (1-.35) | = 10,400 |
| 5 | 62,000 | x .28 | x (1-.35) | = 10,075 |

LOST VALUE ON A.T. BASIS

| Yr. (n) | B.Tax MV (n) | BV in (n) | Cap Gain if Sold in (n) | A. Tax MV(n) |
|---|---|---|---|---|
| -1 | 72,000 | 27,888 | 44,112 x 0.28 = 12,351 | 59,649 |
| 1 | 70,000 | 16,738 | 53,262 x 0.28 = 14,913 | 55,087 |
| 2 | 68,000 | 5,575 | 62,425 x 0.28 = 17,479 | 50,521 |
| 3 | 66,000 | 0 | 66,000 x 0.28 = 18,480 | 47,520 |
| 4 | 64,000 | 0 | 64,000 x 0.28 = 17,920 | 46,080 |
| 5 | 62,000 | 0 | 62,000 x 0.28 = 17,360 | 44,640 |

| Yr. (n) | A.T. Value if Sold begin of (n) | | A.T. Value if Sold end of (n) | Lost A.T. Value in (n) |
|---|---|---|---|---|
| 1 | 59,649 | - | 55,087 = | 4,562 |
| 2 | 55,087 | - | 50,521 = | 4,566 |
| 3 | 50,521 | - | 47,520 = | 3,001 |
| 4 | 47,520 | - | 46,080 = | 1,440 |
| 5 | 46,080 | - | 44,640 = | 1,440 |

TOTAL AFTER-TAX MARGINAL COSTS

| Yr (n) | Fore Cap g/l Loss in (n) | A.T Marg Costs in (n) | Foregone Int. in (n) | Lost A.T Value in (n) | TOTAL A.T. Marg |
|---|---|---|---|---|---|
| 1 | 12,351 | 50,700 | 11,375 | 4,562 | 78,988 |
| 2 | 14,913 | 55,900 | 11,050 | 4,566 | 86,429 |
| 3 | 17,479 | 60,100 | 10,725 | 3,001 | 91,305 |
| 4 | 18,480 | 66,950 | 10,400 | 1,440 | 97,270 |
| 5 | 17,920 | 72,800 | 10,075 | 1,440 | 102,235 |

The A.T. marginal costs are strictly increasing, thus we can employ Replacement Analysis Technique #1 on an A.T. basis. We compare the A.T. marginal cost of the defender against the min. A.T. EUAC of the challenger. This was given as $90,000 in the problem.

Thus we would keep the defender <u>four more years</u> and then replace with the challenger asset at that time.

# 12-28

Here we use the Opportunity Cost Approach for finding the first costs

*a. Problem as given*
<u>Defender:</u>  Depr S/L = (50,000-15,000)/10 = 3,500 per year
                Market Value (today) = $30,000

|  | Yr. | BTCF | DEPR | TI | IT | ATCF |
|---|---|---|---|---|---|---|
| (sell) | 0 | 30,000 |  | 4,500* | -2250 | 27,750 |
| (keep) | 0 | -30,000 |  | -4,500 | +2250 | - 27,750 |

*Cap G/L = 30,000 - [50,000- (7)(3,500)] = $4,500

<u>Challenger</u> 

|  | Yr. | BTCF | DEPR | TI | IT | ATCF |
|---|---|---|---|---|---|---|
|  | 0 | -85,000 |  |  | +8,500 | -76,500 |

*b.      Defender Market value = $25,500*
<u>Defender:</u>  Depr S/L = (50,000-15,000)/10 = 3,500 per year
                Market Value (today) = $30,000

|  | Yr. | BTCF | DEPR | TI | IT | ATCF |
|---|---|---|---|---|---|---|
| (sell) | 0 | 30,000 |  | 0* | 0 | 30,000 |
| (keep) | 0 | -30,000 |  | 0 | 0 | -30,000 |

*Cap G/L = 25,500 - [50,000- (7)(3,500)] = $0

<u>Challenger</u>

|  | Yr. | BTCF | DEPR | TI | IT | ATCF |
|---|---|---|---|---|---|---|
|  | 0 | -85,000 |  | +8,500 | -76,500 |  |

*c.      Defender Market Nalue = $18,000*
<u>Defender:</u>  Depr S/L = (50,000-15,000)/10 = 3,500 per year

Market Value (today) = $18,000

| | Yr. | BTCF | DEPR | TI | IT | ATCF |
|---|---|---|---|---|---|---|
| (sell) | 0 | 30,000 | | -7,500* | +3,750 | 33,750 |
| (keep) | 0 | -30,000 | | +7,500 | -3,750 | -33,750 |

*Cap G/L = 18,000 - [50,000- (7)(3,500)] = $-7,500

Challenger

| | Yr. | BTCF | DEPR | TI | IT | ATCF |
|---|---|---|---|---|---|---|
| | 0 | -85,000 | | | +8,500 | -76,500 |

# 12-29

*a:*    The defender was implemented six years ago with a cost basis (1st cost) of $5,000. The estimated salvage value for tax purposes was $1,000 and the straight line depreciation method was used.

Depr. S/L = (B-S)/N    500=(5,000-1,000)/N    N=<u>8 years</u>

*b.*    the ATCFs for defender and challenger are as follows:

Defender:    - 3 year remaining life
- depreciated over 8 years (six in the past)
- $2,500 expensed at time 0
- present MV = $1,000
- MV in 3 years = $500

| | Yr. | BTCF | DEPR | TI | IT | ATCF |
|---|---|---|---|---|---|---|
| (sell) | 0 | 1,000 | | -1,000* | +280 | 1,280 |
| (keep) | 0 | -1,000 | | 1,000 | -280 | -1,280 |
| | 0 | -2,500 | | -2,500 | +875 | -1,625 |
| | 1 | -600 | 500 | -1,100 | +385 | -215 |
| | 2 | -750 | 500 | -1,250 | +438 | -312 |
| | 3 | -900 | - | -900 | +315 | -585 |
| | 3 | 500 | | -500** | +140 | 640 |

*Cap G/L = 1,000 - [5,000- (6)(500)] = $-1,000
**Cap G/L = 500 - [5,000- (8)(500)] = $-500

<u>Challenger</u>   - 6 year useful life
- MACRS deprec. w/ 7-yr class life
- MV @ 6 years = 1,000

| Yr. | BTCF | DEPR | TI | IT | ATCF |
|---|---|---|---|---|---|
| 0 | -10,000 | | | | -10,000 |
| 1 | -100 | 1,429 | -1,529 | 535 | 435 |
| 2 | -150 | 2,449 | -2,599 | 910 | 760 |
| 3 | -200 | 1,749 | -1,949 | 682 | 482 |
| 4 | -250 | 1,249 | -1,499 | 525 | 275 |
| 5 | -300 | 893 | -1,193 | 418 | 118 |
| 6 | -350 | 446* | -796 | 279 | -71 |
| 6 | 1,000 | | -785** | 220 | 1,220 |

*MACRS deprec = (0.50) (10,000)(0.0892)
**Cap G/L = 1,000 - [10,000(.0446+.0893+.0446)] = $-785

*c.*   Here we use Replacement Analysis Technique #3

AW(def) = [-1,280-1,625 -215(P/F,18%,1)-312(*P/F*,18%,2)-(585-
640)(*P/F*,18%,3)](*A/P*,18%,3)  =  $1,507

AW(chal) = [-10,000 +435(*P/F*,18%,1)+760(*P/F*,18%,2)+482
(*P/F*,18%,3)+275(*P/F*,18%,4)+118(*P/F*,18%,5)+
(-71+1,220)(*P/F*,18%,6)](*A/P*,18%,6)  =  $2,337

The assumptions that are made here are the Repeatability
Replacement Assumptions: the same challenger will always be available
at the current cost, and there is an indefinite need of this asset for
operations.

Solutions to Spreadsheet supplement problems are after Chapter 19 .

# Inflation And Deflation

$$F = P(F/P, \text{\ss}\%, 10\text{yrs}) = 10(F/P, 7\%, 10) = 10(1.967) = \$19.67$$

$$i'_{\text{equivalent}} = i'_{\substack{\text{inflation} \\ \text{corrected}}} + \text{\ss}\% + i'_{\substack{\text{inflation} \\ \text{corrected}}} \times \text{\ss}$$

In this problem: $i'_{\text{equiv}} = 5\%$ $\quad \text{\ss} = +2\%$

$$i'_{\substack{\text{inflation} \\ \text{corrected}}} = \text{Unknown}$$

$$0.05 = i'_{\substack{\text{inflation} \\ \text{corrected}}} + 0.02 + 0.02\, i'_{\substack{\text{inflation} \\ \text{corrected}}}$$

$$i'_{\substack{\text{inflation} \\ \text{corrected}}} = \frac{0.05 - 0.02}{1 + 0.02} = 0.02941 = 2.941\%$$

That this is correct may be proved by the year-by-year computations.

| Yr | Cash Flow | $(1+\text{\ss})^{-n}$ $(P/F, \text{\ss}, n)$ | Cash Flow in Year 0 dollars | Present Worth at 2.941% |
|---|---|---|---|---|
| 0 | -1000 | 0 | -1000.00 | -1000.00 |
| 1 | +50 | .9804 | +49.02 | +47.62 |
| 2 | +50 | .9612 | +48.06 | +45.35 |
| 3 | +50 | .9423 | +47.12 | +43.20 |
| 4 | +50 | .9238 | +46.19 | +41.13 |
| 5 | +50 | .9057 | +45.29 | +39.18 |
| 6 | +50 | .8880 | +44.40 | +37.31 |
| 7 | +50 | .8706 | +43.53 | +35.54 |
| 8 | +50 | .8535 | +42.68 | +33.85 |
| 9 | +50 | .8368 | +41.84 | +32.23 |
| 10 | +50 | .8203 | +41.02 | +30.70 |
| 11 | +50 | .8043 | +40.22 | +29.24 |
| 12 | +50 | .7885 | +39.43 | +27.85 |
| 13 | +50 | .7730 | +38.65 | +26.52 |
| 14 | +50 | .7579 | +37.90 | +25.26 |
| 15 | +50 | .7430 | +37.15 | +24.05 |
| 16 | +50 | .7284 | +36.42 | +22.90 |
| 17 | +50 | .7142 | +35.71 | +21.82 |
| 18 | +50 | .7002 | +35.01 | +20.78 |
| 19 | +50 | .6864 | +34.32 | +19.79 |
| 20 | +1000 | .6730 | +706.65 | +395.76 |
|  |  |  |  | +0.08 |

$$\therefore i'_{\substack{\text{inflation} \\ \text{corrected}}} = 2.94\%$$

# 13-3

<u>No inflation situation</u>

Alt. (a)  PW of Cost = 6000

Alt. (b)  PW of Cost = $4500 + 2500(P/F, 8\%, 8)$

$$= 4500 + 2500(0.5403) = 5851$$

Alt. (c)  PW of Cost = $2500 + 2500(P/F, 8\%, 4) + 2500(P/F, 8\%, 8)$

$$= 2500 + 2500(0.7350) + 2500(0.5403)$$

$$= 5688$$

To minimize PW of Cost, choose Alt. (c)

<u>For  $f = +5\%$  (inflation)</u>

Alt. (a) PW of Cost = 6000

Alt. (b) PW of Cost in year O dollars

$$= 4500 + 2500 \overset{(1+5\%)^n}{(F/P, 5\%, 8)}(P/F, 8\%, 8)$$

$$= 4500 + 2500(1.477)(0.5403)$$

$$= 4500 + 1995 = 6495$$

Alt. (c) PW of Cost in year O dollars

$$= 2500 + 2500(F/P, 5\%, 4)(P/F, 8\%, 4)$$

$$+ 2500(F/P, 5\%, 8)(P/F, 8\%, 8)$$

$$= 2500 + 2500(1.216)(0.7350) + 2500(1.477)(0.5403)$$

$$= 2500 + 2234 + 1995 = 6729.$$

To minimize PW of Cost in year O dollars, choose Alt. (a)

This problem illustrates the fact that the prospect of future inflation encourages current expenditures to be able to avoid higher future expenditures.

# 13-4

20,000 in Year O dollars

n=14 yrs

P= Lump Sum deposit

Actual Dollars = $20,000(1+f)^n$
14 yrs hence

$$= 20,000(1+0.08)^{14} = 58,744$$

At 5% interest

$$P = F(1+i)^{-n} = 58{,}744(1+0.05)^{-14} = 29{,}670.$$

Since the inflation rate (8%) exceeds the interest rate (5%), the money is annually losing purchasing power.

Deposit $29,670

# 13-5

To buy $1 worth of goods today will require

$$F = P(F/P, 8\%, n) \quad n \text{ years hence}$$

$$F = \$1 (1+0.08)^5 = \$1.47 \quad \text{five years hence}$$

For the subsequent 5 years the amount required will increase

to $1.47 (F/P, 6\%, n) = 1.47(1+0.06)^5 = \$1.97$

Thus for the ten-year period $1 must be increased to $1.97

The average price change per year is

$$\frac{\$1.97 - 1.00}{10 \text{ yrs}} = 9.7\% \text{ per year}$$

# 13-6

$$97{,}000 (1 + 7\%)^n$$
$$97{,}000 (1+0.07)^{15} = 97{,}000(F/P, 7\%, 15)$$
$$= 97{,}000(2.759) = \$268{,}000$$

If there is 7% inflation per year, a $97,000 house today is equivalent to $268,000 fifteen years hence. But will one have "profited" from the inflation?

Whether one will profit from owning the house depends somewhat on an examination of the alternate use of the money. "Only the differences between alternatives are relevant." If the alternate is a 5% savings account, neglecting income taxes, the profit from owning the house, rather than the savings account, would be
$268,000 - $97,000(F/P,5%,15) = $66,300.
On the other hand, compared to an alternative investment at 7%, the profit is $0. And if the alternative investment is at 9% there is a loss. If "profit" means an enrichment, or being better off, then multiplying the price of everything does not enrich one in real terms.

# 13-7

(a)

| Year | Before-Tax Cash Flow | SL Deprec | Taxable Income | 34% Income Taxes | After-Tax Cash Flow | NPW at 5% | NPW at 6% |
|---|---|---|---|---|---|---|---|
| 0 | -85,000 | | | | -85,000 | -85,000 | -85,000 |
| 1 | 8000 | 1500 | 6500 | -2210 | 5790 | 5514 | 5462 |
| 2 | 8000 | 1500 | 6500 | -2210 | 5790 | 5252 | 5153 |
| 3 | 8000 | 1500 | 6500 | -2210 | 5790 | 5001 | 4861 |
| 4 | 8000 | 1500 | 6500 | -2210 | 5790 | 4763 | 4586 |
| 5 | 8000 77,500 | 1500 | 6500 0 | -2210 - | 83,290 | 65,258 | 62,243 |
| | | 7500 | | | | +788 | -2645 |

$$\text{SL Deprec} = \frac{67,500 - 0}{45} = 1500$$

Book Value at end of 5 yrs = 85,000 - 5(1500) = 77,500

After-tax Rate of Return ≃ 5.2%

(b)

| YEAR | Before-Tax Cash Flow | SL Deprec | Taxable Income | 34% Income Taxes | Actual Dollars After-Tax Cash Flow | NPW at 15% | NPW at 12% |
|---|---|---|---|---|---|---|---|
| 0 | -85,000 | | | | -85,000 | -85,000 | -85,000 |
| 1 | 8560 | 1500 | 7060 | -2400 | 6160 | 5357 | 5500 |
| 2 | 9159 | 1500 | 7659 | -2604 | 6555 | 4956 | 5226 |
| 3 | 9800 | 1500 | 8300 | -2822 | 6978 | 4588 | 4967 |
| 4 | 10486 | 1500 | 8986 | -3055 | 7431 | 4249 | 4722 |
| 5 | 11220 136,935 | 1500 | 9720 59,435* | -3305 -20 208 | 124,642 | 61,972 | 70722 |
| | | 7500 | | | | -3878 | 6137 |

Selling Price = 85,000 (F/P, 10%, 5) = 85,000(1.611) = 136,935

*Capital gain = 136,935 - 77,500 = 59,435

Tax on Capital gain = 34% (59,435) ≈ 20,208

$$\text{After-tax Rate of Return} = 15\% - (3\%)\left(\frac{3878}{3878 + 6137}\right) = 13.84\%$$

(HP-12C Solution: 13.78%)

(b) Con't
After-Tax Rate of Return in Year O Dollars

| YEAR | Actual Dollars After-Tax Cash Flow | multiply by | Year O $ After-Tax Cash Flow | NPW at 8% | NPW at 6% |
|------|------|------|------|------|------|
| 0 | -85,000 | 1 | -85,000 | -85,000 | -85,000 |
| 1 | 6160 | $1.07^{-1}$ | 5757 | 5330 | 5431 |
| 2 | 6555 | $1.07^{-2}$ | 5725 | 4908 | 5095 |
| 3 | 6978 | $1.07^{-3}$ | 5696 | 4521 | 4782 |
| 4 | 7431 | $1.07^{-4}$ | 5669 | 4167 | 4490 |
| 5 | 124,642 | $1.07^{-5}$ | 88,868 | 60,484 | 66,411 |
|  |  |  |  | -5,590 | 1209 |

In Year O Dollars
After-Tax Rate of Return = 6.36%
( HP-12C Solution = 6.34%)

**13-8**

| Year | Before-Tax Cash Flow | Taxable Income | 42% Income Taxes | After-Tax Cash Flow | multiply by | YEAR O $ after-Tax Cash Flow |
|------|------|------|------|------|------|------|
| 0 | -10,000 |  |  | -10,000 | 1 | -10 000 |
| 1 | 1200 | 1200 | -504 | 696 | $1.07^{-1}$ | 650 |
| 2 | 1200 | 1200 | -504 | 696 | $1.07^{-2}$ | 608 |
| 3 | 1200 | 1200 | -504 | 696 | $1.07^{-3}$ | 568 |
| 4 | 1200 | 1200 | -504 | 696 | $1.07^{-4}$ | 531 |
| 5 | { 1200 \ 10,000 | 1200 | -504 } | 10,696 | $1.07^{-5}$ | 7626 |
|  |  |  |  |  |  | -17 |

(a)   Before-tax rate of return ignoring inflation.
Since the $10,000 principal is returned unchanged,

$$i = \frac{A}{P} = \frac{1,200}{10,000} = 12\%$$

If this is not observed, then the rate of return may be
computed by conventional means.

10,000 = 1200(P/A,i%,5) + 10,000(P/F,i%,5)

Rate of return = 12%

(b) After-tax rate of return ignoring inflation.

Solved in the same manner as Part (a):

$$i = \frac{A}{P} = \frac{696}{10,000} = 6.96\%$$

(c) After-tax rate of return after taking inflation into account.

An examination of the Year 0 dollars after-tax cash flow shows the algebraic sum of the cash flow is -17. Stated in Year 0 dollars, the total receipts are less than the cost, hence there is <u>no positive rate of return</u>.

# 13-9

Let X = selling price

then Long term capital gain = X - 18,000

$$tax = 0.15(X - 18,000)$$

After-tax cash flow in Year 10 = X - 0.15(X - 18000)

$$= 0.85X + 2700$$

| Year | After-Tax Cash Flow | multiply by | YEAR 0 $ After-tax Cash Flow |
|------|---------------------|-------------|------------------------------|
| 0    | -18,000             | 1           | -18,000                      |
| 10   | +0.85X + 2700       | $1.06^{-10}$ | 0.4746X + 1508              |

For a 10% rate of return

$$18000 = (0.4746X + 1508)(P/F, 10\%, 10)$$
$$= 0.1830X + 581 \qquad \therefore X = \$95,186$$

<u>alternate Solution</u> using an equivalent interest rate

$$i_{equiv} = i' + \xi + i'(\xi) = 0.10 + 0.06 + 0.10(0.06) = 0.166$$

So $18,000(1 + 0.166)^{10} = 0.85X + 2700$

$$83,610 = 0.85X + 2700$$

Selling Price of the lot $(X) = \dfrac{83,610 - 2700}{0.85} = \$95,188$

# 13-10

$(1 + f)^5 = 1.50$     $(1 + f) = 1.50^{1/5} = 1.0845$

$$f = 0.0845 = 8.45\%$$

# 13-11

Number of dollars required five years hence to have the buying power of one dollar today = $1(F/P,7\%,5) = \$1.403$

Number of cruzados required five years hence to have the buying power of 15 cruzados today = $15(F/P,25\%,5) = 45.78$ cruzados.

Combining:  $\$1.403 = 45.78$ cruzados,  or $\$1.00 = 32.6$ cruzados.

(Brazil uses cruzados)

# 13-12

Cash Flow:

| Year | $500 Kit | $900 Kit |
|------|----------|----------|
| 0    | -$500    | -$900    |
| 5    | -500     | 0        |

(a)  $PW_{\$500\ kit} = 500 + 500(P/F,10\%,5) = \$810$

$PW_{\$900\ kit} = \$900$

To minimize PW of Cost, choose
$500 Kit

(b)  Replacement cost of $500 kit, five years hence
   $=\$500(F/P,7\%,5) = \$701.5$

$PW_{\$500\ kit} = 500 + 701.5(P/F,10\%,5) = \$935.60$

$PW_{\$900\ kit} = \$900.$      To minimize PW of Cost, choose
$900 Kit

# 13-13

Price increase = $(1 + 0.12)^8$ = 2.476 x present price.

Therefore, required fuel rating = 10 x 2.476 = 24.76 km/liter.

# 13-14

If one assumes the 5-year hence cost of the Filterco unit is 7000(F/P,8%,5) = $10,283 in Actual Dollars and $7000 in Yr 0 dollars:

| Year | Year 0 $ Cash Flow Filterco | Duro | Duro minus Filterco | |
|------|------|------|------|------|
| 0 | -7,000 | -10,000 | -3,000 | |
| 5 | -7,000 | 0 | +7,000 | ΔROR=18.5% Buy Filterco |

# 13-15

NOW: Taxable Income = 60,000
    Income taxes = 5850 + 0.28(60,000 - 39000) = 11,730
    After-tax income = 60,000 - 11,730 = 48,270

TWENTY YEARS Hence: To have same buying power, need
    an after-tax income = 48270 $(1.07)^{20}$ = 186,789
    After-tax Income = Taxable income − Income taxes
    Income taxes = 77262 + 0.396 (Taxable income − 256,500)
    Taxable income = After-tax income + Income taxes
                   = 186,789 + 77,262 + 0.396 (taxable income)
                     − 101,376
                   = (162,675)/(0.604) = $ 269,329

# 13-16

P = 1.00    F = 1.80    n = 10    f = ?

1.80 = 1.00(F/P,f%,10)

(F/P,f%,10) = 1.80

From tables, f is slightly greater than 6%
(f is exactly 6.05%)

# 13-17

Depreciation charges that a firm makes in its accounting records
allow a profitable firm to have that amount of money available for
replacement equipment without any deduction for income taxes.

If the money available from depreciation charges is inadequate to
purchase needed replacement equipment, then the firm may need also
to use after-tax profit for this purpose.

Depreciation charges produce a tax-free source of money; profit
has been subjected to income taxes.  Thus substantial inflation
forces a firm to increasingly finance replacement equipment out
of (costly) after-tax profit.

# 13-18

| Year | Cost to City | Benefits to City |
|------|-------------|------------------|
| 0 | ... -$50,000 Yr 0$ | |
| 1-10 | .... -5,000/yr Yr 0$ | ..... +A Fixed annual sum in then current dollars |
| 10 | ........................ | +50,000 in then current dollars |

$$i = i' + \textit{f} + i'\textit{f}$$
$$= 0.03 + 0.07 + 0.03(0.07) = 0.1021 = 10.21\%$$

$$PW \text{ of } Cost = PW \text{ of } Benefits$$

$$50,000 + 5000 \underset{8.530}{(P/A, 3\%, 10)} = A \underset{6.0895*}{(P/A, 10.21\%, 10)} + 50000 \underset{0.3783*}{(P/F, 10.21\%, 10)}$$

$$92,650 = 6.0895A + 18915$$

\* computed on
   hand calculator

$$A = \frac{92,650 - 18915}{6.0895} = \$12,109$$

# 13-19

| YEAR | Before Tax Cash Flow | MACRS Deprec | Taxable Income | 50% Income Taxes | Actual $ After Tax Cash Flow | Conv. Factor | Yr-0$ After Tax Cash Flow | PW at 15% |
|------|------|------|------|------|------|------|------|------|
| 0 | -10000 | | | | -10,000 | | -10,000 | -10,000 |
| 1 | 2000 | 2000 | 0 | 0 | $2000 \times 1.07^{-1}$ | | 1869 | 1625 |
| 2 | 3000 | 3200 | (200) | +100 | $3100 \times 1.07^{-2}$ | | 2708 | 2048 |
| 3 | 4000 | 1920 | 2080 | -1040 | $2960 \times 1.07^{-3}$ | | 2416 | 1589 |
| 4 | 5000 | 1152 | 3848 | -1924 | $3076 \times 1.07^{-4}$ | | 2347 | 1342 |
| 5 | 6000 | 1152 | 4848 | -2424 | $3576 \times 1.07^{-5}$ | | 2550 | 1268 |
| 6 | 7000 | 576 | 6424 | -3212 | $3788 \times 1.07^{-6}$ | | 2524 | 1091 |
| 7 | 8000 | 0 | 8000 | -4000 | $4000 \times 1.07^{-7}$ | | 2491 | 936 |
| | | | | | | | | -101 |

Thus the Yr-0 $ after-tax rate of return just under 15%
(actually 14.67%)

∴ Purchase justified

# 13-20

$$i = i' + f + i'f$$

$$0.15 = i' + 0.12 + i'(0.12)$$

$$1.12\, i' = 0.03 \qquad\qquad i' = \frac{0.03}{1.12} = 0.027 = 2.7\%$$

# 13-21

| month | Before Tax Cash Flow |
|-------|-----------------------|
| 0 | 0 |
| 1-36 | -1000 |
| 36 | +40,365 |

$$1000\,(F/A, i\%, 36\,mo) = 40,365$$
$$(F/A, i\%, 36\,mo) = 40.365$$

| $(F/A, i\%, 36)$ | $i\%$ |
|------------------|-------|
| 41.153 | 3/4% |
| 39.336 | 1/2% |

interpolation

$$i = 0.50\% + 0.25\% \left(\frac{40.365 - 39.336}{41.153 - 39.336}\right) = 0.6416\%\ \text{per month}$$

Equivalent annual interest rate

$$i\,(\text{per year}) = (1 + 0.006416)^{12} - 1 = 0.080 = 8\%$$

So

$$i = 8\%\quad f = 8\%\quad \text{what is } i'?$$
$$i = i' + f + i'f$$
$$0.08 = i' + 0.08 + i'(0.08)\qquad \therefore\ i' = 0\%$$

Before tax rate of return = 0%

# 13-22

Compute equivalent interest/3 mo. = x

Effective $i = (1+x)^n - 1$

$$0.1925 = (1+x)^4 - 1\qquad (1+x) = 1.1925^{0.25} = 1.045$$
$$x = 0.045 = 4\tfrac{1}{2}\%\ /3\,mo$$

$3.00

n=?
i=4.5%

$2.50

$$2.50 = 3.00 \, (P/F, 4\tfrac{1}{2}\%, n)$$

$$(P/F, 4\tfrac{1}{2}\%, n) = \frac{2.50}{3.00} = 0.833$$

n slightly > 4

So purchase pads of paper - one for immediate use
plus 4 extra pads

# 13-23

| Year | Before Tax Cash Flow | MACRS Deprec | Taxable Income | 35% Income Taxes | After Tax Cash Flow | PW at 6% | PW at 7% |
|------|------|------|------|------|------|------|------|
| 0 | -150000 | | | | -150,000 | -150000 | -150000 |
| 1 | 15750 | 3607 | 12143 | -4250 | 11,500 | 10,847 | 10,746 |
| 2 | 15750 | 3763 | 11987 | -4195 | 11555 | 10,285 | 10,093 |
| 3 | 15750 | 3763 | 11987 | -4195 | 11555 | 9,702 | 9,433 |
| 4 | 15750 | 3763 | 11987 | -4195 | 11555 | 9,154 | 8,816 |
| 5 | { 14438 | 3607 | 10831 | -3791 } | | | |
|   | 150,000 | | 18503 | -5181* } | 155,466 | 116,180 | 110,847 |
|   | | 18,503 | capital gain | | | +6168 | -65 |

\* 28% capital gain tax rate
MACRS depreciation
   home = 150,000 - 46,500 = 103,500
Year
1   3.485%(103 500) = 3607
2   3.636%(103 500) = 3763
3   3.636%(103 500) = 3763
4   3.636%(103 500) = 3763
5   3.485%(103 500) = 3607
                      18,503

after tax rate of return:
with capital gains taxed at 35%:  6.84%
   "      "      "      "    28%:  6.99%

# 13-24

| YEAR | Actual $ Before Tax Cash Flow | mkt value of property +12%/yr | MACRS Deprec | Taxable Income | 35% Income Taxes | Actual $ after-tax Cash Flow |
|---|---|---|---|---|---|---|
| 0 | -150 000 | 150000 | | | | -150,000 |
| 1 | 12000 | 168000 | 3602 | 8398 | -2939 | 9061 |
| 2 | 13440 | 188160 | 3767 | 9673 | -3386 | 10 054 |
| 3 | 15053 | 210739 | 3767 | 11,286 | -3950 | 11 103 |
| 4 | 16859 | 236028 | 3767 | 13,092 | -4582 | 12 277 |
| 5† | 17308* , 261,991 ← 261,991* | 261,991* | 3602 ⎯⎯ 18,505 | 13,706 130,496 Capital gain | -4797 -45,674 | 228, 828 |

\* assumes 11 months rent and 11 mo. increase in Yr 5 mkt value

| Yr | Actual $ after tax Cash Flow | PW at 12% | Pw at 15% |
|---|---|---|---|
| 0 | -150,000 | -150000 | -150000 |
| 1 | 9 061 | 8091 | 7879 |
| 2 | 10 054 | 8015 | 7602 |
| 3 | 11 103 | 7903 | 7300 |
| 4 | 12 277 | 7802 | 7020 |
| 5 | 228 828 | 129,837 | 113,773 |
| | | +11, 648 | -6426 |

Part (a)

actual $ after-tax
Rate of Return:

$= 12\% + (3\%)\left(\dfrac{11648}{11648+6426}\right)$

$= 13.93\%$

Solution assumes "average tax rate of 35%" includes the capital gain.

† note there is a slight error assuming the 11 mo values occur at end of Yr 5.

Part (b)

1. The easy way:

$i = i' + f + i'f$   $0.1388 = i' + 0.10 + 0.10 i'$

$i' = \dfrac{0.0388}{1.10} = 0.0353 = 3.53\%$

Solution con't on next page.

Part (b) cont

2. A more lengthy solution

| Yr | Actual $ After tax cash flow | 10% Inflation adjustment | | Year 0 $ After tax cash flow | PW at 3½% | PW at 4% |
|---|---|---|---|---|---|---|
| 0 | -150,000 | | | -150 000 | -150 000 | -150,000 |
| 1 | 9061 | × 1.10⁻¹ | = | 8237 | 7959 | 7920 |
| 2 | 10 054 | × 1.10⁻² | = | 8309 | 7756 | 7682 |
| 3 | 11 103 | × 1.10⁻³ | = | 8342 | 7524 | 7416 |
| 4 | 12 277 | × 1.10⁻⁴ | = | 8385 | 7307 | 7168 |
| 5 | 228,828 | × 1.10⁻⁵ | = | 142 084 | 119,635 | 116,779 |
| | | | | | + 181 | -3035 |

Yr 0 $
After Tax ROR = 3.53%

# 13-25

$g = 0.06$    $i' = 0.10$    $i = 0.10 + 0.06 + (0.10)(0.06) = 16.6\%$

# 13-26

The <u>stable price</u> assumption is really the same as analysing a problem in Year 0 dollars, where <u>all</u> the costs and benefits change at the same rate.  Allowable depreciation charges are based on the original equipment cost and do not increase. Thus the stable price assumption may be suitable in some before-tax computations, but is not satisfactory where depreciation affects the income tax computations.

# 13-27

(a)    $109.6 = 90.9 (F/P, g, 5)$

$(F/P, g, 5) = \dfrac{109.6}{90.9} = 1.2057$    $g = 3.81\%$

(b)    $CPI_{1996} = 113.6 (F/P, 3.81\%, 9)$

$= 113.6 (1 + 0.0381)^9 = 159.0$

# 13-28

<u>ALTERNATIVE 1:</u> **Continue to rent the duplex home**
Compute the Present Worth of renting and utility costs in Year 0 dollars
Assuming end-of-year payments, the Year 1 payment is
$(450 + 139)(12) = 7068$
The equivalent Year 0 payment in Year 0 dollars $= 7068(1\ 0.05)^{-1} = 6713.40$
Compute an equivalent $i$
$i_{\text{equivalent}} = i' + f + i\ f$
   Where $i'$ = interest rate without inflation = 15.5%
      $f$ = inflation rate = 5%
$i_{\text{equivalent}} = 0.155 + 0.05 + (0.155)(0.05) = 0.21275 = 21.275\%$

PW of 10 years of rent plus utilities
   $= 6731.40(P/A, 21.275\%, 10)$

$$= 6731.40\left[\frac{(1+0.21275)^{10-1}}{0.21275(1+0.21275)^{10}}\right]$$

$= 6731.40(4.9246) = \$33,149$

An alternative computation- but a lot more work
Compute the PW of the 10 years of inflation adjusted rent plus utilities using 15.5% interest.
$Pw_{\text{year0}} = 12[589(1+0.155)^{-1} + 619(1+0.155)^{-2} + ... + 914(1+0.155)^{-10}]$.
   $= 12(2762.44) = \$33,149$

<u>BUYING A HOUSE</u>

$3750 down payment plus about $750 in closing costs for a cash requirement of $4500
Mortgage interest rate per month = 8%/12 = 0.667%; $n$ = 30 years × 12 = 360 payments.
Monthly Payment, $A = (75,000 - 3750)(A/P, 0.667\%, 360)$

$$A = (71,250)\frac{.00667(1.00667)^{360}}{(1.00667)^{360} - 1} = -\$523.00$$

Mortgage Balance After The 10-Year Comparison Period:
$A' = 523(P/A, 0.667\%, 240)$

$$A' = (523)\frac{(1.00667)^{240}-1}{0.00667(1.00667)^{240}} = \$62,504$$

Thus:
  $523 \times 12 \times 10$  $= \$62,760$ total payments
$71,250 - \$62,504$  $= \underline{\$ 8,746}$  principal repayment (12.28% of loan)
          $54,014$  interest payments

The couple is in the 30% marginal income tax bracket. Assuming sufficient other deductions, and the interest averages 87.72% of the loan payment, their monthly tax saving will be:
  $523\ (0.8772)(0.30) = \$138$/month
The after-tax cost of the mortgage = $523 - 138 = \$385$
Sale of the property at 6% appreciation per year in year 10:
  $F = 75,000(1.06)^{10}$  $= \$134,314$
  Less 5% commission   $= -\ 6,716$
  Less mortgage bal.   $= \underline{-\ 62,504}$
  Net Income from the sale  $= \underline{\$ 65,094}$

Assuming No Capital Gain Tax Is Imposed, The Present Worth of Cost is:
PW = + 4500 (Down payment + closing costs in constant dollars)
      $+385*12(P/A, 15.5\%,10)$ - actual dollar mortgage
      $+160*12(P/A, 10\%, 10)$ - constant dollar utilities
      $+50.00*12(P/A,10\%,10)$ - constant dollar insurance and maintenance
      $-65,094(P/F,15.5\%,10)$ - actual dollar net income from sale
PW = +4,500
  $+385*12(4.9246) = +\$22,752$
  $+160*12(6.145)$   $= +11,798$
  $+\$50*12(6.145)$  $= +\ 3,687$
  $-\$65,094(0.2367) = -15,408$
The PW of Cost of owning the house for 10 years = $27,329 in Year 0 dollars.
Thus $33,149 > \$27,329$ - Buying a house is the more attractive alternative.

# 13-29

$F = 20,000\ (F/P,4\%,10) = \$29,600$

# 13-30

| Alt | Year | Cash Flow in Yr0 $ | Cash Flow in Actual $ | SL Deprec | Taxable Income | 25%Income Tax | ATCF in Actual $ | ATCF in Yr0 $ |
|---|---|---|---|---|---|---|---|---|
| A | 0 | -$420 | -$420 | | | | -$420 | -$420 |
| | 1 | 200 | 210 | $140 | $70 | -$17.5 | 192.5 | 183.3 |
| | 2 | 200 | 220.5 | 140 | 80.5 | -20.1 | 200.4 | 181.8 |
| | 3 | 200 | 231.5 | 140 | 91.5 | -22.9 | 208.6 | 180.2 |

| B | 0 | -$300 | -$300 | | | | -$420 | -$420 |
|---|---|---|---|---|---|---|---|---|
| | 1 | 150 | 157.5 | $100 | $57.5 | -$14.4 | 143.1 | 136.3 |
| | 2 | 150 | 165.4 | 100 | 65.4 | -16.4 | 149.0 | 135.1 |
| | 3 | 150 | 173.6 | 100 | 73.6 | -18.4 | 155.2 | 134.1 |

Quick Approximation of Rates of Return:
A   $420 = 182(P/A,i,3); (P/A,i,3) = 420/182 = 2.31$
   $12\% < ROR_A < 15\%$
   (Actual $ROR_A$ - 14.3%)
B   $300 = 135(P/A,i,3); (P/A,i,3) = 300/135 = 2.22$
   $15\% < ROR_B < 18\%$
   (Actual $ROR_B$ - 16.8%)

Incremental ROR analysis for A-B

| Year | A | B | A-B |
|---|---|---|---|
| 0 | -$420 | -$300 | -$120 |
| 1 | 183.3 | 136.3 | 47 |
| 2 | 181.8 | 135.1 | 46.7 |
| 3 | 180.2 | 134.1 | 46.1 |

Try i = 7%
NPW = -120 + 47(P/F,7%,1) + 46.7(P/F,7%,2) + 46.1(P/F,7%,3)
   = -120 + 43.9 + 40.8 + 37.6 = +2.3
So the rate of return for the increment A-B is greater than 7% (actually 8.1%) Choose the higher cost alternative--Choose A.

# 13-31

Compute an equivalent $i$

$i_{equivalent} = i' + f + i'f$

$i_{equivalent} = 0.05 + 0.06 + (0.05)(0.06) = 0.113 = 11.3\%$

Compute the PW of Benefits of the annuity:

PW of Benefits $= 2500(P/A, 11.3\%, 10)$
$$= 2500 \left[ \frac{(1 + 0.113)^{10} - 1}{0.113(1 + 0.113)^{10}} \right] = \$14,540$$

Since the cost is $15,000, the benefits are less than the cost computed at a 5% real rate of return. Thus the actual real rate of return is less than 5% and the annuity should not be purchased.

# 13-32

| Year | Cost-1 | Cost-2 | Cost-3 | Cost-4 | TOTAL | PW-total |
|------|--------|--------|--------|--------|-------|----------|
| 1 | 4500 | 7000 | 10000 | 8500 | 30000 | 24000 |
| 2 | 4613 | 7700 | 10650 | 8288 | 31250 | 20000 |
| 3 | 4728 | 8470 | 11342 | 8080 | 32620 | 16702 |
| 4 | 4846 | 9317 | 12079 | 7878 | 34121 | 13976 |
| 5 | 4967 | 10249 | 12865 | 7681 | 35762 | 11718 |
| 6 | 5091 | 11274 | 13701 | 7489 | 37555 | 9845 |
| 7 | 5219 | 12401 | 14591 | 7302 | 39513 | 8286 |
| 8 | 5349 | 13641 | 15540 | 7120 | 41649 | 6988 |
| 9 | 5483 | 15005 | 16550 | 6942 | 43979 | 5903 |
| 10 | 5620 | 16506 | 17626 | 6768 | 46519 | 4995 |

PW $= -60,000 - (24,000+20,000+16,702+ ...+4995) + 15,000(P/F,25\%,10)$
$$= \underline{\$ 180,802}$$

# 13-33

(a) $F=10,000 \ (F/P,10\%,15)= \underline{\$41,770}$

(b)

| Year | Inflation |
|------|-----------|
| 1 –5 | 3% |
| 6-10 | 5% |
| 11-15 | 8% |

R$ in today's base $= 41,770 \ (P/F, 8\%, 5) \ (P/F, 5\%, 5) \ (P/F, 3\%, 5)$
$\qquad\qquad\qquad = 18,968$

Thus, the real growth in purchasing power has been:
$$18,968 = 10,000 \ (i + i^*)^{15}$$
$$\underline{i^* = 4.36\%}$$

# 13-34

a. Unknown Quantities are calculated as follows:

(a. % change $= (100-89)/89 \ x \ 100\% = \underline{12.36\%}$
(b. PSI $= 100 \ (1.04) = \underline{104}$
(c. % change $= (107-104)/104 = \underline{2.88\%}$
(d. % change $= (116 – 107)/107 = \underline{8.41\%}$
(e. PSI $= 116 \ (1.0517) = \underline{122}$

b.   The base year is 1993.  This is the year of which the index has a value of 100.

c.       (i) PSI (1991) = 82         h = 4 years
            PSI (1995) = 107        $i^* = ?$

$i^* = (107/82)^{0.25}-1 = \underline{6.88\%}$

(ii)  PSI (1992) = 89     n = 6 years
         PSI (1998) = 132     $i^* = ?$

$i^* = (132/89)^{1/6} = \underline{6.79\%}$

# 13-35

$1 = .20 \, (1.06)^n$

$\log (1/.20) = n \log (1.06)$

$n = 27.62$ years

# 13-36

(a)       LCI (-1970) = 100       n = 9
            LCI (-1979) = 250       $i^* = ?$

$i^* = (250/100)^{1/9} - 1 = 10.7\%$

(b)       LCI (1980) =250       n =9
            LCI (1989) = 417       $i^* = ?$

$i^* = (250/100)^{1/9} - 1 = 5.85\%$

(c)       LCI (1990) = 417       n = 8
            LCI (1998) = 550       $i^* = ?$

$i^* = (550/417)^{1/8} - 1 = 3.12\%$

# 13-37

(a) Overa ll LCl change = $\dfrac{250-100}{100}$ $x100\% = 150\%$

(b)  "  $= \dfrac{417-250}{250}$ $x100\% = 66.8\%$

(c)  "  $= \dfrac{550-417}{250}$ $x100\% = 31.9\%$

# 13-38

(a)  CPI (1978) = 65.2    n = 4
CPI (1982) = 96.5    i* = ?
$i^* = (96.5/65.2)^{\frac{1}{4}} - 1 = \underline{10.3\%}$

(b)  (1980) = 82.4    n = 9
(1989) = 124.0    $i^*$ = ?
$i^* = 124/82.4)^{1/9} - 1 = \underline{4.6\%}$

(c)  (1985) = 107.6    n = 12
(1997) = 160.3    $i^*$ = ?
$i^* = (160.3/107.6)^{1/12} - 1 = \underline{3.4\%}$

332 Chapter 13 Inflation And Price Change

# 13-39

a.    $F = 2,500 (1.10)^{50} = \underline{\$293,477}$    in A\$ today

b.    $R$ \$ today in (-50) purchasing power $= 293,477 (P/F, 4\%, 50)$
$$= \underline{41,296\$}$$

# 13-40

(a)    $PW = 2,000 (P/A, i_c, 8)$

$i$ combine $= i$ real $+ f = .03 + .05 + (.03)(0.5)$
$$= \underline{0.0815}$$

$= 2000 (P/A, 8.15\%, 8) = \underline{\$11,428}$

(b)    $PW = 2,00 (P/A, 3\%, 8) = \$14,040$

# 13-41

Find PW of each <u>Plan</u> over next 5 year period

$$i_r = \frac{(i_c - f)}{(1 + f)} = \frac{(.08 - .06)}{(1.06)} = 1.19\%$$

$PW(A) - \$50,000(P/A, 11.5\%, 5) = \$236,359$

$PW (B) = \$45,000 (P/A, 8\%, 5) + 2,500 (P/G, 8\%, 5) = \$198,115$

PW (C) = $65,000 (*P/A*, 1.19, 5) (*P/F*, 6%, 5) = $229,612

Here we choose Company A's salary to maximize PW.

# 13-42

(a)    R today $ in year 15 = 10,000 (*P/F*, $i_r$%, 15)

$$i_r = \frac{(0.15 - 0.08)}{1.08} = 6.5\%$$

=10,000 (1.065)$^{15}$ = 25,718

(b)    $i_c$ = 15% f = 8%

$F$= 10,000 (1.15)$^{15}$ = 81,371

# 13-43

|  | year | brick cost | CBI |
|---|---|---|---|
| a. | 1970 | 2.10 | 442 |
|  | 1998 | x | 618 |

$$\frac{x}{2.10} = 618/442 \quad \text{thus} \quad x = \$2.94$$

**Total Material Cost = 800 x 2.94 = $2,350**

b.      Here we need f % of brick cost
        CBI (1970) = 442            n = 18
        CBI (1998) = 618            i* = ?

$i* = (618/442)^{1/18} - 1 = 0.0188 = \underline{1.9\%}$

We assume the past average inflation rate continues for 10 more years

Brick Unit Cost in 2008 = 2.94 (*F/P*, 0.019%, 10) = \$3.54

Total Material Cost = 800 x 3.54 = $2,833

# 13-44

EAT (today) = 330 (*F/P*, 12%, 10) = <u>1025</u>

# 13-45

F year $^{-16}$ = 100 (*F/A*, 12/34, 5 x 4) = $\underline{\$2687}$

F year $^{-5}$ = 2687 (*F/D*, 4, 20) + 100 (*F/A*, 16/4, 5 x 4) = $\underline{\$8865}$

F year $^{today}$ = 8865 (*F/D*, 2, 20) + 100 (*F/A*, 8/4, 5 x 4) = $\underline{\$15,603}$

# 13-46

| Item | Yr 1 | Yr 2 | Yr 3 |
|------|------|------|------|
| Structural | 125,160 | 129,165 | 137,690 |
| Roofing | 14,280 | 14,637 | 15,076 |
| Heat etc. | 35,560 | 36,306 | 37,614 |
| Insulating | 9,522 | 10,093 | 10,850 |
| Labor | 89,250 | 93,266 | 97,463 |
| Totals | 273,772 | 283,467 | 298,693 |

a)89,250;  93,266;  97,463

b) average = 5 + 4.5 + 4.5/3 = $\underline{4.67\%}$

c) PW = 9522 (*P/F*, 25%, 1)
      +10093 (*P/F*, 25%, 2)
      +10850 (*P/F*, 25%, 3)      = $\underline{\$19,632}$

(c) FW = (9,522 + 89,250) (*F/P*, 25%, 2)
      +(10,093 + 93,266)(*F/P*, 25%, 1)
      + (10,850 + 97,463)      = $\underline{\$391,843}$

(d) PW = 273,772 (*P/F*, 25%, 1)
      + 283,467 (*P/F*, 25%, 2)
      + 298,693 (*P/F*, 25%, 3)    = $553,367

# Estimation Of Future Events

## 14-1

| Grade | Instructor A Grade Distribution | Instructor A Expected Grade Point | Instructor B Grade Distribution | Instructor B Expected Grade Point |
|---|---|---|---|---|
| A 4.0 | 0.10 | 0.40 | 0.15 | 0.60 |
| B 3.0 | 0.15 | 0.45 | 0.15 | 0.45 |
| C 2.0 | 0.45 | 0.90 | 0.30 | 0.60 |
| D 1.0 | 0.15 | 0.15 | 0.20 | 0.20 |
| F 0 | 0.15 | 0 | 0.20 | 0 |
| | 1.00 | 1.90 | 1.00 | 1.85 |

To maximize the Expected Grade Point,
Select Instructor A.

## 14-2

Expected outcome = $2000(0.3) + 1500(0.1) + 1000(0.2)$
$+ 500(0.3) + 0(0.1)$
$= 1100$

## 14-3

The sum of probabilities for all possible outcomes is one.
An inspection of the <u>Regular Season</u> situation reveals that the sum
of the probabilities for the outcomes enumerated is 0.95.
Thus one outcome (win less than three games), with probability 0.05,
has not been tabulated.  This is not a faulty problem statement.
The student is expected to observe this difficulty.

Similarly, the complete probabilities concerning a post-season
<u>Bowl Game</u> are:  probability of playing     = 0.10
                       probability of not playing = 0.90

Expected Net Income for the team
  = $(0.05 + 0.10 + 0.15 + 0.20)(\$250,000)$
    $+ (0.15 + 0.15 + 0.10)(\$400,000) + (0.07 + 0.03)(\$600,000)$
    $+ (0.10)(\$600,000)$

  = $0.50(250,000) + 0.40(400,000) + 0.10(600,000) + 0.10(100,000)$
    $+ 0.90(0)$

  = $\$355,000$.

# 14-4

(a)  Some reasons why a pole might be removed from useful service:

1.  The pole has deteriorated and can no longer perform its function of safely supporting the telephone lines.

2.  The telephone lines are removed from the poles and put underground.  The poles, no longer being needed, are removed.

3.  Poles are destroyed by damage from fire, automobiles, etc.

4.  The street is widened and the pole no longer is in a suitable street location.

5.  The pole is where someone wants to construct a driveway.

(b)  Telephone poles face varying weather and soil conditions, hence there may be large variations in their useful lives.
Typical values for Pacific Telephone Co. in California are:
Optimistic life:  59 years
Most Likely life: 28 years
Pessimistic life:  2.5 years

Recognizing there is a mortality dispersion it would be possible, but impractical, to define optimistic life as the point where the last one from a large group of telephone poles is removed (for Pacific Telephone this would be 83.5 years).  This is <u>not</u> the accepted practice.  Instead, optimum life is where only a small percentage (often 5%) of the group remain in service.  Similarly, pessimistic life is when, say, 5% of the original group of poles have been removed from the group.

# 14-5

Determine the different ways of throwing an 8 with a pair of dice.

| Die 1 | Die 2 |
|-------|-------|
| 2 | 6 |
| 3 | 5 |
| 4 | 4 |
| 5 | 3 |
| 6 | 2 |

The five ways of throwing an 8 have equal probability of 0.20.

The probability of winning is 0.20
The probability of lossing is 0.80

The outcome of a $1 bet = 0.20($4) + 0.80($0) = 80¢ *which means a 20¢ loss!*

# 14-6

$$
\left.\begin{array}{l} 1+6 \\ 2+5 \\ 3+4 \\ 4+3 \\ 5+2 \\ 6+1 \end{array}\right\} \text{6 ways to roll a 7}
$$

$$
\left.\begin{array}{l} 5+6 \\ 6+5 \end{array}\right\} \text{2 ways to roll an 11}
$$

Probability of rolling a 7 or 11 = $\frac{6+2}{36} = \frac{8}{36}$

# 14-7

**(a)**
Since the student must create his own grade distribution, what follows may, or may not, be a typical solution.

| Grade Point | Probability | GPA Group (used in Part (c) |
|---|---|---|
| 0.00 - 0.80 | 0.05 | 1 |
| 0.81 - 1.60 | 0.10 | 2 |
| 1.61 - 2.40 | 0.30 | 3 |
| 2.41 - 3.20 | 0.40 | 4 |
| 3.21 - 4.00 | 0.15 | 5 |
| | 1.00 | |

**(b)**

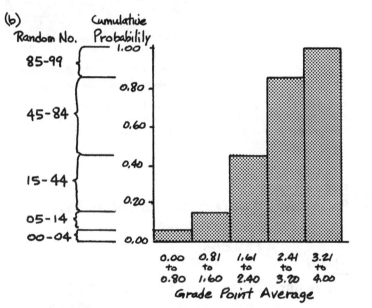

**(c)**
Read 25 values from the table of random numbers:

| Random Number | GPA Group | | Random Number | GPA Group |
|---|---|---|---|---|
| 66 | 4 | | 03 | 1 |
| 34 | 3 | | 69 | 4 |
| 20 | 3 | | 55 | 4 |
| 92 | 5 | | 19 | 3 |
| 78 | 4 | | 00 | 1 |
| 48 | 4 | | 74 | 4 |
| 45 | 4 | | 87 | 5 |
| 84 | 4 | | 16 | 3 |
| 66 | 4 | | 45 | 4 |
| 88 | 5 | | 05 | 1 |
| 14 | 2 | | 24 | 3 |
| 75 | 4 | | 76 | 4 |
| 50 | 4 | | | |

Summary of the 25 random numbers
on the previous page:

| GPA Group | Frequency |
|-----------|-----------|
| 0.00 - 0.80 | 3 |
| 0.81 - 1.60 | 1 |
| 1.61 - 2.40 | 5 |
| 2.41 - 3.20 | 13 |
| 3.21 - 4.00 | 3 |
| | 25 |

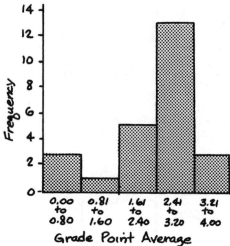

In this typical solution the bar graph is only a very rough
approximation of the actual distribution established in part (a).
This is no doubt due to the small size of the random sample.

# 14-8

<u>Leave the valve as it is</u>

Expected PW of Cost $= 0.60(\$10,000) + 0.50(\$20,000)$
$$+ 0.40(\$30,000)$$
$$= \$28,000$$

<u>Repair the valve</u>

Expected PW of Cost $= \$10,000$ repair $+ 0.40(\$10,000)$
$$+ 0.30(\$20,000) + 0.20(\$30,000)$$
$$= \$26,000$$

<u>Replace the valve</u>

Expected PW of Cost $= \$20,000$ replacement $+ 0.30(\$10,000)$
$$+ 0.20(\$20,000) + 0.10(\$30,000)$$
$$= \$30,000$$

To minimize Expected PW of Cost,
Repair the valve

# 14-9

Expected number of wins in 100 attempts = $\frac{100}{38}$ = 2.6316

Results of a win = $35 \times \$5 + \$5$ bet returned = $180.00

Expected winnings = $180.00 \times 2.6316 = \$473.69$

$$\text{Expected loss} = 500^{00} - 473.69 = \$26.31$$

# 14-10

$$\text{mean life} = \frac{12 + 4(5) + 4}{6} = 6 \text{ yrs}$$

PW of Cost = PW of Benefits

$$80,000 = 20,000 (P/A, i\%, 6)$$

Rate of Return between 12% and 15%

$$\simeq 13\%$$

# 14-11

Do Nothing

   EUAC = Expected annual damage = 0.20 (10,000) + 0.10 (25,000)

$$= \$4500$$

$15,000 Building Alteration

   Expected annual damage = 0.10 ($10,000)      = $1000

   Annual Cost of floodproofing = 15,000 (A/P, 15%, 15) = $\underline{\phantom{xx}2565}$

                        EUAC = $3565

$20,000 Building Alteration

   Expected annual damage                    =      0

   Annual Cost of floodproofing = 20,000 (A/P, 15%, 15) = $\underline{\phantom{xx}3420}$

                        EUAC = $3420

To minimize expected EUAC,

           Recommend $20,000 Building Alteration

# 14-12

Al's score was $\bar{x} + \frac{5}{20}S = \bar{x} + 0.25S$

Bill's score was $\bar{x} + \frac{2}{4}S = \bar{x} + 0.50S$

$\therefore$ Bill ranked higher in his class.

# 14-13

Expected fire loss in any year = $0.010 (10,000) + 0.003(40,000)$
$$+ 0.001(200,000)$$
$$= 420.00$$

The engineer buys the fire insurance because

    1.  a catastrophic loss is an unacceptable risk.

or 2.  he has a loan on the home and fire insurance is required by the lender.

# 14-14

| Height above roadway | Annual Probability of flood damage | x Damage = | Expected Annual Damage |
|---|---|---|---|
| 2 meters | 0.333 | $300,000 | $100,000 |
| 2½ | 0.125 | 300,000 | 37,500 |
| 3 | 0.04 | 300,000 | 12,000 |
| 3½ | 0.02 | 300,000 | 6,000 |
| 4 | 0.01 | 300,000 | 3,000 |

| Height above roadway | Initial Cost | x (A/P, 12%, 50) = | EUAC of Embankment | Expected Annual Damage | Total Expected Annual Cost |
|---|---|---|---|---|---|
| 2 meters | $100 000 | 0.1204 | $12,040 | $100 000 | $112 040 |
| 2½ | 165 000 | 0.1204 | 19,870 | 37 500 | 53 370 |
| 3 | 300 000 | 0.1204 | 36,120 | 12 000 | 48 120 ← |
| 3½ | 400 000 | 0.1204 | 48,160 | 6 000 | 54 160 |
| 4 | 550 000 | 0.1204 | 66,220 | 3 000 | 69 220 |

Select 3 meter embankment to minimize total Expected Annual Cost.

# 14-15

Since 250,000 of dam repairs must be done in all alternatives, this 250,000 can be included or ignored in the analysis. Here it is ignored. ("only the differences between the alternatives are relevant.")

| Flood | Probability of damage in any Year = 1/yr Flood | Downstream Damage | Spillway Damage |
|-------|------------------|-------------------|-----------------|
| 25 yr | 0.04 | 50,000 | |
| 50 yr | 0.02 | 200,000 | |
| Fn 10 yrs: 100 yr | 0.01 | 1,000,000 | 250,000 |
| Thereafter: 100 yr | 0.01 | 2,000,000 | 250,000 |

Alternative 1

Repair existing dam but make no other alterations.

Spillway damage

    Probability that spillway capacity equaled or exceeded in any year is 0.02.

    Damage if spillway capacity exceeded: 250,000

Expected annual cost of spillway damage
   = 250,000 (0.02) = 5000.

Solution continued on next page

<u>Downstream Damage during next 10 years:</u>

| Flood | Probability that flow* will be equaled or exceeded | Damage | Δ Damage over more frequent flood | Annual Cost of flood risk |
|---|---|---|---|---|
| 25 yr | 0.04 | 50 000 | 50 000 | 2000 |
| 50 yr | 0.02 | 200 000 | 150 000 | 3000 |
| 100 yr | 0.01 | 1,000 000 | 800 000 | 8000 |

Next 10 year expected annual cost of downstream damage $13,000

<u>Downstream Damage after 10 years:</u>

Following the same logic as above,
Expected annual cost of downstream damage
$$= 2000 + 3000 + 0.1(2,000,000 - 200,000) = \$23,000$$

<u>Present Worth of Expected Spillway and Downstream Damage:</u>

$$PW = 5000\,(P/A, 7\%, 50) + 13000\,(P/A, 7\%, 10)$$
$$+ 23000\,(P/A, 7\%, 40)(P/F, 7\%, 10)$$
$$= 5000(13.801) + 13000(7.024) + 23000(13.332)(0.5083)$$
$$= 316,180$$

<u>Equivalent Uniform Annual Cost:</u>

$$\text{Annual Cost} = 316,180\,\underset{0.0725}{(A/P, 7\%, 50)} = 22,920$$

\* An N-year flood will be equaled or exceeded at an average internal of N years.

---

**Alternative 2**

Repair the dam and redesign the spillway
Additional cost to redesign/reconstruct the spillway = 250,000
<u>Present Worth to Reconstruct Spillway and Expected Downstream Damage</u>

Downstream damage – same as alternative 1.
$$PW = 250000 + 13000\,\underset{7.024}{(P/A, 7\%, 10)} + 23000\,\underset{13.332}{(P/A, 7\%, 40)}\underset{0.5083}{(P/F, 7\%, 10)}$$
$$= 497,180$$

<u>Equivalent Uniform Annual Cost:</u>

$$\text{Annual Cost} = 497,180\,\underset{0.0725}{(A/P, 7\%, 50)} = 36,050$$

---

**Alternative 3**

Repair the dam and build flood control dam upstream
Cost of flood control dam = $1,000,000.

Equivalent Uniform Annual Cost:

$$\text{Annual Cost} = 1,000,000 \underset{0.0725}{(A/P, 7\%, 50)} = 72,500$$

Note:   One must be careful not to confuse the frequency of a flood
and when it might be expected to occur.  The occurrence of a
100-year flood this year is no guarantee that it won't happen
again next year.  In any 50 year period, for example, there are
4 chances in 10 that a 100-year flood (or greater) will occur.

Conclusion
Since we are dealing with conditions of risk, it is not possible to
make an absolute statement concerning which alternative will result
in the least cost to the community.  Using a probabilistic approach,
however, Alternative 1 is most likely to result in the least
equivalent uniform annual cost.

# 14-16

*a.* Note the first payment is 24 months after the loan was obtained.

$A = \$20$ million $(F/P, 10\%,1)(A/P,10\%,10) = \$20$ million $(1.10)(0.1627)$
$=\$3,579,400$

*b.* Expected number of students
$$= 8000(0.6) + 9000(0.3) + 10,000(0.1) = 8500$$

*c.* Additional Tuition $= 3,579,400/8500 = \$421$

*d.*
| Year | Expense | PW Computation | PW of Cost |
|------|---------|----------------|------------|
| 1 | $14,000 | $14,000(P/F,10\%,1)$ | 12,727 |
| 2 | 15,400 | $15,400(P/F,10\%,2)$ | 12,727 |
| 3 | 16,800 | $16,800(P/F,10\%,3)$ | 12,622 |
| 4 | 18,200 | $18,200(P/F,10\%,4)$ | <u>12,431</u> |
| | | Required deposit $=$ | $50,507 |

*e.* The 2002 payment will be the present worth of all the subsequent payments

Payment$_{2002}$ $= 3,579,400[1+(P/A,10\%,6)]$
$= 3,579,400(5.355)$
$= \$19,167,700$

*f.* Amount owed at time of 1999 payment

Amount $= \$20$ million $(1+0.10)^2 = \$24.2$ million
Interest due $= (0.10)(24.2$ million$) = \$2.42$ million
Payment $=$ Principal $+$ Interest $= \$3,579,400$ (from part *a.*)

*g.* Annual loan payment $(A) = (0.10)(10,000)(8500) = \$8.5$ million
Amount of loan at beginning of 1999 $= \$20$ million $(1+0.10) = \$22$ million
$P = A(P/A,10\%,n)$
$\$22$ million $= 8.5$ million $(P/A,10\%,n)$
$(P/A,10\%,n) = 22/8.5 = 2.588$
From 10% compound interest table:
$(P/A,10\%,3) = 2.487$
$(P/A,10\%,4) = 3.170$
So it will take more than three and less than four full payments to repay the loan.
If we interpolate, the answer is:
No. Of payments $= 3 + (2.588 - 2.487) / (3.170 - 2.487) = 3.15$

*h.* The $20 million loan would be repaid the end of the fourth year.
Repayment amount (F) $= \$20$ million $(1 + 0.10)^4 = \$29.282$ million

*i.* 1999 tuition $= 7500$ increasing $500/year after that
Equivalent uniform annual tuition $= 7500 +500(A/G,10\%,5) = \$8405$

# Selection Of A MARR

## 15-1

The interest rates on these securities vary greatly over time, making it impossible to predict rates. Three factors that distinguish the three securities:

|  | Bond Income | Bond Duration | Bond Safety |
|---|---|---|---|
| U.S. Treasury Bond | Taxable | 5 yrs | safest |
| Municipal Bond | Not Taxable | 20 yrs | safe |
| Corporate Bond | Taxable | 20 yrs | less safe |

The importance of the non-taxable income feature usually makes the municipal bond the one with the lowest interest rate. Next higher, with its safety and a shorter duration, is the Treasury bond. The corporate bond generally will have the highest interest rate.

## 15-2

As this is a situation of "neither input nor output fixed," incremental analysis is required.

|  | C-D | B-C | B-D | D-A |
|---|---|---|---|---|
| $\Delta$ Cost | $25 | $50 | $75 | $25 |
| $\Delta$ Benefit | 4 | 6.31 | 10.31 | 5.96 |
| $\Delta$Rate of Return | 9.6% | 4.5% | 6.2% | 20% |

Using the incremental rates of return one may determine the preferred alternative at any interest rate.

For Interest
Rates Between    0% ——— 4.5% ——— 9.6% ——— 20% ——— ∞%

Choose Alternative    B          C          D          A

The problem here concerns Alternative C.

C preferred for

$$4.5\% < \text{Interest Rate} \leqslant 9.6\%$$

## 15-3

Lease

Pay $267 per month for 24 months.

Purchase

$A = \$9400(A/P,1\%,24) = 9400(0.0471) = \$442.74$

Salvage (resale) value = $4700.

Purchase rather than Lease

Purchase rather
than Lease

Δ Monthly payment = $442.74 - 267.  = ,175.74
Δ Salvage (resale) value = 4700 - 0 = 4700.00

Δ Rate of Return

FW of Cost     = FW of Benefit

$$175.74(F/A,i\%,24) = 4700$$
$$(F/A,i\%,24) = \frac{4700.00}{175.74} = 26.74 \qquad i = 0.93\% \text{ per month}$$

Nominal interest rate = 0.93 x 12
= 11.2%

Thus the additional monthly payment of $175.74 would yield an
11.2% rate of return.  Leasing is therefore preferred at all
interest rates above 11.2%.

(b) Items that might make leasing more desirable:

1. One does not have, or does not want to spend, the
additional $175.74 per month.

2. One can make more than 11.2% rate of return in other
investments.

3. One does not have to be concerned about the resale
value of the car at the end of the two years.

# 15-4

Investment opportunities may include

1. Deposit of the money in a Savings & Loan Association
or a Bank.
2. Purchase of common stock, US Treasury bonds, or
corporate bonds.
3. Investment in a new business, or an existing business.
And so on.

Assuming the student proposes a single investment, in which more
than $2000 could be invested, the MARR equals the projected rate
of return for the investment.

# 15-5

Venture capital syndicates typically invest money in situations with
a substantial amount of risk.  And the process of identifying and
selecting investments is a time-consuming (and hence costly)
process.  The group would therefore only make a venture capital
investment where (they think) the rate of return will be high -
probably 25% or more.

# Economic Analysis In Government

Benefit-Cost ratio = $\dfrac{PW \text{ of Benefits}}{PW \text{ of Cost}} = \dfrac{20,000(P/A, 7\%, 9)(P/F, 7\%, 1)}{100,000 + 50,000(P/F, 7\%, 1)}$

$= \dfrac{20,000(6.515)(0.9346)}{100,000 + 50,000(0.9346)} = 0.83$

This problem requires the student to use calculus. The text points out in Example 8-9 (of Chapter 8) that one definition of the point where $\Delta B = \Delta C$ is that the slope of the benefits curve equals the slope of the NPW = 0 line.

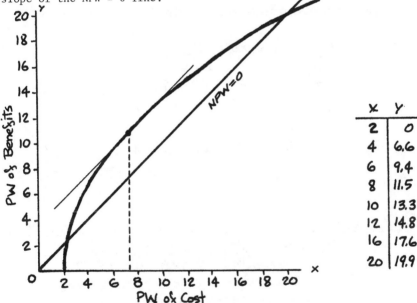

| x | y |
|---|---|
| 2 | 0 |
| 4 | 6.6 |
| 6 | 9.4 |
| 8 | 11.5 |
| 10 | 13.3 |
| 12 | 14.8 |
| 16 | 17.6 |
| 20 | 19.9 |

Let $x = PW$ of Cost and $y = PW$ of Benefits

$y^2 - 22x + 44 = 0$  or  $y = (22x - 44)^{1/2}$

$\dfrac{dy}{dx} = \dfrac{1}{2}(22x - 44)^{-\frac{1}{2}}(22) = 1$  $\left\{ \begin{array}{l} \text{Note that the slope of the} \\ \text{NPW=0 line equals 1} \end{array} \right.$

$22x - 44 = (\frac{1}{2} \times 22)^2$  $x = \dfrac{11^2 + 44}{22} = 7.5 = $ Optimum PW of Cost

# 16-3

Since we have a 40-year analysis period, the problem could be solved by any of the exact analysis techniques.  Here the problem specifies a present worth analysis.  The annual cost solution, with a 10% interest rate, is presented in Problem 6-42.

## Gravity Plan

$$PW \text{ of } Cost = 2,800,000 + 10,000 \underset{11.925}{(P/A, 8\%, 40)}$$

$$= 2,919,250$$

## Pumping Plan

$$PW \text{ of } Cost = 1,400,000 + 200,000 \underset{0.4632}{(P/F, 8\%, 10)}$$

$$+ (25,000 + 50,000) \underset{11.925}{(P/A, 8\%, 40)}$$

$$+ 50,000 \underset{11.258}{(P/A, 8\%, 30)} \underset{0.4632}{(P/F, 8\%, 10)}$$

$$= 2,647,700$$

To minimize PW of Cost: __Pumping Plan__

# 16-4

Part (a)

PW of Benefits $= 60,000(P/A, 5\%, 10) + 64,000(P/A, 5\%, 10)(P/F, 5\%, 10)$
$$+ 66,000(P/A, 5\%, 20)(P/F, 5\%, 20)$$
$$+ 70,000(P/A, 5\%, 10)(P/F, 5\%, 40)$$

$$= 60,000(7.722) + 64,000(7.722)(0.6139)$$
$$+ 66,000(12.462)(0.3769)$$
$$+ 70,000(7.722)(0.1420)$$

$$= 1,153,468$$

For B/C ratio $= 1$,   PW of Cost $=$ PW of Benefits
Justified capital expenditure
$$= 1,153,468 - 15,000(P/A, 5\%, 50)$$
$$= 1,153,468 - 15,000(18.256)$$
$$= 879,628$$

Part (b)

Same equation as on previous page except use 8% interest.

PW of Benefits = 60,000(6.710) + 64,000(6.710)(0.4632)

   + 66,000(9.818)(0.2145)

   + 70,000(6.710)(0.0460)

   = 762,116

Justified capital expenditure

   = 762,116 - 15,000(12.233)

   = 578,621

# 16-5

PLAN A

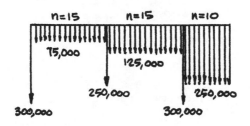

PLAN B

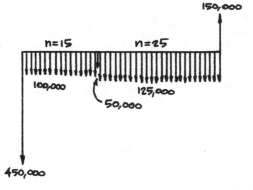

Differences
Between the
Alternatives

PLAN B - PLAN A

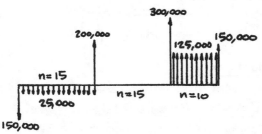

An examination of the differences between the alternatives will
allow us to quickly determine which plan is preferred.

| | CASH FLOW | | | Present Worth | |
|---|---|---|---|---|---|
| Year | A | B | B-A | AT 7% | AT 5% |
| 0 | -300 | -450 | -150 | -150 | -150 |
| 1-15 | -75 | -100 | -25 | -228 | -259 |
| 15 | -250 | -50 | +200 | +72 | +96 |
| 16-30 | -125 | -125 | 0 | 0 | 0 |
| 30 | -300 | 0 | +300 | +39 | +69 |
| 31-40 | -250 | -125 | +125 | +115 | +223 |
| 40 | 0 | +150 | +150 | +10 | +21 |
| | | | +1375* | -142 | 0 |

*This is sum of  -150 -25(15) +200 + ⋯

Part (a)

When the Present Worth of the  B - A  cash flow is computed at 7%,
the NPW = -142.   The increment is not desirable at i = 7%.

Choose Plan A.

Part (b)

For Plan B to be choosen, the increment B - A must be desirable.
The last column in the table above shows that the B - A increment
has a 5% rate of return.   In other words, at all interest rates
at or below 5%, the increment is desirable and hence Plan B is the
preferred alternative.

The value of MARR would have to
be 5% or less.

# 16-6

Overpass cost $1,800,000    salvage value $100,000  n=30  i=6%
Is built,

Benefits to the Public

Time Saving
1000 vehicles/day
$\begin{cases} 400 \text{ trucks} \times \frac{2}{60} \times \$18/hr = \$240 \text{ per day} \\ 600 \text{ others} \times \frac{2}{60} \times \$5/hr = \underline{100} \end{cases}$

$340 per day

Benefits to the State

Saving in accident investigation costs, etc.    = $2000 per year

Combined Benefits = Benefits to Public + Benefits to State
= 340 (365 days) + 6000 = $130,100 per year

Benefits to the Railroad
    Saving in Crossing guard expense  $48,000 per year
    Saving in accident case expense   60,000
                                         $108,000 per year

Should the overpass be built?

Benefit-Cost ratio analysis

$$\text{Annual Cost (EUAC)} = 1,700,000(A/P, 6\%, 30) + 100,000(0.06)$$
$$= 1,700,000(0.0726) + 6000$$
$$= \$129,420$$

$$\text{Annual Benefits (EUAB)} = 130,100 + 108,000 = \$238,100$$

$$B/c = \frac{EUAB}{EUAC} = \frac{238,100}{129,420} = 1.84$$

With a B/c ratio > 1, the project is economically justified.

Allocation of the $1,800,000 cost

The railroad should contribute to the project in proportion to the benefits received.

$$\text{PW of Cost} = 1,800,000 - 100,000(P/F, 6\%, 30)$$
$$= 1,800,000 - 100,000(0.1741) = \$1,782,590$$

The railroad portion would be

$$\frac{108,000}{238,100}(1,782,590) \qquad\qquad = 808,570$$

The State portion would be

$$\frac{130,100}{238,100}(1,782,590) + 100,000(P/F, 6\%, 30) = 991,430$$
$$\overset{0.1741}{\phantom{x}}$$
$$\underline{\$1,800,000}$$

While this problem is a simplified representation of the situation, it illustrates a realistic statement of benefits and an economic analysis solution to the allocation of costs.

# 16-7

|  | Existing | Plan A | Plan B | Plan C |
|---|---|---|---|---|
| Length (miles) | 10 | 10 | 10 | 10.3 |
| Number of Lanes | 2 | 4 | 4 | 4 |
| Average ADT | 20,000 | 20,000 | 20,000 | 20,000 |
|     Autos | 19,000 | 19,000 | 19,000 | 19,000 |
|     Trucks | 1,000 | 1,000 | 1,000 | 1,000 |
| Time Savings (minutes) |  |  |  |  |
|     Autos |  | 2 | 3 | 5 |
|     Trucks |  | 1 | 3 | 4 |
| Accident Rate/MVM | 4.58 | 2.50 | 2.40 | 2.30 |
| Initial Cost per mile (P) | - | 450,000 | 650,000 | 800,000 |
| Annual Maintenance |  |  |  |  |
|     Per lane per mile | 1500 | 1250 | 1000 | 1000 |

Total Annual Maintenance $30,000  $50,000  $40,000  $41,200

EUAC of Initial Cost
$$= (P \times miles)(A/P, 5\%, 20)$$
$$0.0802$$
                           0   360,900  521,300  660,850

Total Annual Cost of
EUAC + maintenance  $30,000  $410,900  $561,300  $702,050

## Annual Incremental Operating Costs due to distance

None for Plans A and B same length as Existing road

Plan C   Autos    19,000 × 365 × 0.3 mi × $0.06 = 124,830

            Trucks    1,000 × 365 × 0.3 mi × $0.18    <u>19,710</u>

                                             $144,540/yr

## Annual Accident Savings compared to Existing Highway

Plan A
$$(4.58 - 2.50)(10^{-6})(10 \text{ mi})(365 \text{ days})(20,000 \text{ ADT})(\$1200) = \$182,200$$

Plan B
$$(4.58 - 2.40)(10^{-6})(10 \text{ mi})(365 \text{ days})(20,000 \text{ ADT})(\$1200) = 190,970$$

Plan C
$$(4.58 - 2.30)(10^{-6})(10.3 \text{ mi})(365 \text{ days})(20,000 \text{ ADT})(\$1200) = 205,720$$

## Time Savings Benefits to Road Users compared to Existing Highway

### Plan A

| | | |
|---|---|---|
| Autos | $19,000 \times 365\text{ days} \times 2\text{ min} \times \$0.03$ | $= \$416,100$ |
| Trucks | $1000 \times 365\text{ days} \times 1\text{ min} \times \$0.15$ | $= \underline{\phantom{00}54,750}$ |
| | | $\$470,850$ |

### Plan B

| | | |
|---|---|---|
| Autos | $19,000 \times 365\text{ days} \times 3\text{ min} \times \$0.03$ | $= \$624,150$ |
| Trucks | $1000 \times 365\text{ days} \times 3\text{ min} \times \$0.15$ | $= \underline{\phantom{0}164,250}$ |
| | | $\$788,400$ |

### Plan C

| | | |
|---|---|---|
| Autos | $19,000 \times 365\text{ days} \times 5\text{ min} \times \$0.03$ | $= \$1,040,250$ |
| Trucks | $1000 \times 365\text{ days} \times 4\text{ min} \times \$0.15$ | $= \underline{\phantom{0}219,000}$ |
| | | $\$1,259,250$ |

## Summary of Annual Costs and Benefits

| | Existing | Plan A | Plan B | Plan C |
|---|---|---|---|---|
| Annual Highway Costs | $30,000 | $410,900 | $561,300 | $702,050 |
| **Annual Benefits** | | | | |
| Accident Savings | | $182,200 | $190,970 | $205,720 |
| Time Savings | | 470,850 | 788,400 | 1,259,250 |
| Additional Operating Cost* | | | | -144,540 |
| Annual Benefits: | | 653,050 | 979,370 | 1,320,430 |

*User costs considered as a disbenefit.

## Benefit-Cost Ratios

Plan A rather than Existing: $\quad B/c = \dfrac{653,050}{410,900-30,000} = 1.71$

Plan B rather than Plan A: $\quad B/c = \dfrac{979,370-653,050}{561,300-410,900} = 2.17$

Plan C rather than Plan B: $\quad B/c = \dfrac{1,320,430-979,370}{702,050-561,300} = 2.42$

Plan C is preferred

# 16-8

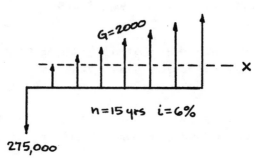

Compute X for NPW = 0

NPW = PW of Benefits - PW of Costs

= X(P/A,6%,15) + 2000(P/G,6%,15) - 275,000 = 0

= X(9.712) + 2000(57.555) - 275,000 = 0

$$X = \frac{275,000 - 2000(57.555)}{9.712} = 16,463$$

Therefore NPW$_{\text{at yr } 0}$ turns positive for the first time when

X is greater than 16,463.  This indicates that construction should not be done prior to 19X5 as NPW is not positive.  The problem thus reduces to deciding whether to proceed in 19X5 or 19X6. The appropriate criterion is to Max NPW at some point.  If we choose the beginning of 19X5 for convenience,

<u>Construct in 19X5</u>

NPW$_{\text{at 19X5}}$ = 18,000(P/A,6%,15) + 2000(P/G,6%,15) - 275,000

= 18,000(9.712) + 2000(57.555) - 275,000

= +14,926

<u>Construct in 19X6</u>

NPW$_{\text{at 19X5}}$ = [20,000(P/A,6%,15) + 2000(P/G,6%,15)

 - 275,000 ](P/F,6%,1)

= [20,000(9.712) + 2000(57.555) - 275,000] (0.9434)

= +32,406

Conclusion: Construct in 19X6

# 16-9

It is important to recognize that if Net Present Worth analysis is done, then the criterion is to Max NPW. But, of course, the NPW's must be computed at a common point in time, like Year 0.

## Repair Now

NPW at yr 0

$= 5000(P/F, 15\%, 1) + 10000(P/G, 15\%, 5) + 50000(P/A, 15\%, 5)(P/F, 15\%, 5)$
$\quad -150,000$

$= 5000(0.8696) + 10000(5.775) + 50000(3.352)(0.4972) - 150,000$

$= -4571$

## Repair Two Years Hence

NPW at yr 2

$= 20000(P/A, 15\%, 3) + 10000(P/G, 15\%, 3) + 50000(P/A, 15\%, 7)(P/F, 15\%, 3)$
$\quad -150,000$

$= 20000(2.283) + 10000(2.071) + 5000(4.160)(0.6575) - 150,000$

$= +53,130$

NPW at yr 0 $= +53,130(P/F, 15\%, 2) = +53130(0.7561) = +40,172$

## Repair Four Years Hence

NPW at Yr 4

$= 50000(P/A, 15\%, 10) - 10000(P/F, 15\%, 1) - 150000$

$= 50000(5.019) - 10000(0.8696) - 150000 = +92,254$

NPW at Yr 0 $= +92254(P/F, 15\%, 4) = +92254(0.5718) = +52,751$

## Repair Five Years Hence

NPW at yr 5

$= 50,000(P/A, 15\%, 10) - 150000$

$= 50,000(5.019) - 150,000 = +100,950$

NPW at yr 0 $= +100,950(P/F, 15\%, 5) = +100,950(0.4972) = +50,192$

Solution continued on next page

To max NPW at Year 0
    <u>Repair the road four years hence</u>

It might be worth noting in this situation that since the benefits
in the early years (Yrs 1, 2, and 3) are less than the cost times
the interest rate ($150,000 x 0.15 = $22,500), delaying the
project will increase the NPW at Year 0.   In other words, we
would not expect the project to be selected (if it ever would be)
until the annual benefits are greater than $22,500.

If a "Repair three years hence" alternative were considered we
would find it has a NPW at Year 0 of +49,945.   So the decision to
repair the road four years hence is correct.

# 16-10

This problem will require some student thought on how
to structure the analysis.   This is a situation of providing
the necessary capacity when it is needed - in other words
Fixed Output.   Computing the cost is easy, but what is the
benefit?

One cannot compute the B/C ratio for either alternative,
but the incremental B/C ratio may be computed on the difference
between the alternatives.

| Year | A<br>Half capacity tunnel now plus second half capacity tunnel in 20 years | B<br>Full Capacity tunnel | B-A<br>Difference between the alternatives |
|------|------|------|------|
| 0 | -$300,000 | -$500,000 | -$200,000 |
| 10 | -16,000 | -20,000 | -4,000 |
| 20 | $\left\{\begin{array}{l} -16,000 \\ -400,000 \end{array}\right.$ | -20,000 | +396,000 |
| 30 | -32,000 | -20,000 | +12,000 |
| 40 | -32,000 | -20,000 | +12,000 |
| 50 | 0 | 0 | 0 |

$$\frac{\Delta B}{\Delta C} = \frac{396,000\,(P/F, 5\%, 20) + 12000\,(P/F, 5\%, 30) + 12000\,(P/F, 5\%, 40)}{200,000 + 4000\,(P/F, 5\%, 10)}$$

$$= \frac{153,733}{202,456} = 0.76$$

This is an undesirable increment of
investment.   Build the half-capacity
tunnel now.

# 16-11

The time required to initiate, study, fund and construct public projects is generally several years (or even decades). Because of this it is not uncommon for there to be turnover in public policy makers. Politicians, who generally strive to maintain a positive public image, have been known to "stand up and gain political capital" from projects that originally began many years previous to their taking office.

# 16-12

a).   The conventional and modified versions of the B/C Ratio will always give consistent recommendations in terms of "invest" or "do not invest". However the magnitude of the B/C Ratio will be different for the two methods. Advocates of a project may use the method with the larger ratio to bolster their advocacy.

(b)   Larger interest rates raise the "cost of capital" or "lost interest" for public projects because of the sometimes quite expensive construction costs. A person favoring a 200 M $ turnpike project would want to use lower i% values in the B/C Ratio calculations to offset the large capital costs.

c)   A decision maker in favor of a particular public project would advocate the use of a longer project in the calculation of the B/C ratio. Longer durations spread the large initial costs over a greater number of years.

d)   Benefits, costs and disbenefits are quantities that have various amounts of "certainty" associated with this. And although this is true for all engineering economy estimates it is particularly true for public projects. It is much easier to estimate labor savings in a production environment than it is to estimate the impact on local hotels of new signage along a major route through town. Because benefits, costs and disbenefits tend to have more uncertainty it is therefore easier to manipulate their values to make a B/C Ratio indicate a decision with your position.

# 16-13

**This is a list of potential costs, benefits and disbenefits for a nuclear power plant.**

| Costs | Benefits | Disbenefits |
|---|---|---|
| Land Acquisition | Environment | Fission product |
| Site Preparation | *no greenhouse gas | material to |
| Cooling System | *no leakage | contend with |
| *Reservoir dams | *no combustion | forever |
| *Reservoir cooling | Jobs & Economy | Not in my back |
| Construction | *at enrichment plants | yard |
| *Reactor vessel/core | *at power plant | Risk of Reactor |
| *Balance of plant | *increase tax base | *real |
| *Spent fuel storage | Increase Demand | *psychological |
| *Water cleaning | *Uranium plants | Loss to economy |
| | | *coal |
| | | *electric |

# 16-14

(a) **Conventional B / C Ratio** = $\dfrac{\text{PW (Benefits - Disabilities)}}{\text{PW (1st Cost + Annual Cost)}}$

$= \dfrac{(500,000 - 25,000)(P/A,10\%35)}{1,200,000 + 125,000(P/A,10\%35)} = 1.9$

(b) **Modified B / C Ratio** = $\dfrac{\text{PW(Benefits - Disbenefits - Costs)}}{\text{PW (1st Cost)}}$

$= \dfrac{(500,000 - 25,000 - 125,000)(P/A,10\%35)}{1,200,000} = 2.8$

# 16-15

Using the Conventional B/C Ratio

(i) Using PW    B/C Ratio = 1.90 (as above)

(ii) Using AW
    B/C = (500,000-25,000)/(1,200,000($A/P$,10%,35)+125,000)
        = 1.90
 (iii) Using FW
    B/C = (500,000-25,000)($F/A$,10%,35)/ (1,200,000($F/P$,10%,35)+125,000($F/A$,10%,35))
        = 1.90

# 16-16

$$(a) \quad B\ /\ C \ \text{R a t i o} \quad = \quad \frac{(5\,5\,0\ -\ 3\,5)(\ P\ /\ A\,,8\,\%\ ,2\,0\ )}{(7\,5\,0\ +\ 2\,7\,5\,0\ )\ +\ 1\,8\,5(\ P\ /\ A\,,8\,\%\ ,2\,0\ )} = 0.9\,5$$

$(b)$   Let's find the breakeven number of years at which B / C $= 1.0$

$$1.0\ = \quad \frac{(5\,5\,0\ -\ 3\,5)(\ P\ /\ A\,,8\,\%\ ,2\,0\ )}{(7\,5\,0\ +\ 2\,7\,5\,0\ )\ +\ 1\,8\,5(\ P\ /\ A\,,8\,\%\ ,\ x\ )}$$

By trial and error:
@ x = 24 years          B/C ratio = 0.995
@ x = 25 years          B/C ratio = 1.004
@ x = 26 years          B/C ratio = 1.031

One can see how Big City Carl arrived at his value of "at least" 25 years for the project duration. This is the minimum number of years at which the B/C ratio is greater than 1.0 (nominally).

# 16-17

Annual Travel Volume = (2500)(365) = 912,500 cars/year

The High Road
$1^{st}$ Cost = 200,000 (35) = 7,000,000
Annual Benefits = 0.015 (912,500) (35) = 479,063
Annual O & M Cost = 2000 (35) = 70,000

The Low Road
$1^{st}$ Cost = 450,000 (10) = 4,500,000
Annual Benefits = 0.045 (912,500) 10 = 410,625

Annual O & M Cost = 10,000 (10) = 100,000

These are two mutually exclusive alternatives, we use an incremental analysis process.

Rank Order based on denominator = Low Road, High Road

|  | (Do Nothing-to-Low) | (Low-to-High) |
|---|---|---|
| Δ 1st Cost | 4,500,000 | 2,500,000 |
| Δ Annual Benefits | 410,625 | 68,438 |
| Δ Annual O & M Cost | 100,000 | -30,000 |
| Δ B/ΔC | 1.07[a] | 0.61[b] |
| Justified? | Yes | Yes |

Recommend investing in the Low Road, it is the last justified increment.

(a) $$\frac{(410,625 - 100,000)(15,456)}{4,500,000} = 1.07$$

(b) $$\frac{(68,438 \quad +30,000)(15456)}{2,500,000} = .61$$

# 16-18

|                         | ALT.A  | ALT.B  | ALT.C  |
|-------------------------|--------|--------|--------|
| First Cost              | 9,500  | 12,500 | 14,000 |
| Annual O&M Costs        | 550    | 175    | 325    |
| Salvage Value           | 1,000  | 6,000  | 3,500  |
| PW of Denominator       | 15592  | 13874  | 17,311 |
| Annual Benefits         | 2,200  | 1,500  | 1,000  |
| Annual Disbenefits      | 350    | 150    | 75     |
| PW of Numerator         | 20827  | 15198  | 10413  |
| B/C RATIO               | 1.34   | 1.10   | 0.60   |

We eliminate ALT.C from consideration
Our rank order is B,A,D

|                          | (dn--->B) | (B ---> A) | (A --->D) |
|--------------------------|-----------|------------|-----------|
| Δ(First Cost)            | 12,500    | -3,000     | 6,250     |
| Δ(Annual O&M Costs)      | 175       | 375        | -405      |
| Δ(Salvage Value)         | 6,000     | -5,000     | 6,500     |
| PW of Δ (Denominator)    | 13874     | 1719       | 1045      |
| Δ(Annual Benefits)       | 1,500     | 700        | 300       |
| Δ(Annual Disbenefits)    | 150       | 200        | 350       |
| PW of Δ (Numerator)      | 15198     | 5629       | -563      |
| Δ(B/C RATIO)             | 1.10      | 3.28       | -0.54     |
| JUSTIFIED                | YES       | YES        | NO        |

**We would choose Alt. A because it is associated with the last justified increment of investment.**

# 16-19

|                      | 1    | 2    | 3    | 4    | 5    | 6    |
|----------------------|------|------|------|------|------|------|
| AW Costs (sponsor)   | 15.5 | 13.7 | 16.8 | 10.2 | 17   | 23.3 |
| AW Benefits (users)  | 20   | 16   | 15   | 13.7 | 22   | 25   |
| B/C Ratio            | 1.29 | 1.17 | 0.89 | 1.34 | 1.29 | 1.07 |

We can eliminate project #3 from consideration.  Our rank order is 4,2,1,5 and 6.

|                         | (dn->4) | (4->2) | (4->1) | (1->5) | (5->6) |
|-------------------------|---------|--------|--------|--------|--------|
| $\Delta$(AW Costs (sponsor))  | 10.2 | 3.5  | 5.3  | 1.5  | 6.3  |
| $\Delta$(AW Benefits (users)) | 13.7 | 2.3  | 6.3  | 2    | 3    |
| $\Delta$(B/C Ratio)           | 1.34 | 0.66 | 1.19 | 1.33 | 0.48 |
| JUSTIFIED ?             | YES  | NO   | YES  | YES  | NO   |

We would choose Alt 5 because it is associated with the last justified increment of investment.

# 16-20

|                     | A      | B      | C      |
|---------------------|--------|--------|--------|
| Initial Investment  | 9,500  | 18,500 | 22,000 |
| Annual Savings      | 3,200  | 5,000  | 9,800  |
| Annual Costs        | 1,000  | 2,750  | 6,400  |
| Salvage Value       | 6,000  | 4,200  | 14,000 |

(a)  Conventional B/C

|                 | A     | B     | C     |
|-----------------|-------|-------|-------|
| PW Numerator    | 21795 | 34054 | 66746 |
| PW Denominator  | 15215 | 36463 | 63032 |
| B/C Ratio       | 1.43  | 0.93  | 1.06  |

Here we eliminate Alt. B
Rank order is A then C

| Incremental Analysis   | (dn-->A) | (A-->C) |
|------------------------|----------|---------|
| Δ(Initial Investment)  | 9,500    | 12,500  |
| Δ(Annual Savings)      | 3,200    | 6,600   |
| Δ (Annual Costs)       | 1,000    | 5,400   |
| Δ (Salvage Value)      | 6,000    | 8,000   |
| Δ (PW Numerator)       | 21795    | 44952   |
| Δ (PW Denominator)     | 15215    | 47817   |
| Δ (B/C Ratio)          | 1.43     | 0.94    |
| JUSTIFIED ?            | YES      | NO      |

We recommend ALT. A

(b) Modified B/C

|  | A | B | C |
|---|---|---|---|
| PW Numerator | 14984 | 15324 | 23157 |
| PW Denominator | 8404 | 17733 | 19442 |
| B/C Ratio | 1.78 | 0.86 | 1.19 |

Here we eliminate Alt. B
Rank order is A then C

| Incremental Analysis | (dn-->A) | (A-->C) |
|---|---|---|
| Δ (Initial Investment) | 9,500 | 12,500 |
| Δ (Annual Savings) | 3,200 | 6,600 |
| Δ (Annual Costs) | 1,000 | 5,400 |
| Δ (Salvage Value) | 6,000 | 8,000 |
| Δ (PW Numerator) | 14984 | 8173 |
| Δ (PW Denominator) | 8404 | 11038 |
| Δ (B/C Ratio) | 1.78 | 0.74 |
| JUSTIFIED ? | YES | NO |

We recommend ALT. A

|  | A | B | C |
|---|---|---|---|
| Year 0 | -9,500 | -18,500 | -22,000 |
| Year 1 | 2,200 | 2,250 | 3,400 |
| Year 2 | 2,200 | 2,250 | 3,400 |
| Year 3 | 2,200 | 2,250 | 3,400 |
| Year 4 | 2,200 | 2,250 | 3,400 |
| Year 5 | 2,200 | 2,250 | 3,400 |
| Year 6 | 2,200 | 2,250 | 3,400 |
| Year 7 | 2,200 | 2,250 | 3,400 |
| Year 8 | 2,200 | 2,250 | 3,400 |
| Year 9 | 2,200 | 2,250 | 3,400 |
| Year 10 | 2,200 | 2,250 | 3,400 |
| Year 11 | 2,200 | 2,250 | 3,400 |
| Year 12 | 2,200 | 2,250 | 3,400 |
| Year 13 | 2,200 | 2,250 | 3,400 |
| Year 14 | 2,200 | 2,250 | 3,400 |
| Year 15 | 8,200 | 6,450 | 17,400 |
| (c) Present Worth | 6,580 | -2,408 | 3,715 |

We recommend Alt. A.

(d) IRR Method          23%          10%          15%
Here we need incremental analysis method.
Eliminate Alt. B because IRR < MARR.

| Incremental Analysis | dn--> A | A--> C |
|---|---|---|
| Δ (year 0) | -9500 | -12500 |
| Δ (year 1) | 2200 | 1200 |
| Δ (year 2) | 2200 | 1200 |
| Δ (year 3) | 2200 | 1200 |
| Δ (year 4) | 2200 | 1200 |
| Δ (year 5) | 2200 | 1200 |
| Δ (year 6) | 2200 | 1200 |
| Δ (year 7) | 2200 | 1200 |
| Δ (year 8) | 2200 | 1200 |
| Δ (year 9) | 2200 | 1200 |
| Δ (year 10) | 2200 | 1200 |
| Δ (year 11) | 2200 | 1200 |
| Δ (year 12) | 2200 | 1200 |
| Δ (year 13) | 2200 | 1200 |
| Δ (year 14) | 2200 | 1200 |
| Δ (year 15) | 8200 | 9200 |
| Δ (IRR) | 23% | 8% |
| Justified? | Yes | No |

Recommend Alt. A.

(d) Simple
Payback

|         | A      | B       | C      |
|---------|--------|---------|--------|
| Year 0  | -9500  | -18500  | 22000  |
| Year 1  | -7300  | -16250  | -18600 |
| Year 2  | -5100  | -14000  | -15200 |
| Year 3  | -2900  | -11750  | -11800 |
| Year 4  | -700   | -9500   | -8400  |
| Year 5  | 1500   | -7250   | -5000  |
| Year 6  | 3700   | -5000   | -1600  |
| Year 7  | 5900   | -2750   | 1800   |
| Year 8  | 8100   | -500    | 5200   |
| Year 9  | 10300  | 1750    | 8600   |
| Year 10 | 12500  | 4000    | 12000  |
| Year 11 | 14700  | 6250    | 15400  |
| Year 12 | 16900  | 8500    | 18800  |
| Year 13 | 19100  | 10750   | 22200  |
| Year 14 | 21300  | 13000   | 25600  |
| Year 15 | 29500  | 19450   | 43000  |

Alt A (SPB) = 4+[700/(700+2200)] = 4.32 years
Alt B (SPB) = 8+[500/(500+1750)] = 8.22 years
Alt C (SPB) = 6+[1600/(1600+1800)] = 6.47 years

(a)

With no budget constraint do all projects except project no. 4.
   Cost = $115,000

(b)

Ranking the 9 projects by NPW/cost

| Project | Cost | Uniform Benefit | NPW at 12% | NPW/cost |
|---|---|---|---|---|
| 1 | 5 | 1.03 | 0.82 | 0.16 |
| 2 | 15 | 3.22 | 3.19 | 0.21 |
| 3 | 10 | 1.77 | 0 | 0 |
| 5 | 5 | 1.19 | 1.72 | 0.34 |
| 6 | 20 | 3.83 | 1.64 | 0.08 |
| 7 | 5 | 1.00 | 0.65 | 0.13 |
| 8 | 20 | 3.69 | 0.85 | 0.04 |
| 9 | 5 | 1.15 | 1.50 | 0.30 |
| 10 | 10 | 2.23 | 2.60 | 0.26 |

Projects ranked in order of desirability

| Project | Cost | NPW at 12% | NPW/cost | Cumulative Cost |
|---|---|---|---|---|
| 5 | 5 | 1.72 | 0.34 | 5 |
| 9 | 5 | 1.50 | 0.30 | 10 |
| 10 | 10 | 2.60 | 0.26 | 20 |
| 2 | 15 | 3.19 | 0.21 | 35 |
| 1 | 5 | 0.82 | 0.16 | 40 |
| 7 | 5 | 0.65 | 0.13 | 45 |
| 6 | 20 | 1.64 | 0.08 | 65 |
| 8 | 20 | 0.85 | 0.04 | 85 |
| 3 | 10 | 0 | 0 | 95 |

(c)

At $55,000 we have more money than needed for the first six projects
($45,000), but not enough for the first seven projects ($65,000).
This is the "lumpiness" problem.

There may be a better solution than simply taking the first
six projects, with total NPW equal to 10.48.   There is in

**371**

this problem.  By trial and error we see that if we forego
Projects 1 and 7, we have ample money to fund Project 6.
For this set of projects $\Sigma$ NPW = 10.65.

To maximize NPW the proper set of projects for a $55,000 capital
budget is
        Projects 5, 9, 10, 2, and 6.

# 17-2

(a)

Select projects, given MARR = 10%
Incremental analysis is required.

| Project | | $\Delta$ Cost | $\Delta$ Uniform Annual Benefit | $\Delta$ Rate of Return | |
|---|---|---|---|---|---|
| 1 | Alt 1A – Alt 1C | 15 | 2.22 | 7.8% | Reject 1A |
| | Alt 1B – Alt 1C | 40 | 7.59 | 13.7% | Reject 1C |
| | | | | | Select Project 1B |
| 2 | Alt. 2B – Alt 2A | 15 | 2.57 | 11.2% | Reject 2A |
| | | | | | Select Project 2B |
| 3 | Alt. 3A – Alt 3B | 15 | 3.41 | 18.6% | Reject 3B |
| | | | | | Select Project 3A |
| 4 | | 10 | 1.70 | 11% | Select Project 4 |

Conclusion: Select Projects 1B, 2B, 3A, and 4

(b)

Rank Separable increments of investment by rate of return

| Alternative | COST OR $\Delta$ COST | $\Delta$ Rate of Return | For Budget of $100,000 | |
|---|---|---|---|---|
| 1C | 10 | 20% | ~~1C~~ | ~~10~~ |
| 3A | 25 | 18 | 3A | 25 |
| 2A | 20 | 16 | 2A | 20 |
| 1B – 1C | 40 | 13.7 | →1B | 50 |
| 2B – 2A | 15 | 11.2 | $\Sigma$ = 95 | |
| 4 | 10 | 11 | | |

Conclusion: Select Projects 3A, 2A, and 1B

(c)

The cutoff rate of return equals the cost of the best project
foregone.  Project 1B, with a  Rate of Return of 13.7% is accepted
and Project 2B with a  Rate of Return of 11.2% is rejected.
Therefore the cutoff rate of return is actually 11.2%, but could
be considered as midway between 11.2% and 13.7%.

                    Interest rate = 12%

(d) Compute NPW/cost at $i=12\%$ for the various alternatives

| Project | Cost | Uniform Benefit | NPW | NPW/Cost |
|---|---|---|---|---|
| 1A | 25 | 4.61 | 1.05 | 0.04 |
| 1B | 50 | 9.96 | 6.28 | 0.13 |
| 1C | 10 | 2.39 | 3.50 | 0.35 |
| 2A | 20 | 4.14 | 3.39 | 0.17 |
| 2B | 35 | 6.71 | 2.91 | 0.08 |
| 3A | 25 | 5.56 | 6.42 | 0.26 |
| 3B | 10 | 2.15 | 2.15 | 0.21 |
| 4 | 10 | 1.70 | -0.39 | -0.03 |

Project Ranking

| Project | Cost | NPW/COST |
|---|---|---|
| 1C | 10 | 0.35 |
| 3A | 25 | 0.26 |
| 3B | 10 | 0.21 |
| 2A | 20 | 0.17 |
| 1B | 50 | 0.13 |
| 2B | 35 | 0.08 |
| 1A | 25 | 0.04 |
| 4 | 10 | -0.03 |

(e) For Budget of 100 $(\times 10^3)$:

Select:  3A   25
         2A   20
         1B   $\underline{50}$
              95

# 17-3

(a) Cost to maximize total ohs. – no budget limitation
    Select the most appropriate gift for each of the seven people.

| Recipient | Gift | oh rating | Cost |
|---|---|---|---|
| Father | Shirt | 5 | $20 |
| Mother | Camera | 5 | 30 |
| Sister | Sweater | 5 | 24 |
| Brother | Camera | 5 | 30 |
| Aunt | Candy | 5 | 20 |
| Uncle | Sweater | 4 | 24 |
| Cousin | Shirt | 4 | $\underline{20}$ |

$168   Cost of best gifts

## (b)

This problem differs from those described in the book where a project may be rejected by selecting the do-nothing alternative. Here, each person <u>must</u> be provided a gift. Thus while we can move the gift money around to maximize ohs, we cannot eliminate a gift. This constraint destroys the validity of the NPW - p(PW of Cost) or Ohs - p(Cost) technique.

The best solution is to simplify the problem as much as possible and then to proceed with incremental analysis. The number of alternatives may be reduced by observing that since the goal is to maximize ohs, for any recipient one should not pay more than necessary for a given number of ohs, or more dollars for less ohs.

For example, for Mother the seven feasible alternatives (the three 0-oh alternatives are not feasible) are:

| Alternative | Cost | Ohs |
|---|---|---|
| No. 1 | $20 | 4 |
| 4 | 20 | 3 |
| 5 | 24 | 4 |
| 6 | 30 | 5 |
| 8 | 16 | 3 |
| 9 | 18 | 4 |
| 10 | 16 | 2 |

Careful examination shows that for five ohs one must pay $30, for four ohs, $18, and $16 for three ohs. The other three and four oh alternatives cost more, and the two oh alternative costs the same as the three oh alternative.

Thus for Mother the three dominate alternatives are:

| Alternative | Cost | Ohs |
|---|---|---|
| No. 6 | $30 | 5 |
| 9 | 18 | 4 |
| 8 | 16 | 3 |

All other alternatives are either infeasible or inferior.

If the situation is examined for each of the gift recipients we obtain:

| ohs | Father | | Mother | | Sister | | Brother | | Aunt | | Uncle | | Cousin | |
|---|---|---|---|---|---|---|---|---|---|---|---|---|---|---|
| | Cost | Cost per oh | Cost | Cost per oh | Cost | Cost per oh | Cost | Cost per oh | Cost | Cost per oh | Cost | Cost per oh | Cost | Cost per oh |
| 5 | $20 | >$4 | $30 | >$12 | $24 | >$8 | $30 | >$14 | $20 | >$2 | | | | |
| 4 | 16 | >4 | 18 | >2 | 16 | | 16 | | 18 | >2 | $24 | >$8 | $20 | >$4 |
| 3 | 12 | | 16 | | | >3.3 | | >1.3 | 16 | | 16 | | 16 | >4 |
| 2 | | | | | | | | | | >5 | | >2 | 12 | >6 |
| 1 | | | | | 6 | | 12 | | 6 | >3.5 | 12 | | 6 | >4.6 |

In Part (a) we found that the most appropriate gifts cost $ *168*. This
table confirms that the gifts with the largest oh for each person
costs $ *20+30+24+30+20+24+20 = 168*        (This can be found
be reading across the top of the table on the previous page.)

For a budget limited to $*112* we must forego increments of Cost/Oh
that consume excessive dollars.  The best saving available is to go
from a five-oh to a four-oh gift for Brother thereby saving $ *14.*
This makes the cost of the seven gifts = $ *168-14= 154.*  Further
adjustments are required, first on Mother, then Sister, then Father
and finally a further adjustment of Sister.  The selected gifts are:

|        | Gift     | Ohs | Cost |
|--------|----------|-----|------|
| Father | Shirt    | 5   | $*20* |
| Mother | Book     | 4   | *18* |
| Sister | Magazine | 4   | *16* |
| Brother | Magazine | 4  | *16* |
| Aunt   | Candy    | 5   | *20* |
| Uncle  | Necktie  | 3   | *16* |
| Cousin | Calendar | 1   | *6* |
|        |          | 26  | $*112* |

**(c)**
For a budget of $*90* the process described above must be continued.
The selected gifts are:

|        | Gift     | Ohs | Cost |
|--------|----------|-----|------|
| Father | Cigars   | 3   | $*12* |
| Mother | Book     | 4   | *18* |
| Sister | Magazine | 4   | *16* |
| Brother | Magazine | 4  | *16* |
| Aunt   | Calendar | 1   | *6* |
| Uncle  | Necktie  | 3   | *16* |
| Cousin | Calendar | 1   | *6* |
|        |          | 20  | $*90* |

# 17-4

This problem is based on unlimited capital and a 12% MARR.
Replacements (if needed) in the 16-year analysis period will produce
a 12% rate of return.

In the Present Worth computations at 12% the NPW of the replacements
will be zero.  In this situation the replacements do not enter into
the computation of NPW.

See the data and computations
of NPW on the next page for
this problem.  For each project
select the alternative which
maximizes NPW

| For Project | Select Alternative |
|-------------|--------------------|
| 1           | B                  |
| 2           | A                  |
| 3           | F                  |
| 4           | A                  |
| 5           | A                  |

DATA FOR PROBLEMS 17-4, 17-5 and 17-7.

| Project | Cost | Useful Life | Problem 17-4 Alternative at useful life NPW | Problem 17-5 Alternative & identical replacements for 16 years NPW | Problem 17-7 NPW (computed for Prob. 17-5) and p = 0.20 NPW - p(Cost) |
|---|---|---|---|---|---|
| 1A | 40 | 2 | Negative | Negative | Negative |
| 1B | 10 | 16 | +3.86 | +3.86 | +1.86 |
| 1C | 55 | 4 | 0 | 0 | Negative |
| 1D | 30 | 8 | +3.23 | +4.53 | Negative |
| 1E | 15 | 2 | +3.30 | +13.60 | +10.60 |
| 2A | 10 | 16 | +3.65 | +3.65 | +1.65 |
| 2B | 5 | 8 | +1.46 | +2.05 | +1.05 |
| 2C | 5 | 8 | +0.63 | +0.88 | Negative |
| 2D | 15 | 4 | +1.95 | +4.46 | +1.46 |
| 3A | 20 | 16 | 0 | 0 | Negative |
| 3B | 5 | 16 | +0.86 | +0.86 | Negative |
| 3C | 10 | 16 | Negative | Negative | Negative |
| 3D | 15 | 16 | +2.57 | +2.57 | Negative |
| 3E | 10 | 4 | +0.63 | +1.45 | Negative |
| 3F | 15 | 16 | +3.14 | +3.14 | +0.14 |
| 4A | 10 | 8 | +2.97 | +4.17 | +2.17 |
| 4B | 5 | 16 | +1.76 | +1.76 | +0.76 |
| 4C | 5 | 16 | +2.10 | +2.10 | +1.10 |
| 4D | 15 | 8 | +1.59 | +2.23 | Negative |
| 5A | 5 | 8 | +0.75 | +1.05 | +0.05 |
| 5B* | 10 | 4 | +0.63 | +1.45 | Negative |
| 5C | 15 | 8 | 0 | 0 | Negative |

*5B and 3E have the same parameters

# 17-5

This problem is based on unlimited capital, a 12% MARR, and identical replacement throughout the 16-year analysis period. The NPW is computed for each alternative together with any identical replacements. From the table above the alternatives that maximize NPW will be selected.

| For Project | Select Alternative |
|---|---|
| 1 | E |
| 2 | D |
| 3 | F |
| 4 | A |
| 5 | B |

# 17-6

To solve this problem with neither input nor output fixed,
incremental analysis is required with rate of return methods.
With 22 different alternatives, the problem could be lengthly.
By careful examination, most of the alternatives may be eliminated
by inspection.

Project 1    Reject 1A.   Rate of return (ROR) $<$ MARR.
             Reject 1B.   Alt. 1E has a greater investment and a
                          greater ROR.

| Increment 1D - 1E | Yr | Cash Flow 1D | Cash Flow 1E | Cash Flow 1D - 1E |
|---|---|---|---|---|
| | 0 | -30 | -15 | -15 |
| | 1-8 | +6.69 | +3.75 | +2.94 |
| | 8 | -30 | 0 | -30 |
| | 9-16 | +6.69 | +3.75 | +2.94 |

$i*$ very close to 1-1/2%. By inspection we can see there must
be an external investment prior to year 8 (actually in years
6 and 7). Assuming $e* = 6\%$, $i*$ will still be less than 12%.
             Reject 1D.

             Reject 1C.   Higher cost alternative has ROR = MARR,
                          and lower cost alternative has ROR $>$ MARR.
                          The increment between them must have a
                          $\Delta$ROR $<$ MARR.
                                    Select Alternative 1E

Project 2    Reject 2A.   The increment between 2D and 2A has a
                          desirable $\Delta$ROR = 18%.
             Reject 2C.   Higher cost Alternative 2D has a higher ROR.

| Increment 2D - 2B | Yr | Cash Flow 2D | Cash Flow 2B | Cash Flow 2D - 2B |
|---|---|---|---|---|
| | 0 | -15 | -5 | -10 |
| | 1-4 | +5.58 | +1.30 | +4.28 |
| | 4 | -15 | 0 | -15 |
| | 5-8 | +5.58 | +1.30 | +4.28 |

(The next 8 years duplicates the first 8.)

15% $<$ $i*$ $<$ 18%.  There is not net investment throughout the
             8 years, but at $e* = 6\%$, $i*$ still appears to
             be $>$ 12%.
                                    Select Alternative 2D

Project 3    Reject 3C.   ROR $<$ MARR.
             Reject 3B, 3D, and 3E.  Alt. 3F with the same ROR
                          has higher cost.  Therefore,
                          $\Delta$ROR = 15%.
             Reject 3A.   The increment 3A - 3F must have a
                          $\Delta$ROR $<$ 12%.
                                    Select Alternative 3F

Project 4    Reject 4B and 4C.  These alternatives are dominated by
                          Alt. 4A with its higher cost and
                          greater ROR.

```
Increment 4D - 4A           Cash Flow
                    Year     4D - 4A
                     0         -5
                    1-8       +0.73
```

Computed i* = 3.6%.  Reject 4D

Select Alternative 4A

Project 5    Reject 5A.   Alt. 5B with the same ROR has a higher
                          cost.  Therefore, **Δ**ROR = 15%.
             Reject 5C.   The increment 5C - 5B must have an
                          **Δ**ROR <12%.

Select Alternative 5B

Answer: Select 1E, 2D, 3F, 4A, and 5B
                (Note that this is also the answer to
                Problem 17-5.)

# 17-7

This problem may be solved by the method outlined in Figure 17-3.

With no budget constraint the best alternatives were identified in
Problem 17-5 with a total cost of $65,000.  Here we are limited to
$55,000.

Using  NPW - p(Cost), the problem must be solved by trial and error
until a suitable value of p is determined.  A value of p = 0.20
proves satisfactory.  The computation for NPW - 0.20(Cost) is
given in the table between Solutions 17-4 and 17-5.

Selecting the alternative from each project with the largest
positive NPW - 0.2(Cost) gives:

| For Project | Select Alternative | Cost |
|---|---|---|
| 1 | E | $15,000 |
| 2 | A | 10,000 |
| 3 | F | 15,000 |
| 4 | A | 10,000 |
| 5 | A | 5,000 |
| | | $55,000 |

# 17-8

The solution will follow the approach of Example 17-5.
The first step is to compute the rate of return for each increment
of investment.

**Project A1 — no investment**

**Project A2**
**(A2-A1)**

| YEAR | Cash Flow | PW at 20% |
|------|-----------|-----------|
| 0 | -500,000 (keep land) | -500,000 |
| 1-20 | +98,700 | +480,669 |
| 20 | +750,000 | + 19,575 |
| | | +244 |

∴ Rate of Return ≈ 20%

**Project A3 (A3-A1)**

Expected Annual Rental Income
$$= 0.1(1,000,000) + 0.3(1,100,000) + 0.4(1,200,000) + 0.2(1,900,000)$$
$$= 1,290,000$$

| YEAR | Cash Flow | PW at 18% |
|------|-----------|-----------|
| 0 | -5,000,000 | -5,000,000 |
| 1-2 | 0 | 0 |
| 3-20 | +1,290,000 | +4,885,200 |
| 20 | +3,000,000 | + 109,500 |
| | | -5,300 |

∴ Rate of Return ≈ 18%

Incremental Rate of Return : Project A3 - Project A2

| YEAR | Project A3 | Project A2 | A3-A2 |
|------|-----------|-----------|--------|
| 0 | -5,000,000 | - 500,000 | -4,500,000 |
| 1 | 0 | + 98,700 | - 98,700 |
| 2 | 0 | + 98,700 | - 98,700 |
| 3-20 | +1,290,000 | + 98,700 | + 1,191,300 |
| 20 | +3,000,000 | +750,000 | + 2,250,000 |

| YEAR | A3-A2 | PW at 15% | PW at 18% |
|------|-------|-----------|-----------|
| 0 | -4,500,000 | -4,500,000 | -4,500,000 |
| 1 | -98,700 | -85,830 | -83,650 |
| 2 | -98,700 | -74,630 | -70,890 |
| 3-20 | +1,191,300 | +5,519,290 | +4,511,450 |
| 20 | +2,250,000 | +137,480 | +82,120 |
| | | +996,310 | -60,970 |

$$\Delta \text{Rate of Return} \approx 17.7\%$$
$$(\text{HP-12C answer} = 17.8\%)$$

Project B

$$\text{Rate of return} = i_{eff} = e^r - 1 = e^{0.1375} - 1 = 0.1474 = 14.74\%$$

Project C

| YEAR | CASH FLOW | PW at 25% |
|------|-----------|-----------|
| 0 | -2,000,000 | -2,000,000 |
| 1-10 | +500,000 | +1,785,500 |
| 10 | +2,000,000 | +214,800 |
| | | +300 |

$$\text{actually the rate of return is exactly } \frac{500,000}{2,000,000} = 25\%$$

Project D

$$\text{Rate of return} = 16\%$$

Project E

$$i_{eff} = \left(1 + \frac{0.1406}{12}\right)^{12} - 1 = 15.00\%$$

Project F

| YEAR | Cash Flow | PW at 18% |
|------|-----------|-----------|
| 0 | -2,000,000 | -2,000,000 |
| 1 | +1,000,000 | +847,500 |
| 2 | +1,604,800 | +1,152,600 |
| | | +100 |

$$\text{Rate of return} = 18\%$$

Rank Order the increments of investment by rate of return

| Project | Increment | Rate of Return |
|---------|-----------|----------------|
| C | $2,000,000 | 25% |
| A2 | 500,000 | 20 |
| F | 2,000,000 | 18 |
| A3- A2 | 4,500,000 | 17.7 |
| D | 500,000 | 16 |
| E | any amount > 100,000 | 15 |
| B | amt not stated | 14.7 |

Note that $500,000 value of Project A land is included

Part (a) Budget = $4 million (or 4.5 million including Project A land)

Go down the project list until the budget is exhausted.

Choose Project C, A2, and F.

MARR = Cutoff Rate of Return = Opportunity Cost

≈ 17.7 - 18%

Part (b) Budget = $9 million (or 9.5 million including Project A land)

Again, go down the project list until the budget is exhausted

Choose Projects C, F, A3, D

Note that this would become a <u>lumpiness problem</u> at a capital budget of $5 million (or many other amounts).

# 17-9

*Project 1.   Liquid storage tank.*
   *Saving at 0.1 cent per kg of soap:*
   *First five years = $0.001 x 22,000 x 1000 = $22,000*
   *Subsequent years = $0.001 x 12,000 x 1000 =   12,000*

   *How long must the tank remain in service to produce a*
   *15% rate of return?*

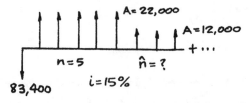

$$83,400 = 22,000 \, (P/A, 15\%, 5) + 12000 (P/A, 15\%, \hat{n})(P/F, 15\%, 5)$$
$$= 22,000 \, (3.352) + 12000 (P/A, 15\%, \hat{n})(0.4972)$$
$$(P/A, 15\%, \hat{n}) = 1.619$$

   $\hat{n} \sim 2$ years (beyond the 5 yr Taker contract)

   *Thus the storage tank will have a 15% rate of return for a*
   *useful life of 7 years.   This appears to be far less than*
   *the actual useful life of the tank to Raleigh.*
                    *Install the Liquid Storage Tank.*


*Project 2.   Another sulfonation unit.*
   *There is no alternative available, so the project must be*
   *undertaken to provide the necessary plant capacity.*
                    *Install Sulfonation Unit.*

*Project 3.   Packaging department expansion.*

Cost $150,000
Salvage value at end of 5 yrs $42,000
Annual saving in wage premium  $35,000

Rate of Return:
$$150,000 - 42,000(P/F, i\%, 5) = 35,000(P/A, i\%, 5)$$

Try $i = 12\%$
$$150,000 - 42,000(0.5674) = 35,000(3.605)$$
$$126,169 = 126,175$$

The rate of return is 12%.

Reject the packaging department expansion and plan on two shift operation.

*Projects 4 & 5.   New warehouse or leased warehouse.*

Cash Flow

| YEAR | Leased Warehouse | New Warehouse | New rather than Leased |
|------|------------------|---------------|------------------------|
| 0 | 0 | -225,000 | -225,000 |
| 1-4 | -49,000 | -5,000 | +44,000 |
| 5 | -49,000 | $\left\{ \begin{array}{c} -5,000 \\ +200,000 \end{array} \right\}$ | +244,000 |

Compute the rate of return on the difference between the alternatives.
$$225,000 = 44,000(P/A, i\%, 5) + 200,000(P/F, i\%, 5)$$

Try $i = 18\%$
$$225,000 = 44,000(3.127) + 200,000(0.4371)$$
$$= 225,008$$

The incremental rate of return is 18%.

*Build the new warehouse.*

# 17-10

This is a variation of Problem 17-1.

(a)  Approve all projects except D.

(b)  Ranking Computations for NPW/Cost

| Project | Cost | Uniform Benefit | NPW at 14% | NPW/Cost |
|---------|------|-----------------|------------|----------|
| A | 10 | 2.98 | 0.23 | 0.023 |
| B | 15 | 5.58 | 4.16 | 0.277 |
| C | 5 | 1.53 | 0.25 | 0.050 |
| D | 20 | 5.55 | -0.95 | -0.048 |
| E | 15 | 4.37 | 0 | 0 |
| F | 30 | 9.81 | 3.68 | 0.123 |
| G | 25 | 7.81 | 1.81 | 0.072 |
| H | 10 | 3.49 | 1.98 | 0.198 |
| I | 5 | 1.67 | 0.73 | 0.146 |
| J | 10 | 3.20 | 0.99 | 0.099 |

Ranking:

| Project | Cost | NPW/Cost | Cumulative Cost |
|---------|------|----------|-----------------|
| B | 15 | 0.277 | 15 |
| H | 10 | 0.198 | 25 |
| I | 5 | 0.146 | 30 |
| F | 30 | 0.123 | 60 |
| J | 10 | 0.099 | 70 |
| G | 25 | 0.072 | 95 |
| C | 5 | 0.050 | 100 |
| A | 10 | 0.023 | 110 |
| E | 15 | 0 | 125 |
| D | 20 | -0.048 | 145 |

(c)  Budget = $85,000.
The first five projects (B, H, I, F, and J) equal $70,000.
There is not enough money to add G, but there is enough to add
C and A.  Alternately, one could delete J and add G.  So two
possible selections are:  B H I F G  $NPW_{14\%}$ = 28.36

B H I F J C A  $NPW_{14\%}$ = 28.26

For $85,000. maximize NPW

Select: B, H, I, F, and G.

# 17-11

| Proj/Alt | Cost (P) | Annual benefit (A) | (A/P, i, 10) | ROR |
|---|---|---|---|---|
| 1A | $5000 | $1192.50 | 0.2385 | 20% |
| 1B-1A | 5000 | 800.50 | 0.1601 | 9.6% |
| 2A | 15,000 | 3337.50 | 0.2225 | 18% |
| 2B-2A | 10,000 | 1087.50 | 0.1088 | 1.6% |

*a.* 1A
*b.* 18%
*c.* 1B and 2A

# A Further Look At Rate Of Return

| Year | Cash Flow | Accumulated Cash Flow | Net Investment at i = 0% |
|------|-----------|-----------------------|--------------------------|
| 0 | -500 | -500 | -500 |
| 1 | +2000 | +1500 | +1500 |
| 2 | -1200 | +300 | +300 |
| 3 | -300 | 0 | 0 |
|   | 0 |   |   |

Sign changes in the cash flow = 2
Sign changes in accumulated cash flow = 1

(a) <u>Cash Flow Rule of Signs</u>: There may be as many as two positive rates of return.

<u>Accumulated Cash Flow Sign Test</u>: Conditions insuring a single rate of return not met.

<u>Algebraic Sum of the Cash Flow</u>: Zero percent is a rate of return.

<u>Net Investment Conditions</u>: Conditions insuring a single rate of return not met.

(b) $i^* = 0\%$

(c) Given $e^* = 6\%$, compute $i^*$. There is external investment.

At $e^* = 6\%$ and $i = 20.2\%$:

| Year | Cash Flow | | Net Investment |
|------|-----------|--|----------------|
| 0 | -500 | | = -500 |
| 1 | +2000 | -500(1.202) + 2000 = | +1399 |
| 2 | -1200 | +1399(1.06) - 1200 = | +282.94 |
| 3 | -300 | +282.94(1.06) - 300 = | -0.08 |

For $e^* = 6\%$, $i^*$ very close to 20.2%

| Year | Cash Flow | Accumulated Cash Flow |
|------|-----------|-----------------------|
| 0 | -500 | -500 |
| 1 | +200 | -300 |
| 2 | -500 | -800 |
| 3 | +1200 | +400 |
|   | +400 |   |

Sign changes in the cash flow = 3
Sign changes in the accumulated cash flow = 1

(a) <u>Cash Flow Rule of Signs</u>: There may be as many as three positive rates of return.

<u>Accumulated Cash Flow Sign Test</u>: There is a single positive rate of return.

**387**

Algebraic Sum of the Cash Flow:   A positive rate of return is
                                  indicated.

Net Investment Conditions:   By inspection we can see that for
                             a positive rate of return there
                             will be net investment throughout
                             the life of the project.

(b)   Solve for i*

500 + 500(P/F,i%,2) - 200(P/F,i%,1) - 1200(P/F,i%,3) = 0

At i = 21.1%
          840.94 - 840.84 = 0.10

                           i* is close to 21.1%

(c)   With no external investment i* remains at about 21.1%

# 18-3

| Year | Cash Flow | Accumulated Cash Flow |
|------|-----------|------------------------|
| 0 | -500 | -500 |
| 1 | +200 | -300 |
| 2 | -500 | -800 |
| 3 | +200 | -600 |
|   | -600 |   |

Sign changes in the cash flow = 3
Sign changes in accumulated cash flow = 0

(a)   Cash Flow Rule of Signs:   There may be as many as three
                                positive rates of return.

      Accumulated Cash Flow Sign Test:   Conditions insuring a single
                                         positive rate of return not met.

      Algebraic Sum of the Cash Flow:   The negative sum suggests
                                        there may not be a positive rate of
                                        return.

(b) & (c)

Search for a positive value of i*

500 + 500(P/F,i%,2) - 200(P/F,i%,1) - 200(P/F,i%,3) = 0

                           No positive value of i* located.

# 18-4

| Year | Cash Flow | Accumulated Cash Flow | PW of Cash Flow at 35% |
|------|-----------|-----------------------|------------------------|
| 0 | -100 | -100 | -100 |
| 1 | +360 | +260 | +267 |
| 2 | -570 | -310 | -313 |
| 3 | +360 | +50 | +146 |
|   | +50 |   | 0 |

Sign changes in the cash flow = 3
Sign changes in accumulated cash flow = 3

(a)   Cash Flow Rule of Signs: There may be as many as three positive rates of return.

Accumulated Cash Flow Sign Test: Conditions insuring a single positive rate of return were not met.

Algebraic Sum of the Cash Flow: A positive rate of return is indicated.

Net Investment Conditions: The large end-of-year 1 positive cash flow indicates there is not net investment at this point and hence the conditions insuring a single positive rate of return will not be met.

(b)   Solve for a i*

These computations were made in Problem 7A-6.  The Present Worth calculations at 35% shown above also prove that this is a rate of return.

Check net investment.

| Year | Cash Flow | Net Investment |
|------|-----------|----------------|
| 0 | -100 | -100 |
| 1 | +360 | -100(1.35) + 360 = +225 |
| 2 | -570 | +225(1.35) - 570 = -266 |
| 3 | +360 | -266(1.35) + 360 =   0 |

Thus the evaluation of Net Investment Conditions was correct.

(c)   Given e* = 6%, compute i*.  This value of e* will diminish the computed i*.

With e* = 6%, try i* = 15%

| Year | Cash Flow | Net Investment |
|------|-----------|----------------|
| 0 | -100 | -100 |
| 1 | +360 | -100(1.15) + 360 = +245 |
| 2 | -570 | +245(1.06) - 570 = -310 |
| 3 | +360 | -310(1.15) + 360 =   +3 |

With e* = 6%, i* is close to 15%

# 18-5

| Year | Cash Flow | Accumulated Cash Flow | PW at 20% | | | at i* = 20% Net Investment |
|------|-----------|----------------------|-----------|--------------------|------|-----------------|
| 0 | -200 | -200 | -200.00 | | | -200.0 |
| 1 | +100 | -100 | +83.33 | -200.0(1.20) + 100 | = | -140.0 |
| 2 | +100 | 0 | +69.44 | -140.0(1.20) + 100 | = | -68.0 |
| 3 | +100 | +100 | +57.87 | -68.0(1.20) + 100 | = | +18.4 |
| 4 | -300 | -200 | -144.68 | +18.4(1.20) - 300 | = | -277.9 |
| 5 | +100 | -100 | +40.19 | -277.9(1.20) + 100 | = | -233.5 |
| 6 | +200 | +100 | +66.98 | -233.5(1.20) + 200 | = | -80.2 |
| 7 | +200 | +300 | +55.82 | -80.2(1.20) + 200 | = | +103.8 |
| 8 | -124.5 | +124.5 | -28.95 | +103.8(1.20) - 124.5 | = | 0 |
| | +175.5 | | 0 | | | |

The sign changes in the cash flow and accumulated cash flow suggest the possibility of multiple positive rates of return. The present worth of the cash flow at 20% is zero, indicating that 20% is a positive rate of return.

Additional computations (not shown here) do not reveal additional positive rates of return. 20% may, therefore, be the single positive rate of return. The net investment computation at 20% (above) shows that there is <u>not</u> net investment throughout the 8-year life.

For Part (a):   <u>i* = e* = 20%</u>

(b)   For e* = 6%, compute i*.

For e* reduced from the 20% in Part (a), the benefits will decline somewhat. Thus i* will decline from 20%. Several trial computations (not shown here) reveal that i* is close to 18.9%. The computation at e* = 6% and i = 18.9% is as follows:

| Year | Cash Flow | | | Net Investment |
|------|-----------|--------------------|-----|-----------------|
| 0 | -200 | | | -200.0 |
| 1 | +100 | -200.0(1.189) + 100 | = | -137.8 |
| 2 | +100 | -137.8(1.189) + 100 | = | -63.8 |
| 3 | +100 | -63.8(1.189) + 100 | = | +24.1 |
| 4 | -300 | +24.1(1.060) - 300 | = | -274.5 |
| 5 | +100 | -274.5(1.189) + 100 | = | -226.4 |
| 6 | +200 | -226.4(1.189) + 200 | = | -69.2 |
| 7 | +200 | -69.2(1.189) + 200 | = | +117.7 |
| 8 | -124.5 | +117.7(1.060) - 124.5 | = | +0.2 |

For Part (b):   <u>With e* = 6%,   i* = 18.9%</u>

# 18-6

In either method any net external investment is at the external interest rate e*. Examination of this cash flow shows that there will be the same external investment using either method. Thus i* will be 8.4% for both methods. The calculations below confirm this.

| Year | Cash Flow | Net Investment |
|------|-----------|----------------|
| 0 | +19 | +19.0 |
| 1 | +10 | +19.0(1.060) + 10 = +30.1 |
| 2 | -50 | +30.1(1.060) - 50 = -18.1 |
| 3 | -50 | -18.1(1.084) - 50 = -69.6 |
| 4 | +20 | -69.6(1.084) + 20 = -55.4 |
| 5 | +60 | -55.4(1.084) + 60 = 0 |

For both methods with e* = 6%,  i* = 8.4%

# 18-7

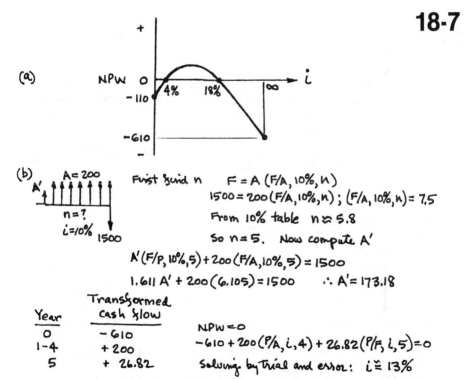

(a)

(b)

First find n

$F = A\ (F/A, 10\%, n)$

$1500 = 200\ (F/A, 10\%, n)$ ; $(F/A, 10\%, n) = 7.5$

From 10% table $n \approx 5.8$

So n = 5. Now compute A'

$A'(F/P, 10\%, 5) + 200\ (F/A, 10\%, 5) = 1500$

$1.611\ A' + 200\ (6.105) = 1500$   $\therefore A' = 173.18$

| Year | Transformed cash flow |
|------|------------------------|
| 0 | - 610 |
| 1-4 | + 200 |
| 5 | + 26.82 |

NPW = 0

$-610 + 200\ (P/A, i, 4) + 26.82\ (P/F, i, 5) = 0$

Solving by trial and error:  $i \cong 13\%$

(c) For this cash flow the Chapter 7A and Chapter 18 transformations are the same, hence both would produce the same 13% answer.

# 18-8

(a)  The Present Worth computation at 70.7% in the problem
     statement is based on the assumption that i* = e*.

$$\text{Thus } i^* = e^* = 70.7\%$$

(b)  Compute the transformed cash flow with e* = 0%, and then
     calculate i*.

| Year | Cash Flow | | | Transformed Cash Flow | PW at 50% |
|------|-----------|--|--|-----------------------|-----------|
| 0 | -$200 | | | -200 | -200 |
| 1 | +400 | -100(1 + 0) ↘ | | +300 | +200 |
| 2 | -100 | | +100 | 0 | 0 |
| | | | | | 0 |

$$i^* = 50\%$$

# 18-9

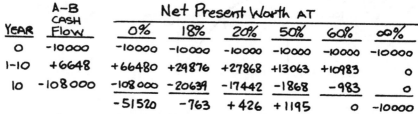

| YEAR | A-B CASH Flow | Net Present Worth AT | | | | | |
|------|---------------|------|-----|-----|-----|-----|-----|
| | | 0% | 18% | 20% | 50% | 60% | ∞% |
| 0 | -10000 | -10000 | -10000 | -10000 | -10000 | -10000 | -10000 |
| 1-10 | +6648 | +66480 | +29876 | +27868 | +13063 | +10983 | 0 |
| 10 | -108000 | -108000 | -20639 | -17442 | -1868 | -983 | 0 |
| | | -51520 | -763 | +426 | +1195 | 0 | -10000 |

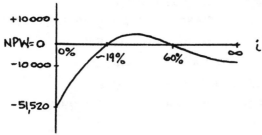

The A-B cash flow has two sign changes and two positive rates of
return.  (Note that the A-B cash flow is primarily a borrowing
situation.)  The problem asks for i*, given e* = 6%.  In this
situation there is no positive i*.

Computations, not shown here, indicate that i* will not be positive
for any value of e* less than 12.2%.

# 18-10

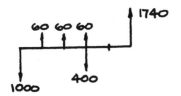

Note that there are three sign changes in the cash flow.  The cash flow rule of signs would warn that there may be as many as 3 rates of return.  Here

there always is net unrecovered investment.  This indicates there is one positive rate of return.

$NPW = 0$

$$-1000 + 60(P/A, i\%, 3) - 400(P/F, i\%, 3) + 1740(P/F, i\%, 5) = 0$$

Try $i = 9\%$

$$-1000 + 60(2.531) - 400(0.7722) + 1740(0.6499) = -26.19$$

Try $i = 8\%$

$$-1000 + 60(2.577) - 400(0.7938) + 1740(0.6806) = +21.34$$

Rate of Return  $i^* = 8\% + (1\%)\left(\dfrac{21.34}{21.34 - (-26.19)}\right) = 8.4\%$

# Microcomputer Programs

Problem 19-1: Solve Problem 6-12 using EA

THE DATA ARE:

Period  Cont.Value  Single Value
--------------------------------

| -5 | 0.00 | 600.00 |
| -4 | 0.00 | 700.00 |
| -3 | 0.00 | 800.00 |
| -2 | 0.00 | 900.00 |
| -1 | 0.00 | 1000.00 |
| 0 | 0.00 | 900.00 |
| 1 | 0.00 | 800.00 |
| 2 | 0.00 | 700.00 |
| 3 | 0.00 | 600.00 |
| 4 | 0.00 | 500.00 |

THE RESULTS ARE:
Present or future worth at NO =   0 and
Interest rate INT =    8.00%              PF =    8056.16

Equivalent uniform amount for the period
from NF =  -5 through NL =    4           A =    756.58

All cash flows are positive. Rate of return is undetermined.

## 19-2

Problem 19-2: Solve Problem 5-40 using EA

THE DATA ARE:

Period  Cont.Value  Single Value
--------------------------------

| 1 | 0.00 | 150.00 |
| 2 | 0.00 | 300.00 |
| 3 | 0.00 | 450.00 |
| 4 | 0.00 | 600.00 |
| 5 | 0.00 | 750.00 |

THE RESULTS ARE:
Present or future worth at NO =   0 and
Interest rate INT =    3.00%              PF =    2020.27

Equivalent uniform amount for the period
from NF =   0 through NL =   0            A =    2020.27

All cash flows are positive. Rate of return is undetermined.

**395**

# 19-3

MORTG     file display

DATA ARE:

| | | |
|---|---|---|
| Present or Future worth | (PF) = | 100000.00 |
| Time Period of PF | (NO) = | 0 |
| Interest Rate    Type = N | (INT) = | 10.00 |
| (Type: Nominal=N, Effective=E) | | |
| Number of Repayment Periods | (N) = | 240 |
| Time Period of First Repayment | (NF) = | 1 |
| Uniform Repayment Amount | (A) | = Not given |

Monthly Compounding System

RESULTS:

Capital recovery factor is:        0.009650
Uniform repayment amount is:     965.02 ◄—(a)

TABLE OF PRINCIPAL AND INTEREST PAYMENTS

| | | | CUMULATIVE | |
|---|---|---|---|---|
| PERIOD | PRINCIPAL | INTEREST | PRINCIPAL | INTEREST |
| 1 | 131.69 | 833.33 | 131.69 | 833.33 |
| 2 | 132.79 | 832.24 | 264.47 | 1665.57 |
| 3 | 133.89 | 831.13 | 398.37 | 2496.70 |
| 4 | 135.01 | 830.01 | 533.38 | 3326.71 |
| 5 | 136.13 | 828.89 | 669.51 | 4155.60 |
| 6 | 137.27 | 827.75 | 806.78 | 4983.36 |
| 7 | 138.41 | 826.61 | 945.19 | 5809.97 |
| 8 | 139.57 | 825.46 | 1084.75 | 6635.42 |
| 9 | 140.73 | 824.29 | 1225.48 | 7459.72 |
| 10 | 141.90 | 823.12 | 1367.38 | 8282.84 |
| 11 | 143.08 | 821.94 | 1510.47 | 9104.78 |
| 12 | 144.28 | 820.75 | 1654.74 | 9925.52 |
| YEAR  1 | 1654.74 | 9925.52 | 1654.74 | 9925.52 |

| | | | CUMULATIVE | |
|---|---|---|---|---|
| PERIOD | PRINCIPAL | INTEREST | PRINCIPAL | INTEREST |
| 157 | 480.61 | 484.41 | 42350.94 | 109157.52 |
| (c)—►158 | 484.61 | 480.41 | 42835.55 | 109637.92 |
| 159 | 488.65 | 476.37 | 43324.21 | 110114.29 |
| 160 | 492.72 | 472.30 | 43816.93 | 110586.59 |
| 170 | 535.36 | 429.66 | 48975.74 | 115078.00 |
| 171 | 539.82 | 425.20 | 49515.56 | 115503.20 |
| (b)—►172 | 544.32 | 420.70 | 50059.88 | 115923.91 |
| 173 | 548.85 | 416.17 | 50608.73 | 116340.08 |
| 174 | 553.43 | 411.59 | 51162.16 | 116751.67 |

Part (a)                    EA.OUT file display              **19-4**

Problem 19-4: van Gogh's "Irises"


THE DATA ARE:
Period   Cont.Value   Single Value
-------------------------------

 -40       0.00       -84.00    } Entries limited to < 1,000,000.
   0       0.00      49000.00   } Problem scaled by dividing by 1000.

ROR Calculation, convergence control:
      INT              PF
      0.00        48916.00000
      3.04        14703.86328
      4.70         7732.95703
      6.53         3815.23169
      8.32         1919.48376
     10.13          948.28033
     11.90          461.93088
     13.58          216.87445
     15.06           94.88084
     16.22           35.93251
     16.92           10.17699
     17.20            1.63145
     17.26            0.09261


THE RESULTS ARE:
  Rate of return                      ROR =      17.26 %


Part (b)                  EA.OUT file display

THE DATA ARE:
Period   Cont.Value   Single Value
-------------------------------

   0       0.00      53900.00        Entry divided by 1000


THE RESULTS ARE:
  Present or future worth at NO =   40 and
  Interest rate INT =    17.26%              PF = 31447406.00 $\times 10^3$

19-4b Shortcut Solution              10% Commission: 3144740   $\times 10^3$

$\dfrac{(49\times10^6)(53.9\times10^6)}{84000}$ = \$31.4 Billion    Selling Price \$ 34,542,146,000

                        3.1  +10%
                      \$ 34.5 Billion

# 19-5

```
          CAPITAL EXPENDITURE ANALYSIS PROGRAM
     FROM NEWNAN - ENGINEERING ECONOMIC ANALYSIS

          EXAMPLE 14-12 Scales for Production Line

    INVESTMENT
          NORMAL DISTRIBUTION WITH MEAN =      1500  AND STD DEV =   150.

    INVESTMENT TIMING
          TOTAL INVESTMENT MADE AT BEGINNING OF  YEAR 1 (YEAR 0)

    ANALYSIS PERIOD
          MAX USEFUL LIFE =  16
          NORMAL DISTRIBUTION WITH MEAN = 15.00  AND STD DEV =  0.80

    DEPRECIATION METHOD
          DEPRECIABLE LIFE =   0 YEARS
          BEFORE TAX DEPRECIATION NOT COMPUTED

    END-OF-LIFE SALVAGE VALUE
          NO SALVAGE VALUE

    BORROWED MONEY
          NO BORROWED MONEY

    EXPENSED COSTS
          NO EXPENSED ANNUAL COST

    INCOME TAX
          INCOME TAXES IGNORED

    BENEFIT SCHEDULE
          UNIFORM BENEFIT =     250.

    BENEFIT TREND
          NO TREND

    EXTERNAL INVESTMENT
          INTEREST RATE EARNED ON ANY EXTERNAL INVESTMENT =  6.0 %


MODEL ITERATIONS =   200
```

```
    HISTOGRAM OF RATE OF RETURN VS. REL FREQUENCY

                        RELATIVE FREQUENCY, %
         MIDPOINT  0      10        20        30        40        50
         ROR, %    |---------+---------+---------+---------+---------+-
           9.5     |*
          10.5     |********
          11.5     |***************
          12.5     |*****************
          13.5     |********
          14.5     |********
          15.5     |********
          16.5     |********
          17.5     |**********
          18.5     |**********
          19.5     |*****
          20.5     |*

         MEAN     = 14.567 %          STD DEV    = 2.821 %
         VARIANCE =  7.955            ITERATIONS =   200

         END
```

EQAN.OUT file display
**********************************************************
EQUIPMENT ECONOMIC ANALYSIS        PROGRAM: EQAN3PC
INPUT FILE:              ;  OUTPUT FILE: EQAN.OUT
**********************************************************

GENERAL DATA OF THE PROJECT

| | | |
|---|---|---|
| PRESENT YEAR | : | 1990 |
| PROJECT STARTS IN YEAR | : | 1991 |
| PROJECT DURATION PERIOD, years | : | 5 |
| EQUIPMENT OPERATION PERIOD, years   ==> | : | 5 |
| LOAN REPAYMENT PERIOD, years | : | 5 |
| LOAN PAYMENT SCHEDULE | : | 2 |
| DEPRECIATION SYSTEM | : | 6 |
| EQUIPMENT OPERATION TIME, hours/year   ==> | : | 4000.0 |
| PRESENT EQUIPMENT COST, k$   ==> | : | 650.0 |
| PERCENT PAID CASH FOR EQUIPMENT, % | : | 50.0 |
| INTEREST ON LOAN, %/year | : | 12.0 |
| FEDERAL/STATE TAX RATE, %   > | : | 34.0 |
| INVESTMENT TAX CREDIT RATE, %   > | : | 0.0 |
| INSURANCE COST AS % OF EQUIPMENT PRICE, % | : | 2.0 |
| PROPERTY TAX AS % OF EQUIPMENT PRICE, % | : | 1.0 |
| EFFECTIVE BEFORE-TAX RETURN ON INVESTMENT,% | : | 0.0 |
| COST INFLATION RATE, % | : | 0.0 |

RESULTS:

| | | |
|---|---|---|
| COST PRESENT VALUE (YEAR 0)   (k$) | : | 1764.5 |
| | | |
| EQUIVALENT O & M COST PER HOUR ($/hour) | : | 50.0 |
| EQUIVALENT OWNERSHIP COST PER HOUR | : | 38.2 |
| EQUIVALENT TOTAL COST PER HOUR | : | 88.2 |

==========================================================

OUTPUT, EQUIPMENT COST ANALYSIS TABLE:
(All values in 1000 $ (k$) unless otherwise noted)

| OPERATING YEARS | : | 1991 | 1992 | 1993 | 1994 | 1995 | 1996 |
|---|---|---|---|---|---|---|---|
| | : | 0 | 1 | 2 | 3 | 4 | 5 |

==========================================================================
DATA, VARIABLE IN TIME, PRESENT COST VALUES:

| | | | | | | |
|---|---|---|---|---|---|---|
| SALVAGE VALUE | : | 300.0 | 200.0 | 150.0 | 120.0 | 100.0 |
| DEPRECIATION, % | : | 14.0 | 24.5 | 17.5 | 12.5 | 5.2 |
| OPER. COST, $/hour | : | 50.0 | 50.0 | 50.0 | 50.0 | 50.0 |
| MAINT. COST, $/hour | : | | | | | |

==========================================================================

```
COST POSITIONS NOT SUBJECT TO TAX:
EQUIPMENT COST, k$   :   650.0
           PAID CASH :   325.0
                LOAN :   325.0
LOAN PAYMENT,PRINC. :            65.0    65.0    65.0    65.0    65.0
INVESTM. TAX CREDIT :
ITC RECAPTURE       :
DEPRECIATION        :           -91.0  -159.2  -113.8   -81.2   -34.1
END BOOK VALUE      :                                          -170.6
------------------------------------------------------------------------
TOTAL PER YEAR      :   325.0   -26.0   -94.2   -48.8   -16.2  -139.8
        PER HOUR ($/h):  81.2    -6.5   -23.6   -12.2    -4.1   -34.9
========================================================================
COST POSITIONS SUBJECT TO TAX:

LOAN REPAYMENT,INT. :            39.0    31.2    23.4    15.6     7.8
DEPRECIATION        :            91.0   159.2   113.8    81.2    34.1
END BOOK VALUE      :                                           170.6
END SALVAGE VALUE   :                                          -100.0
OPERATING COST      :           200.0   200.0   200.0   200.0   200.0
MAINTENANCE COST    :
INS.COST + PROP.TAX :            19.5    19.5    19.5    19.5    19.5
------------------------------------------------------------------------
TOTAL PER YEAR      :     0.0   349.5   410.0   356.6   316.4   332.0
        PER HOUR ($/h):    0.0    87.4   102.5    89.2    79.1    83.0
========================================================================
TOTAL COST PER YEAR :   492.4   310.1   267.1   282.8   291.7   120.3
        PER HOUR ($/h) : 123.1    77.5    66.8    70.7    72.9    30.1

DISCOUNTED COST     :   492.4   310.1   267.1   282.8   291.7   120.3
========================================================================
```

# 19-7

```
        MORTG.OUT file display
        DATA ARE:

        Present or Future worth        (PF)  =      45.00
        Time Period of PF              (NO)  =       0
        Interest Rate     Type = N     (INT) =      12.00
        (Type: Nominal=N, Effective=E)
        Number of Repayment Periods    (N)   = Not given
        Time Period of First Repayment (NF)  =       1
        Uniform Repayment Amount       (A)   =       1.00
        Compounding System           1 compounding periods per year


        RESULTS:

        Repayment period N is: 59   last payment:      0.96

        Effective interest rate per month is     0.9489%
        Nominal interest rate per year is       12.0000%
        Effective interest rate per year is     12.0000%
```

ROR.OUT file display

# 19-8

Problem 19-8: Solve Example 5-9 with e* = 10%, if required.

| YEAR | CASH FLOW | ACCUMULATED CASH FLOW |
|---|---|---|
| 0 | -610.00 | -610.00 |
| 1 | 200.00 | -410.00 |
| 2 | 200.00 | -210.00 |
| 3 | 200.00 | -10.00 |
| 4 | 200.00 | 190.00 |
| 5 | 200.00 | 390.00 |
| 6 | 200.00 | 590.00 |
| 7 | 200.00 | 790.00 |
| 8 | 200.00 | 990.00 |
| 9 | 200.00 | 1190.00 |
| 10 | -1300.00 | -110.00 |

SUM = -110.00

NUMBER OF SIGN CHANGES IN CASH FLOW = 2
IN ACCUMULATED CASH FLOW = 2

FOR THIS CASH FLOW
ACCUMULATED CASH FLOW IN YEAR N = 10 is -110.00
AND NUMBER OF SIGN CHANGES = 2
NO CONCLUSIONS CAN BE REACHED FROM THIS CALCULATION.

TRIAL NUMBER 16 : INTERNAL RATE OF RETURN = 12.96 %
EXTERNAL INTEREST RATE = 10.00 %

| YEAR | CASH FLOW | COMPUTATION | | | INTERNAL INVESTM. | EXTERNAL INVESTM. |
|---|---|---|---|---|---|---|
| 0 | -610.00 | | | | -610.00 | 0.00 |
| 1 | 200.00 | -610.00*(1+0.130)+ | 200.00 = | -489.04 | 200.00 | 0.00 |
| 2 | 200.00 | -489.04*(1+0.130)+ | 200.00 = | -352.40 | 200.00 | 0.00 |
| 3 | 200.00 | -352.40*(1+0.130)+ | 200.00 = | -198.06 | 200.00 | 0.00 |
| 4 | 200.00 | -198.06*(1+0.130)+ | 200.00 = | -23.72 | 200.00 | 0.00 |
| 5 | 200.00 | -23.72*(1+0.130)+ | 200.00 = | 173.21 | 26.79 | 173.21 |
| 6 | 200.00 | 173.21*(1+0.100)+ | 200.00 = | 390.53 | 0.00 | 200.00 |
| 7 | 200.00 | 390.53*(1+0.100)+ | 200.00 = | 629.58 | 0.00 | 200.00 |
| 8 | 200.00 | 629.58*(1+0.100)+ | 200.00 = | 892.54 | 0.00 | 200.00 |
| 9 | 200.00 | 892.54*(1+0.100)+ | 200.00 = | 1181.79 | 0.00 | 200.00 |
| 10 | -1300.00 | 1181.79*(1+0.100)+ | -1300.00 = | -0.03 | -0.03 | -1299.97 |

AFTER 16 TRIALS, THE TRUE INTERNAL RATE OF RETURN WAS FOUND
TO BE VERY CLOSE TO 12.957 %. THIS VALUE IS CONSIDERED THE ANSWER.

RESULTS OF RATE OF RETURN COMPUTATION WITH EXTERNAL INTEREST
RATE = 10.00 % :
EXTERNAL INTEREST RATE NEEDED IN COMPUTATION.
COMPUTED INTERNAL RATE OF RETURN EQUALS 12.96 %

# 19-9

```
          ROR.OUT file display
        RATE OF RETURN COMPUTATION
   FROM NEWNAN - ENGINEERING ECONOMIC ANALYSIS
   ==============================================

    Problem 19-9: Compute Rate of Return in Example 7A-2.
                              ACCUMULATED
          YEAR     CASH FLOW    CASH FLOW
           0         19.00        19.00
           1         10.00        29.00
           2        -50.00       -21.00
           3        -50.00       -71.00
           4         20.00       -51.00
           5         60.00         9.00

          SUM =      9.00


   NUMBER OF SIGN CHANGES IN CASH FLOW =   2
              IN ACCUMULATED CASH FLOW =   2

   CASH FLOW RULE OF SIGNS:
        THERE MAY BE AS MANY POSITIVE RATES OF RETURN AS THERE
        ARE SIGN CHANGES IN THE CASH FLOW.  FOR THIS CASH FLOW
        POSSIBLE NUMBER OF POSITIVE RATES RETURN
        IS BETWEEN 0 AND   2


   TRIAL NUMBER 13 : INTERNAL RATE OF RETURN =   8.35 %
                     EXTERNAL INTEREST RATE =   6.00 %

          CASH                                   INTERNAL  EXTERNAL
   YEAR   FLOW          COMPUTATION               INVESTM.  INVESTM.
    0    19.00                                      0.00    19.00
    1    10.00   19.00*(1+0.060)+  10.00 =  30.14   0.00    10.00
    2   -50.00   30.14*(1+0.060)+ -50.00 = -18.05 -18.05   -31.95
    3   -50.00  -18.05*(1+0.084)+ -50.00 = -69.56 -50.00     0.00
    4    20.00  -69.56*(1+0.084)+  20.00 = -55.37  20.00     0.00
    5    60.00  -55.37*(1+0.084)+  60.00 =   0.00  60.00     0.00


   AFTER 13 TRIALS, THE TRUE INTERNAL RATE OF RETURN WAS FOUND
   TO BE VERY CLOSE TO   8.353 %. THIS VALUE IS CONSIDERED THE ANSWER.


   RESULTS OF RATE OF RETURN COMPUTATION WITH EXTERNAL INTEREST
        RATE =   6.00 % :
        EXTERNAL INTEREST RATE NEEDED IN COMPUTATION.
        COMPUTED INTERNAL RATE OF RETURN EQUALS   8.35 %
```

# 19-10

TITLE: Problem 19-10. Solve Problem 11-5a using CEAP..

| | | | | | | | |
|---|---|---|---|---|---|---|---|
| JOB = | 1912 | NMAX = | 20 | IL = | 1 | AVEN = | 0.00 |
| SDN = | 0.00 | KERL1= | 0 | ISWCH= | 1 | IFC = | 1 |
| AVEI= | 93000.00 | SDI = | 0.00 | KERL2= | 0 | | |
| | | | | | | | |
| IT = | 1 | TN = | 0.00 | IB = | 1 | BI = | 0.00 |
| BN = | 1.00 | BPC = | 0.00 | ID = | 2 | ND = | 20 |
| ISV = | 2 | AVESV= | 9000.00 | SVMAX= | 0.00 | SVMIN= | 0.00 |
| | | | | | | | |
| IC = | 1 | AVEC = | 0.00 | SDC = | 0.00 | KERL3= | 0 |
| ITX = | 2 | TAX = | 0.38 | TXCD = | 0.00 | EXT = | 0.00 |
| | | | | | | | |
| IBS = | 1 | AVEB = | 9000.00 | SDB = | 0.00 | KERL4= | 0 |
| ITB = | 1 | TPC = | 0.00 | ITER = | 1 | | |

### NET CASH FLOW CALCULATION TABLE
```
===================================
```

| YR | CUMULATIVE INVESTMENT | ANNUAL INVESTMENT | DEPREC SCHEDULE | BORROWED MONEY | LOAN PAYMT PRINCIPAL | LOAN INTEREST |
|---|---|---|---|---|---|---|
| 0 | 93000. | 93000. | | 0. | | |
| 1 | 93000. | 0. | 8000. | | 0. | 0. |
| 2 | 93000. | 0. | 7600. | | 0. | 0. |
| 3 | 93000. | 0. | 7200. | | 0. | 0. |
| 4 | 93000. | 0. | 6800. | | 0. | 0. |
| 5 | 93000. | 0. | 6400. | | 0. | 0. |
| 16 | 93000. | 0. | 2000. | | 0. | 0. |
| 17 | 93000. | 0. | 1600. | | 0. | 0. |
| 18 | 93000. | 0. | 1200. | | 0. | 0. |
| 19 | 93000. | 0. | 800. | | 0. | 0. |
| 20 | 93000. | 0. | 400. | | 0. | 0. |

### NET CASH FLOW CALCULATION TABLE - CONTINUED
```
=================================================
```

| YR | -INVESTMENT (NET) | - LOAN PAYMT PRIN + INT | + PROJECT BENEFITS | - EXPENSED COSTS | - INCOME TAX | = NET CASH FLOW |
|---|---|---|---|---|---|---|
| 0 | 93000. | | | | | -93000. |
| 1 | 0. | 0. | 9000. | 0. | 380. | 8620. |
| 2 | 0. | 0. | 9000. | 0. | 532. | 8468. |
| 3 | 0. | 0. | 9000. | 0. | 684. | 8316. |
| 4 | 0. | 0. | 9000. | 0. | 836. | 8164. |
| 5 | 0. | 0. | 9000. | 0. | 988. | 8012. |
| 16 | 0. | 0. | 9000. | 0. | 2660. | 6340. |
| 17 | 0. | 0. | 9000. | 0. | 2812. | 6188. |
| 18 | 0. | 0. | 9000. | 0. | 2964. | 6036. |
| 19 | 0. | 0. | 9000. | 0. | 3116. | 5884. |
| 20 | 0. | 0. | 9000. | 0. | 3268. | 14732. |
| 20 | SALV. VAL. | 9000. | | | | |

```
TRIAL NUMBER  9 : INTERNAL RATE OF RETURN =   5.41 %
                  EXTERNAL INTEREST RATE =    0.00 %
```

| YEAR | CASH FLOW | COMPUTATION | INTERNAL INVESTM. | EXTERNAL INVESTM. |
|---|---|---|---|---|
| 0 | -93000.00 | | -93000.00 | 0.00 |
| 1 | 8620.00 | -93000.00*(1+0.054)+ 8620.00 = -89415.08 | 8620.00 | 0.00 |
| 2 | 8468.00 | -89415.08*(1+0.054)+ 8468.00 = -85788.07 | 8468.00 | 0.00 |
| 3 | 8316.00 | -85788.07*(1+0.054)+ 8316.00 = -82116.69 | 8316.00 | 0.00 |
| 4 | 8164.00 | -82116.69*(1+0.054)+ 8164.00 = -78398.54 | 8164.00 | 0.00 |
| 5 | 8012.00 | -78398.54*(1+0.054)+ 8012.00 = -74631.09 | 8012.00 | 0.00 |
| 6 | 7860.00 | -74631.09*(1+0.054)+ 7860.00 = -70811.66 | 7860.00 | 0.00 |
| 15 | 6492.00 | -38013.43*(1+0.054)+ 6492.00 = -33579.50 | 6492.00 | 0.00 |
| 16 | 6340.00 | -33579.50*(1+0.054)+ 6340.00 = -29057.51 | 6340.00 | 0.00 |
| 17 | 6188.00 | -29057.51*(1+0.054)+ 6188.00 = -24442.70 | 6188.00 | 0.00 |
| 18 | 6036.00 | -24442.70*(1+0.054)+ 6036.00 = -19730.05 | 6036.00 | 0.00 |
| 19 | 5884.00 | -19730.05*(1+0.054)+ 5884.00 = -14914.24 | 5884.00 | 0.00 |
| 20 | 14732.00 | -14914.24*(1+0.054)+14732.00 =   -989.71 | 14732.00 | 0.00 |

```
AFTER  9 TRIALS, THE TRUE INTERNAL RATE OF RETURN WAS FOUND
TO BE VERY CLOSE TO   5.414 %. THIS VALUE IS CONSIDERED THE ANSWER.
```

# 19-11

ROR.OUT file display

Problem 19-11: Solve Problem 7A-5 with RORiPC

| YEAR | CASH FLOW | ACCUMULATED CASH FLOW |
|---|---|---|
| 0 | -500.00 | -500.00 |
| 1 | 200.00 | -300.00 |
| 2 | -500.00 | -800.00 |
| 3 | 1200.00 | 400.00 |

```
     SUM =      400.00
```

```
NUMBER OF SIGN CHANGES IN CASH FLOW =   3
              IN ACCUMULATED CASH FLOW =    1
```

```
     THERE IS A SINGLE POSITIVE RATE OF RETURN
ONE SIGN CHANGE IN ACCUMULATED CASH FLOW
```

```
RESULTS OF RATE OF RETURN COMPUTATION WITH EXTERNAL INTEREST
          RATE =   6.00 % :
          EXTERNAL INTEREST RATE NOT NEEDED.
          COMPUTED INTERNAL RATE OF RETURN EQUALS  21.09 %
```

*In Chapter 7A the cash flow was transformed at a 6% external interest rate and that affected the solution. We now see there is only one positive rate of return and no transformation is needed.*

Interest Payments —— Principal Payments

## Problem 4S-1 — LOAN AMORTIZATION SCHEDULES

| LOAN AMOUNT | $15,000 |
|---|---|
| PAYMENTS PER YEAR | 12 |
| YEARS OF PAYMENTS | 3 |
| NOMINAL INTEREST RATE | 8.90% |
| PERIODIC PAYMENT | $476.30 |
| TOTAL INTEREST PAID | $2,146.73 |

| PMT # | INTEREST PAYMENT | PRINCIPAL PAYMENT | LOAN BALANCE |
|---|---|---|---|
| 1 | 111.25 | 365.05 | 14,634.95 |
| 2 | 108.54 | 367.76 | 14,267.20 |
| 3 | 105.82 | 370.48 | 13,896.71 |
| 4 | 103.07 | 373.23 | 13,523.48 |
| 5 | 100.30 | 376.00 | 13,147.48 |
| 6 | 97.51 | 378.79 | 12,768.70 |
| 7 | 94.70 | 381.60 | 12,387.10 |
| 8 | 91.87 | 384.43 | 12,002.67 |
| 9 | 89.02 | 387.28 | 11,615.39 |
| 10 | 86.15 | 390.15 | 11,225.24 |
| 11 | 83.25 | 393.04 | 10,832.20 |
| 12 | 80.34 | 395.96 | 10,436.24 |
| 13 | 77.40 | 398.90 | 10,037.34 |
| 14 | 74.44 | 401.85 | 9,635.49 |
| 15 | 71.46 | 404.83 | 9,230.65 |
| 16 | 68.46 | 407.84 | 8,822.82 |
| 17 | 65.44 | 410.86 | 8,411.95 |
| 18 | 62.39 | 413.91 | 7,998.04 |
| 19 | 59.32 | 416.98 | 7,581.06 |
| 20 | 56.23 | 420.07 | 7,160.99 |
| 21 | 53.11 | 423.19 | 6,737.80 |
| 22 | 49.97 | 426.33 | 6,311.48 |
| 23 | 46.81 | 429.49 | 5,881.99 |
| 24 | 43.62 | 432.67 | 5,449.32 |
| 25 | 40.42 | 435.88 | 5,013.43 |
| 26 | 37.18 | 439.12 | 4,574.32 |
| 27 | 33.93 | 442.37 | 4,131.95 |
| 28 | 30.65 | 445.65 | 3,686.29 |
| 29 | 27.34 | 448.96 | 3,237.34 |
| 30 | 24.01 | 452.29 | 2,785.05 |
| 31 | 20.66 | 455.64 | 2,329.41 |
| 32 | 17.28 | 459.02 | 1,870.38 |
| 33 | 13.87 | 462.43 | 1,407.96 |
| 34 | 10.44 | 465.86 | 942.10 |
| 35 | 6.99 | 469.31 | 472.79 |
| 36 | 3.51 | 472.79 | 0.00 |

| LOAN AMOUNT | $15,000 |
|---|---|
| PAYMENTS PER YEAR | 12 |
| YEARS OF PAYMENTS | 5 |
| NOMINAL INTEREST RATE | 8.90% |
| PERIODIC PAYMENT | $310.65 |
| TOTAL INTEREST PAID | $3,638.87 |

| PMT # | INTEREST PAYMENT | PRINCIPAL PAYMENT | LOAN BALANCE |
|---|---|---|---|
| 1 | 111.25 | 199.40 | 14,800.60 |
| 2 | 109.77 | 200.88 | 14,599.73 |
| 3 | 108.28 | 202.37 | 14,397.36 |
| 4 | 106.78 | 203.87 | 14,193.49 |
| 5 | 105.27 | 205.38 | 13,988.11 |
| 6 | 103.75 | 206.90 | 13,781.21 |
| 7 | 102.21 | 208.44 | 13,572.77 |
| 8 | 100.66 | 209.98 | 13,362.79 |
| 9 | 99.11 | 211.54 | 13,151.25 |
| 10 | 97.54 | 213.11 | 12,938.14 |
| 11 | 95.96 | 214.69 | 12,723.45 |
| 12 | 94.37 | 216.28 | 12,507.17 |
| 13 | 92.76 | 217.89 | 12,289.28 |
| 14 | 91.15 | 219.50 | 12,069.78 |
| 15 | 89.52 | 221.13 | 11,848.65 |
| 16 | 87.88 | 222.77 | 11,625.88 |
| 17 | 86.23 | 224.42 | 11,401.46 |
| 18 | 84.56 | 226.09 | 11,175.37 |
| 19 | 82.88 | 227.76 | 10,947.60 |
| 20 | 81.19 | 229.45 | 10,718.15 |
| 21 | 79.49 | 231.15 | 10,487.00 |
| 22 | 77.78 | 232.87 | 10,254.13 |
| 23 | 76.05 | 234.60 | 10,019.53 |
| 24 | 74.31 | 236.34 | 9,783.19 |
| 25 | 72.56 | 238.09 | 9,545.10 |
| 26 | 70.79 | 239.85 | 9,305.25 |
| 27 | 69.01 | 241.63 | 9,063.62 |
| 28 | 67.22 | 243.43 | 8,820.19 |
| 29 | 65.42 | 245.23 | 8,574.96 |
| 30 | 63.60 | 247.05 | 8,327.91 |
| 31 | 61.77 | 248.88 | 8,079.03 |
| 32 | 59.92 | 250.73 | 7,828.30 |
| 33 | 58.06 | 252.59 | 7,575.71 |
| 34 | 56.19 | 254.46 | 7,321.25 |
| 35 | 54.30 | 256.35 | 7,064.90 |
| 36 | 52.40 | 258.25 | 6,806.65 |

## Problem 4S-2  LOAN AMORTIZATION SCHEDULES

| LOAN AMOUNT | $100,000 | | LOAN AMOUNT | $100,000 |
|---|---|---|---|---|
| PAYMENTS PER YEAR | 12 | | PAYMENTS PER YEAR | 12 |
| YEARS OF PAYMENTS | 30 | | YEARS OF PAYMENTS | 15 |
| NOMINAL INTEREST RATE | 7.50% | | NOMINAL INTEREST RATE | 7.50% |
| PERIODIC PAYMENT | $699.21 | | PERIODIC PAYMENT | $927.01 |
| TOTAL INTEREST PAID | $151,717.22 | | TOTAL INTEREST PAID | $66,862.22 |

| PMT # | INTEREST PAYMENT | PRINCIPAL PAYMENT | LOAN BALANCE | | PMT # | INTEREST PAYMENT | PRINCIPAL PAYMENT | LOAN BALANCE |
|---|---|---|---|---|---|---|---|---|
| 1 | 625.00 | 74.21 | 99,925.79 | | 1 | 625.00 | 302.01 | 99,697.99 |
| 2 | 624.54 | 74.68 | 99,851.11 | | 2 | 623.11 | 303.90 | 99,394.09 |
| 3 | 624.07 | 75.15 | 99,775.96 | | 3 | 621.21 | 305.80 | 99,088.29 |
| 4 | 623.60 | 75.61 | 99,700.35 | | 4 | 619.30 | 307.71 | 98,780.58 |
| 5 | 623.13 | 76.09 | 99,624.26 | | 5 | 617.38 | 309.63 | 98,470.94 |
| 6 | 622.65 | 76.56 | 99,547.70 | | 6 | 615.44 | 311.57 | 98,159.38 |
| 7 | 622.17 | 77.04 | 99,470.66 | | 7 | 613.50 | 313.52 | 97,845.86 |
| 8 | 621.69 | 77.52 | 99,393.13 | | 8 | 611.54 | 315.48 | 97,530.38 |
| 9 | 621.21 | 78.01 | 99,315.13 | | 9 | 609.56 | 317.45 | 97,212.94 |
| 10 | 620.72 | 78.49 | 99,236.63 | | 10 | 607.58 | 319.43 | 96,893.50 |
| 11 | 620.23 | 78.99 | 99,157.64 | | 11 | 605.58 | 321.43 | 96,572.08 |
| 12 | 619.74 | 79.48 | 99,078.17 | | 12 | 603.58 | 323.44 | 96,248.64 |
| 13 | 619.24 | 79.98 | 98,998.19 | | 13 | 601.55 | 325.46 | 95,923.18 |
| 14 | 618.74 | 80.48 | 98,917.71 | | 14 | 599.52 | 327.49 | 95,595.69 |
| 15 | 618.24 | 80.98 | 98,836.73 | | 15 | 597.47 | 329.54 | 95,266.15 |
| 16 | 617.73 | 81.48 | 98,755.25 | | 16 | 595.41 | 331.60 | 94,934.55 |
| 17 | 617.22 | 81.99 | 98,673.26 | | 17 | 593.34 | 333.67 | 94,600.88 |
| 18 | 616.71 | 82.51 | 98,590.75 | | 18 | 591.26 | 335.76 | 94,265.12 |
| 19 | 616.19 | 83.02 | 98,507.73 | | 19 | 589.16 | 337.86 | 93,927.27 |
| 20 | 615.67 | 83.54 | 98,424.19 | | 20 | 587.05 | 339.97 | 93,587.30 |
| 21 | 615.15 | 84.06 | 98,340.12 | | 21 | 584.92 | 342.09 | 93,245.21 |
| 22 | 614.63 | 84.59 | 98,255.53 | | 22 | 582.78 | 344.23 | 92,900.98 |
| 23 | 614.10 | 85.12 | 98,170.42 | | 23 | 580.63 | 346.38 | 92,554.60 |
| 24 | 613.57 | 85.65 | 98,084.77 | | 24 | 578.47 | 348.55 | 92,206.05 |
| 25 | 613.03 | 86.18 | 97,998.58 | | 25 | 576.29 | 350.72 | 91,855.33 |
| 26 | 612.49 | 86.72 | 97,911.86 | | 26 | 574.10 | 352.92 | 91,502.41 |
| 27 | 611.95 | 87.27 | 97,824.59 | | 27 | 571.89 | 355.12 | 91,147.29 |
| 28 | 611.40 | 87.81 | 97,736.78 | | 28 | 569.67 | 357.34 | 90,789.95 |
| 29 | 610.85 | 88.36 | 97,648.42 | | 29 | 567.44 | 359.58 | 90,430.37 |
| 30 | 610.30 | 88.91 | 97,559.51 | | 30 | 565.19 | 361.82 | 90,068.55 |
| 31 | 609.75 | 89.47 | 97,470.04 | | 31 | 562.93 | 364.08 | 89,704.46 |
| 32 | 609.19 | 90.03 | 97,380.02 | | 32 | 560.65 | 366.36 | 89,338.10 |
| 33 | 608.63 | 90.59 | 97,289.43 | | 33 | 558.36 | 368.65 | 88,969.46 |

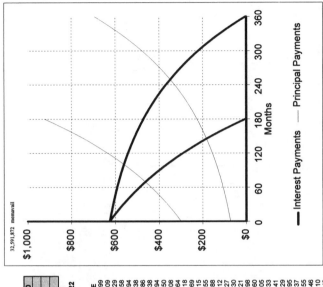

Interest Payments — Principal Payments

## Problem 4S-6
DeferAnn.WB2

| Input Data in Green Shaded Cells | DEPOSITS | ANNUITY |
|---|---|---|
| INTEREST RATE | 2.00% | 2.00% |
| TOTAL # OF PAYMENTS | 1 | |
| INITIAL DEPOSIT | $15,373 | |
| ANNUAL DEPOSIT GRADIENT | $100 | |
| Periods PRIOR TO FIRST ANNUITY PMT | | 19 |
| Half YEARS ANNUITY IS TO BE PAID | | 30 |
| TOTAL DEPOSITS | $15,373 | |
| PRESENT WORTH OF DEPOSITS | $15,373 | |
| FUTURE WORTH OF DEPOSITS | $15,373 | |
| VALUE, YR PRIOR TO FIRST ANNUITY PMT | | $22,396 |
| Semi-annual ANNUITY | | $1,000 |

| Semi-annual Payment | |
|---|---|
| 0 | ($15,373) |
| 1 | |
| 18 | |
| 19 | ($22,396) |
| 20 | $1,000 |
| 21 | $1,000 |
| 22 | $1,000 |
| 23 | $1,000 |
| 24 | $1,000 |
| 25 | $1,000 |
| 26 | $1,000 |
| 27 | $1,000 |
| 28 | $1,000 |
| 29 | $1,000 |
| 30 | $1,000 |
| 31 | $1,000 |
| 32 | $1,000 |
| 33 | $1,000 |
| 34 | $1,000 |
| 35 | $1,000 |
| 36 | $1,000 |
| 37 | $1,000 |
| 38 | $1,000 |
| 39 | $1,000 |
| 40 | $1,000 |
| 41 | $1,000 |
| 42 | $1,000 |
| 43 | $1,000 |
| 44 | $1,000 |
| 45 | $1,000 |
| 46 | $1,000 |
| 47 | $1,000 |
| 48 | $1,000 |
| 49 | $1,000 |

$22,396

## Problem 4S-5
Solve Problem 4-19

| Interest Rate per Period | 2.00% |
|---|---|
| DesiredAnnuity | $1,000 |
| Number of Payments | 30 |
| Interest Periods between deposit and 6 Months prior to birthday | 19 |
| Present Value of Payments | $22,396 |
| 6 Months prior to birthday | $22,396 |
| Cost of single premium Annuity | ($15,374) |

## Problem 4S-7
Solve Problem 4-32

| Interest Rate per Period | 5.00% |
|---|---|
| Desired Annual Annuity | $4,000 |
| Number of Specified Deposits | 4 |
| Amount of Specified Deposits | $600 |
| Interest Periods between initial deposit and one period prior to 18th birthday | 14 |
| Future Value of Total Deposits one period prior to18th birthday | $14,183.80 |
| Future Value of first deposits one period prior to birthday | $4,212.44 |
| Remainder to be raised through additional deposits | $9,971.36 |
| **Magnitude of additional deposits** | **$792.77** |

Chart: Thousands — $5, $0, ($5), ($10), ($15), ($20), ($25); X-axis Payment Period 0–40.

## 5-S1

### COMPARISON OF ALTERNATIVES WITH UNEQUAL LIVE

| **2ALTNPW** | **MARR** | **4.00%** | *Input Data in Green Shaded Cells* |
|---|---|---|---|
| Analysis Period <37yr | IRR GUESS | 20% | |
| | Two stage | Single stage | |
| USEFUL LIFE | 25 | 25 | |
| COMMON MULTIPLE | 25 | 25 | |
| INITIAL COST | $14,200,000 | $22,400,000 | Second Stage construction is treated |
| ANNUAL COSTS | $75,000 | $100,000 | as a negative salvage value in year 25 |
| ANNUAL REVENUE | $0 | $0 | |
| SALVAGE VALUE | ($22,901,006) | $0 | Second Stage construction could |
| NET ANNUAL CASH FLOW | ($75,000) | ($100,000) | cost up to $22.9 M to break even |

| **Net Annual Cash Flow (NACF) Method** | | | |
|---|---|---|---|
| PWB | $0 | $0 | Difference |
| PWC | $23,962,208 | $23,962,208 | $0 |
| NPW=PWB-PWC | ($23,962,208) | ($23,962,208) | $0 |
| | For comparison | | Drive to zero using solver |
| NPW @ USE.LIFE | ($23,962,208) | ($23,962,208) | |

| | A | B | A | B |
|---|---|---|---|---|
| | NPW | NPW | PWC | PWC |
| | (23,962,208) | (23,962,208) | 23,962,208 | 23,962,208 |
| REPEATING CASH FLOW | (37,176,006) | (22,500,000) | | |
| YEAR 0 | (14,200,000) | (22,400,000) | (14,200,000) | (22,400,000) |
| 1 | (75,000) | (100,000) | (75,000) | (100,000) |
| 2 | (75,000) | (100,000) | (75,000) | (100,000) |
| 3 | (75,000) | (100,000) | (75,000) | (100,000) |
| 4 | (75,000) | (100,000) | (75,000) | (100,000) |
| 5 | (75,000) | (100,000) | (75,000) | (100,000) |
| 6 | (75,000) | (100,000) | (75,000) | (100,000) |
| 7 | (75,000) | (100,000) | (75,000) | (100,000) |
| 8 | (75,000) | (100,000) | (75,000) | (100,000) |
| 9 | (75,000) | (100,000) | (75,000) | (100,000) |
| 10 | (75,000) | (100,000) | (75,000) | (100,000) |
| 11 | (75,000) | (100,000) | (75,000) | (100,000) |
| 12 | (75,000) | (100,000) | (75,000) | (100,000) |
| 13 | (75,000) | (100,000) | (75,000) | (100,000) |
| 14 | (75,000) | (100,000) | (75,000) | (100,000) |
| 15 | (75,000) | (100,000) | (75,000) | (100,000) |
| 16 | (75,000) | (100,000) | (75,000) | (100,000) |
| 17 | (75,000) | (100,000) | (75,000) | (100,000) |
| 18 | (75,000) | (100,000) | (75,000) | (100,000) |
| 19 | (75,000) | (100,000) | (75,000) | (100,000) |
| 20 | (75,000) | (100,000) | (75,000) | (100,000) |
| 21 | (75,000) | (100,000) | (75,000) | (100,000) |
| 22 | (75,000) | (100,000) | (75,000) | (100,000) |
| 23 | (75,000) | (100,000) | (75,000) | (100,000) |
| 24 | (75,000) | (100,000) | (75,000) | (100,000) |
| 25 | (22,976,006) | (100,000) | (22,976,006) | (100,000) |

# 5-S2

## COMPARISON OF ALTERNATIVES WITH UNEQUAL LIVES

| 2ALTNPW | MARR | 10.00% | Input Data in Green Shaded Cells |
|---|---|---|---|
| Analysis Period <37yr | IRR GUESS | 20% | |
| | Westinghouse | Itis | |
| USEFUL LIFE | 10 | 15 | |
| COMMON MULTIPLE | 30 | 30 | |
| INITIAL COST | $45,000 | $54,000 | |
| ANNUAL COSTS | $2,673 | $2,850 | Only a $27 reduction in |
| ANNUAL REVENUE | $0 | $0 | operating costs is required for the |
| SALVAGE VALUE | $3,000 | $4,500 | nearly equal alternatives |
| NET ANNUAL CASH FLOW | ($2,673) | ($2,850) | |

| Net Annual Cash Flow (NACF) Method | | | |
|---|---|---|---|
| PWB | $19 | $95 | Difference |
| PWC | $92,477 | $92,553 | |
| NPW=PWB-PWC | ($92,459) | ($92,459) | ($0) |
| | For comparison | | Drive to zero using solver |
| NPW @ USE.LIFE | ($60,266) | ($74,600) | |

| | A | B | A | B |
|---|---|---|---|---|
| | NPW | NPW | PWC | PWC |
| | (92,459) | (92,459) | 92,477 | 92,553 |
| REPEATING CASH FLOW | (44,673) | (52,350) | | |
| YEAR 0 | (45,000) | (54,000) | (45,000) | (54,000) |
| 1 | (2,673) | (2,850) | (2,673) | (2,850) |
| 2 | (2,673) | (2,850) | (2,673) | (2,850) |
| 3 | (2,673) | (2,850) | (2,673) | (2,850) |
| 4 | (2,673) | (2,850) | (2,673) | (2,850) |
| 5 | (2,673) | (2,850) | (2,673) | (2,850) |
| 6 | (2,673) | (2,850) | (2,673) | (2,850) |
| 7 | (2,673) | (2,850) | (2,673) | (2,850) |
| 8 | (2,673) | (2,850) | (2,673) | (2,850) |
| 9 | (2,673) | (2,850) | (2,673) | (2,850) |
| 10 | (44,673) | (2,850) | (44,673) | (2,850) |
| 11 | (2,673) | (2,850) | (2,673) | (2,850) |
| 12 | (2,673) | (2,850) | (2,673) | (2,850) |
| 13 | (2,673) | (2,850) | (2,673) | (2,850) |
| 14 | (2,673) | (2,850) | (2,673) | (2,850) |
| 15 | (2,673) | (52,350) | (2,673) | (52,350) |
| 16 | (2,673) | (2,850) | (2,673) | (2,850) |
| 17 | (2,673) | (2,850) | (2,673) | (2,850) |
| 18 | (2,673) | (2,850) | (2,673) | (2,850) |
| 19 | (2,673) | (2,850) | (2,673) | (2,850) |
| 20 | (44,673) | (2,850) | (44,673) | (2,850) |
| 21 | (2,673) | (2,850) | (2,673) | (2,850) |
| 22 | (2,673) | (2,850) | (2,673) | (2,850) |
| 23 | (2,673) | (2,850) | (2,673) | (2,850) |
| 24 | (2,673) | (2,850) | (2,673) | (2,850) |
| 25 | (2,673) | (2,850) | (2,673) | (2,850) |
| 26 | (2,673) | (2,850) | (2,673) | (2,850) |
| 27 | (2,673) | (2,850) | (2,673) | (2,850) |
| 28 | (2,673) | (2,850) | (2,673) | (2,850) |
| 29 | (2,673) | (2,850) | (2,673) | (2,850) |
| 30 | 327 | 1,650 | 0 | 0 |

## 5-S3   2ALTNPW — COMPARISON OF ALTERNATIVES WITH UNEQUAL LIVES

| | | Alt A | Alt B | Notes |
|---|---|---|---|---|
| | MARR | 10.00% | | Input Data in Green Shaded Cells |
| Analysis Period <37yr | IRR GUESS | 20% | | Solution Cell: +D15  Equal  0 |
| USEFUL LIFE | | 4 | 8 | Variable Cells: @COUNT(C9) |
| COMMON MULTIPLE | | 8 | 8 | Constraints |
| INITIAL COST | | $5,300 | $10,700 | Only a $34 increase in Alternative B |
| ANNUAL COSTS | | $0 | $0 | operating revenue is required for the |
| ANNUAL REVENUE | | $1,800 | $2,134 | nearly equal alternatives |
| SALVAGE VALUE | | $0 | $0 | |
| NET ANNUAL CASH FLOW | | $1,800 | $2,134 | |

### Net Annual Cash Flow (NACF) Method

| | Alt A | Alt B | Difference |
|---|---|---|---|
| PWB | $8,373 | $11,383 | |
| PWC | $7,691 | $10,700 | |
| NPW=PWB-PWC | $683 | $683 | ($0)  Drive to zero using solver |

For comparison:

| | Alt A | Alt B |
|---|---|---|
| NPW @ USE.LIFE | $406 | $683 |

| | A NPW | B NPW | A PWC | B PWC | A PWB | B PWB |
|---|---|---|---|---|---|---|
| NPW / PW | 683 | 683 | 7,691 | 10,700 | 8,373 | 11,383 |

**REPEATING CASH FLOW**

| YEAR | A | B | A PWC | B PWC | A PWB | B PWB |
|---|---|---|---|---|---|---|
| 0 | (5,300) | (10,700) | (5,300) | (10,700) | 0 | 0 |
| 1 | 1,800 | 2,134 | 0 | 0 | 1,800 | 2,134 |
| 2 | 1,800 | 2,134 | 0 | 0 | 1,800 | 2,134 |
| 3 | 1,800 | 2,134 | 0 | 0 | 1,800 | 2,134 |
| 4 | (3,500) | 2,134 | (3,500) | 0 | 0 | 2,134 |
| 5 | 1,800 | 2,134 | 0 | 0 | 1,800 | 2,134 |
| 6 | 1,800 | 2,134 | 0 | 0 | 1,800 | 2,134 |
| 7 | 1,800 | 2,134 | 0 | 0 | 1,800 | 2,134 |
| 8 | 1,800 | 2,134 | 0 | 0 | 1,800 | 2,134 |

# 6S-1

## Problem 6-15

*Input Data in Green Shaded Cells*

| 2ALTEUAW (modified) | Around the Lake MARR | Under the lake 7.00% |
|---|---|---|
| Length,km | 15 | 5 |
| First cost/km | $5,000 | $25,000 |
| Maintenance/km/yr | $200 | $400 |
| Yearly power loss/km | $500 | $500 |
| Salvage Value/km | $3,000 | $5,000 |
| Property tax/.02*first cost/yr | $1,500 | $2,500 |
| USEFUL LIFE | 15 | 15 |
| INITIAL COST | $75,000 | $125,000 |
| ANNUAL COSTS | $12,000 | $7,000 |
| ANNUAL REVENUE | $0 | $0 |
| SALVAGE VALUE | $45,000 | $25,000 |
| Salvage Value as a Reduced Cost | | |
| EUAB | $0 | $0 |
| EUAC(CR) + EUAC(0&M) | $18,444 | $19,729 |
| EUAW | ($18,444) | ($19,729) |

## Breakeven Analysis

*Input Data in Green Shaded Cells*

| | Around the Lake MARR | Under the lake 7.00% |
|---|---|---|
| Length,km | 15 | 5 |
| First cost/km | $5,000 | $23,019 |
| Maintenance/km/yr | $200 | $400 |
| Yearly power loss/km | $500 | $500 |
| Salvage Value/km | $3,000 | $5,000 |
| Property tax/.02*first cost/yr | $1,500 | $2,302 |
| USEFUL LIFE | 15 | 15 |
| INITIAL COST | $75,000 | $115,095 |
| ANNUAL COSTS | $12,000 | $6,802 |
| ANNUAL REVENUE | $0 | $0 |
| SALVAGE VALUE | $45,000 | $25,000 |
| Salvage Value as a Reduced Cost | | |
| EUAB | $0 | $0 |
| EUAC(CR) + EUAC(0&M) | $18,444 | $18,444 |
| EUAW | ($18,444) | ($18,444) |
| | Difference | $0 |

# 6S-2

## Problem 6-21

| Input Data in Green Shaded Cells | Diesel | Gasoline |
|---|---|---|
| 2ALTEUAW modified | MARR | 6.00% |
| Km per year | 50,000 | 50,000 |
| First cost | $13,000 | $12,000 |
| Fuel Cost per liter | $0.48 | $0.51 |
| Mileage, km/liter | 35 | 28 |
| Annual Repairs | $300 | $200 |
| Annual insurance premium | $500 | $500 |
| USEFUL LIFE | 4 | 3 |
| INITIAL COST | $13,000 | $12,000 |
| ANNUAL COSTS | $1,486 | $1,611 |
| ANNUAL REVENUE | $0 | $0 |
| SALVAGE VALUE | $2,000 | $3,000 |
| Salvage Value as a Reduced Cost | | |
| EUAB | $0 | $0 |
| EUAC(CR) + EUAC(0&M) | $4,780 | $5,158 |
| EUAW | ($4,780) | ($5,158) |
| Mileage, km | | |
| 10,000 | $4,232 | $4,429 |
| 20,000 | $4,369 | $4,611 |
| 40,000 | $4,643 | $4,976 |
| 60,000 | $4,917 | $5,340 |
| 80,000 | $5,192 | $5,704 |

There is no crossover, the Diesel is always more economical.

## 6S-3

### Problem 6-30

| Input Data in Green Shaded Cells | MARR | 8.00% | |
|---|---|---|---|
| Current Trucking Cost per month | | $200.00 | |
| Labor Cost per year | | $3,000 | |
| Strapping material cost per bale | | $0.40 | |
| Revenue per Bale | | $2.30 | |
| Bales per year produced | | 500 | |
| USEFUL LIFE | | 30 | |
| Initial cost for Bailer | | $6,000 | |
| ANNUAL COSTS | | $3,200 | |
| Annual Benefits | | $3,550 | |
| SALVAGE VALUE | | $0 | |
| Salvage Value as a Reduced Cost | | | |
| EUAB | | $3,550 | |
| EUAC(CR) + EUAC(O&M) | | $3,733 | |
| EUAW | | ($183) | |

## 6S-4

### Problem 6-34    LOAN REFINANCING

Comments and equations

| | | | |
|---|---|---|---|
| LOAN AMOUNT | | $80,000 | Input Data in Shaded Cells |
| PAYMENTS PER YEAR | | 1 | |
| YEARS OF PAYMENTS | | 25 | |
| NOMINAL INTEREST RATE | | 10.00% | Input as .089 and format as percent |
| ORIGINAL PERIODIC PAYMENT | | $8,813.45 | D7 = @PMT(D3,D6/D4,D4*D5) |
| TOTAL INTEREST to be PAID | | $140,336.14 | D8 = +D7*D4*D5-D3 |
| Penalty Charge Points for refinance | | 2.00% | |
| Refinance at end of year | | 10 | |
| Loan Balance | | $67,035.77 | D11 = @PV(D7,D6/D4,D4*(D5-D10)) |
| Penalty Charge for refinancing | | $1,340.72 | D12 = +C12*D11 |
| Service Charge | | $1,000.00 | |
| New Loan | | $69,376.48 | D13 = @SUM(D11..D13) |
| New Nominal Interest Rate | | 9.00% | |
| New Loan Term | | 15 | |
| New Periodic Payment | | $8,606.77 | D17 = @PMT(D14,D15/D4,D4*D16) |
| Old Payment minus new payment | | $206.68 | D18 = +D7-D17 |

# 6-S5

**COMPARISON OF ALTERNATIVES**

| Problem 6-42 | MARR | 10.00% | Breakeven |
|---|---|---|---|
| *Input Data in Green Shaded Cells* | **Gravity Plan** | **Pumping** | **Pumping** |
| USEFUL LIFE | 40 | 40 | 40 |
| COMMON MULTIPLE | 40 | 40 | 40 |
| INITIAL COST | $2,800,000 | $1,400,000 | $1,400,000 |
| ANNUAL COSTS | $10,000 | $75,000 | $75,000 |
| Additional Cost, 10th year | | $200,000 | $1,541,798 |
| Additional Power Cost, yr 11-40 | | $50,000 | $50,000 |
| ANNUAL REVENUE | $0 | $0 | $0 |
| SALVAGE VALUE | $0 | $0 | $0 |
| NET ANNUAL CASH FLOW | ($10,000) | ($75,000) | ($75,000) |

| Net Annual Cash Flow (NACF) Method | | | |
|---|---|---|---|
| PWB | $0 | $0 | **Difference** |
| PWC | $2,896,765 | $2,379,444 | Drive to zero using solver |
| | | | $0 |
| NPW=PWB-PWC | ($2,896,765) | ($2,379,444) | ($2,896,765) |
| EUAC | $296,222 | $243,321 | $296,222 |

| | A | B | C |
|---|---|---|---|
| | NPW | NPW | NPW |
| | (2,896,765) | (2,379,444) | (2,896,765) |
| REPEATING CASH FLOW | (2,810,000) | (1,475,000) | (1,475,000) |
| YEAR 0 | (2,800,000) | (1,400,000) | (1,400,000) |
| 1 | (10,000) | (75,000) | (75,000) |
| 2 | (10,000) | (75,000) | (75,000) |
| 3 | (10,000) | (75,000) | (75,000) |
| 4 | (10,000) | (75,000) | (75,000) |
| 5 | (10,000) | (75,000) | (75,000) |
| 6 | (10,000) | (75,000) | (75,000) |
| 7 | (10,000) | (75,000) | (75,000) |
| 8 | (10,000) | (75,000) | (75,000) |
| 9 | (10,000) | (75,000) | (75,000) |
| 10 | (10,000) | (275,000) | (1,616,798) |
| 11 | (10,000) | (125,000) | (125,000) |
| 12 | (10,000) | (125,000) | (125,000) |
| 13 | (10,000) | (125,000) | (125,000) |
| 14 | (10,000) | (125,000) | (125,000) |
| 15 | (10,000) | (125,000) | (125,000) |
| 16 | (10,000) | (125,000) | (125,000) |
| 17 | (10,000) | (125,000) | (125,000) |
| 18 | (10,000) | (125,000) | (125,000) |
| 19 | (10,000) | (125,000) | (125,000) |
| 20 | (10,000) | (125,000) | (125,000) |
| 21 | (10,000) | (125,000) | (125,000) |
| 22 | (10,000) | (125,000) | (125,000) |
| 23 | (10,000) | (125,000) | (125,000) |
| 24 | (10,000) | (125,000) | (125,000) |
| 25 | (10,000) | (125,000) | (125,000) |
| 26 | (10,000) | (125,000) | (125,000) |
| 27 | (10,000) | (125,000) | (125,000) |
| 28 | (10,000) | (125,000) | (125,000) |
| 29 | (10,000) | (125,000) | (125,000) |
| 30 | (10,000) | (125,000) | (125,000) |
| 31 | (10,000) | (125,000) | (125,000) |
| 32 | (10,000) | (125,000) | (125,000) |
| 33 | (10,000) | (125,000) | (125,000) |
| 34 | (10,000) | (125,000) | (125,000) |
| 35 | (10,000) | (125,000) | (125,000) |
| 36 | (10,000) | (125,000) | (125,000) |
| 37 | (10,000) | (125,000) | (125,000) |
| 38 | (10,000) | (125,000) | (125,000) |
| 39 | (10,000) | (125,000) | (125,000) |
| 40 | (10,000) | (125,000) | (125,000) |

## Problem 9S-1a

| | Breakeven Revenues | | |
|---|---|---|---|
| | IRR Guess | 25% | |
| 2ALTEL | MARR = | 15.00% | |
| ANALYSIS LIFE (<37yr) | 8 | YEARS | |
| Input Data in Shaded Cells | ALTERNATIVES | | |
| | A | B | |
| INITIAL COST | $15,000 | $30,000 | |
| ANNUAL COSTS | $1,000 | $800 | |
| ANNUAL COST GRADIENT | $100 | $60 | |
| ANNUAL REVENUE | $5,078 | $8,000 | |
| SALVAGE VALUE | $1,500 | $3,000 | |
| **Salvage value as a reduced cost** | | | |
| EUAB | $5,078 | $8,000 | |
| EUAC(CR) + EUAC(O&M) | $4,512 | $7,434 | |
| EUAW | $566 | $566 | |
| **Net Annual Cash Flow (NACF) Method** | | | |
| EUAB | $3,909 | $7,252 | |
| EUAC | $3,343 | $6,686 | |
| EUAW | $566 | $566 | |
| PWB | $17,541 | $32,541 | |
| PWC | $15,000 | $30,000 | |
| NPW = PWB - PWC | $2,541 | $2,541 | |
| B/C = PWB/PWC | 1.169 | 1.085 | |
| INCREMENTAL B/C | | 1.00 | |
| IRR | 20.02% | 17.48% | |
| INCREMENTAL IRR | | 15.00% | |
| Use solver to drive incremental B/C to 1.000 | | | |

## Problem 9S-1b

| | Breakeven MARR | | |
|---|---|---|---|
| | IRR Guess | 25% | |
| 2ALTEL | MARR = | 15.67% | |
| ANALYSIS LIFE (<37yr) | 8 | YEARS | |
| Input Data in Shaded Cells | ALTERNATIVES | | |
| | A | B | |
| INITIAL COST | $15,000 | $30,000 | |
| ANNUAL COSTS | $1,000 | $800 | |
| ANNUAL COST GRADIENT | $100 | $60 | |
| ANNUAL REVENUE | $5,000 | $8,000 | |
| SALVAGE VALUE | $1,500 | $3,000 | |
| **Salvage value as a reduced cost** | | | |
| EUAB | $5,000 | $8,000 | |
| EUAC(CR) + EUAC(O&M) | $4,585 | $7,585 | |
| EUAW | $415 | $415 | |
| **Net Annual Cash Flow (NACF) Method** | | | |
| EUAB | $3,831 | $7,248 | |
| EUAC | $3,417 | $6,833 | |
| EUAW | $415 | $415 | |
| PWB | $16,820 | $31,820 | |
| PWC | $15,000 | $30,000 | |
| NPW = PWB - PWC | $1,820 | $1,820 | |
| B/C = PWB/PWC | 1.121 | 1.061 | |
| INCREMENTAL B/C | | 1.00 | |
| IRR | 19.34% | 17.48% | |
| INCREMENTAL IRR | | 15.67% | |

## Problem 9s-2b

**2ALTUL**  
MARR 16.00%  
IRR GUESS 20%  
Analysis Period <37yr  
*Input Data in Green Shaded Cells*

| | ALT A | ALT B |
|---|---|---|
| USEFUL LIFE | 3 | 6 |
| COMMON MULTIPLE | 15 | 15 |
| INITIAL COST | $15,000 | $30,000 |
| ANNUAL COSTS | $1,000 | $900 |
| ANNUAL REVENUE | $6,946 | $9,200 |
| SALVAGE VALUE | $3,000 | $6,000 |
| NET ANNUAL CASH FLOW | $5,946 | $8,300 |

*Salvage Value as a Reduced Cost*

| | ALT A | ALT B |
|---|---|---|
| EUAB | $6,946 | $9,200 |
| EUAC(CR) + EUAC(O&M) | $6,706 | $8,960 |
| EUAW | $240 | $240 |

*Net Annual Cash Flow (NACF) Method*

| | ALT A | ALT B |
|---|---|---|
| EUAB | $4,422 | $7,370 |
| EUAC   EUAW | $4,181 | $7,129 |
| | $240 | $240 |
| PWB | $25,856 | $43,092 |
| PWC | $24,450 | $41,686 |
| NPW=PWB-PWC | $1,406 | $1,406 |
| | For comparison | |
| NPW @ USE.LIFE | $549 | $806 |
| B/C= PWB/PWC | 1.06 | 1.03 |
| INCREMENTAL B/C | | 1.00 |
| IRR | 17.04% | 16.04% |
| INCREMENTAL IRR | | 15.00% |

## Problem 9s-2a

**2ALTUL**  
MARR < 14.50%  
IRR GUESS 20%  
Analysis Period <37yr  
*Input Data in Green Shaded Cells*

| | ALT A | ALT B |
|---|---|---|
| USEFUL LIFE | 3 | 6 |
| COMMON MULTIPLE | 15 | 15 |
| INITIAL COST | $15,000 | $30,000 |
| ANNUAL COSTS | $1,000 | $900 |
| ANNUAL REVENUE | $7,000 | $9,200 |
| SALVAGE VALUE | $3,000 | $6,000 |
| NET ANNUAL CASH FLOW | $6,000 | $8,300 |

*Salvage Value as a Reduced Cost*

| | ALT A | ALT B |
|---|---|---|
| EUAB | $7,000 | $9,200 |
| EUAC(CR) + EUAC(O&M) | $6,647 | $8,845 |
| EUAW | $353 | $355 |

*Net Annual Cash Flow (NACF) Method*

| | ALT A | ALT B |
|---|---|---|
| EUAB | $4,461 | $7,370 |
| EUAC   EUAW | $4,108 | $7,015 |
| | $353 | $355 |
| PWB | $26,729 | $44,158 |
| PWC | $24,615 | $42,031 |
| NPW=PWB-PWC | $2,114 | $2,127 |
| | For comparison | |
| NPW @ USE.LIFE | $812 | $1,204 |
| B/C= PWB/PWC | 1.09 | 1.05 |
| INCREMENTAL B/C | | 1.00 |
| IRR | 17.50% | 16.04% |
| INCREMENTAL IRR | | 14.52% |

## 9S-3

### Problem 9-4

*Input Data in Green Shaded Cells*

|  | Fearless Bus | Generous Electric |
|---|---|---|
| MARR | 9.00% |  |
| Analysis Period | 5 | 5 |
| Salary per year | $65,000 | $62,000 |
| Shares of Stock per year | 100 | 0 |
| Shares held at the end of period | 500 | 600 |
| Expected Stock Price | $60.00 |  |
| Annual Dividend | $2.00 |  |
| Future Worth of Salary @MARR | $389,006 | $371,052 |
| Future Worth of Stock @MARR | $30,000 |  |
| Future Worth of Dividend | $2,188 |  |
| Total Future Worth | $421,194 | $421,194 |
| Required stock price for breakeven | $1,422 | $83.57 |
| Present Worth of dividends, year 0 |  |  |
| Dividend Income, year 1 |  |  |
| 2 | $200 |  |
| 3 | $400 |  |
| 4 | $600 |  |
| 5 | $800 |  |

## Problem 9S-4

**2ALTUL**
Analysis Period <3/yr
*Input Data in Green Shaded Cells*

## Problem 9-34a

MARR **10.00%**
IRR GUESS **20%**

| | Convent. | Solar |
|---|---|---|
| USEFUL LIFE | 20 | 20 |
| COMMON MULTIPLE | 20 | 20 |
| INITIAL COST | $200 | $1,400 |
| ANNUAL COSTS | $230 | $60 |
| ANNUAL REVENUE | $0 | $0 |
| SALVAGE VALUE | $0 | $1,220 |
| NET ANNUAL CASH FLOW | ($230) | ($60) |

**Net Annual Cash Flow (NACF) Method**

| | | |
|---|---|---|
| EUAB | $0 | $0 |
| EUAC | ($253) | ($260) |
| EUAW | ($253) | ($260) |
| | | |
| PWB | $0 | $0 |
| PWC | $2,158 | $2,214 |
| NPW=PWB-PWC | ($2,158) | ($2,214) |
| | | |
| B/C= PWB/PWC | 0.00 | 0.00 |
| INCREMENTAL B/C | | 0.95 |
| | | |
| IRR | -100.00% | -100.00% |
| INCREMENTAL IRR | | 9.29% |

The cash flow for the 4-year maintanence cycle of the solar heater can be simulated by using 4-year life for the heater with a salvage value equal to the purchase price minus the 4-year maintanence cost or -$240 and deleting the repurchase at the end of 20 years

| | A IRR | B IRR | A PWC | B PWC | A PWB | B PWB | B-A DELTA ROR | B-A PWC | B-A PWB |
|---|---|---|---|---|---|---|---|---|---|
| IRR | -100.00% | -100.00% | 2,158 | 2,214 | 0 | 0 | 9.29% | 1,217 | 1,161 |
| REPEATING CASH FLOW | | | | | | | | | |
| 0 | (430) | (1,400) | (240) | (1,400) | 0 | 0 | (1,200) | (1,200) | (1,200) |
| 1 | (230) | (60) | (230) | (60) | 0 | 0 | 170 | 0 | 170 |
| 2 | (230) | (60) | (230) | (60) | 0 | 0 | 170 | 0 | 170 |
| 3 | (230) | (60) | (230) | (60) | 0 | 0 | 170 | 0 | 170 |
| 4 | (230) | (240) | (230) | (240) | 0 | 0 | (10) | (10) | 0 |
| 5 | (230) | (60) | (230) | (60) | 0 | 0 | 170 | 0 | 170 |
| 6 | (230) | (60) | (230) | (60) | 0 | 0 | 170 | 0 | 170 |
| 7 | (230) | (60) | (230) | (60) | 0 | 0 | 170 | 0 | 170 |
| 8 | (230) | (240) | (230) | (240) | 0 | 0 | (10) | (10) | 0 |
| 9 | (230) | (60) | (230) | (60) | 0 | 0 | 170 | 0 | 170 |
| 10 | (230) | (60) | (230) | (60) | 0 | 0 | 170 | 0 | 170 |
| 11 | (230) | (60) | (230) | (60) | | | 170 | 0 | 170 |

**CUMULATIVE CASH FLOWS**

| YEAR | A | B | B-A |
|---|---|---|---|
| | ($200) | ($1,400) | ($1,200) |
| 1 | ($430) | ($1,460) | ($1,030) |
| 2 | ($660) | ($1,520) | ($860) |
| 3 | ($890) | ($1,580) | ($690) |
| 4 | ($1,120) | ($1,820) | ($700) |
| 5 | ($1,350) | ($1,880) | ($530) |
| 6 | ($1,580) | ($1,940) | ($360) |
| 7 | ($1,810) | ($2,000) | ($190) |
| 8 | ($2,040) | ($2,240) | ($200) |
| 9 | ($2,270) | ($2,300) | ($30) |
| 10 | ($2,500) | ($2,360) | $140 |
| 11 | ($2,730) | ($2,420) | $310 |

**Net Annual Cash Flow, Alt. A** (bar chart) — y-axis: $0, ($50), ($100), ($150), ($200), ($250); x-axis: Year 0–20; legend: Convent.

**Net Annual Cash Flow, Alt. B** (bar chart) — y-axis: $0, ($200), ($400), ($600), ($800), ($1,000), ($1,200), ($1,400); x-axis: Year 0–20; legend: Solar

# Problem 9S-5

*Input Data in Green Shaded Cells*

Chapter 4S example modified to solve Problem 9-54 and play what if with interest rates and annuity payments

14-Dec-97

|  | DeferAnn.WB2 |  |
|---|---|---|
|  | DEPOSITS | ANNUITY |
| INTEREST RATE | 10.00% | 10.00% |
| TOTAL # OF PAYMENTS | 41 | 15 |
| INITIAL DEPOSIT | $2,000 |  |
| ANNUAL DEPOSIT GRADIENT |  |  |
| YEAR # PRIOR TO FIRST ANNUITY PMT |  | 40 |
| YEARS ANNUITY IS TO BE PAID |  | 15 |
| TOTAL DEPOSITS | $82,000 |  |
| PRESENT WORTH OF DEPOSITS | $21,558 |  |
| FUTURE WORTH OF DEPOSITS | $975,704 |  |
| VALUE, YR PRIOR TO FIRST ANNUITY PMT |  | $975,704 |
| YEARLY ANNUITY |  | $128,279 |

Alternatie Solution using @FV(Pmt,Rate,Term)  $975,704

C9: -@SUM(C14..C74)
C10: -@NPV($C$3,C15..C54)-C14
C11: +C10*(1+C3)^(C4-1)
D12:+C10*(1+C3)^D7
D13: @PMT(D12,D3,D8)
C14: -C5
A15: @IF(B15=D$7,+D$12,0)
C16: @IF(B16<$C$4,-C16-$B16*C16,0)
D17: @IF(B17>D$7#AND#B17<=D$7+D$8+1,+D$13,@IF(B17=D$7,-D$12,0))

| YEAR | Age | |
|---|---|---|
| 0 | 25 | ($2,000) |
| 1 | 26 | ($2,000) |
| 2 | 27 | ($2,000) |
| 3 | 28 | ($2,000) |
| 4 | 29 | ($2,000) |
| 5 | 30 | ($2,000) |
| 6 | 31 | ($2,000) |
| 7 | 32 | ($2,000) |
| 8 | 33 | ($2,000) |
| 9 | 34 | ($2,000) |
| 10 | 35 | ($2,000) |
| 11 | 36 | ($2,000) |
| 12 | 37 | ($2,000) |
| 13 | 38 | ($2,000) |
| 14 | 39 | ($2,000) |
| 15 | 40 | ($2,000) |
| 16 | 41 | ($2,000) |
| 17 | 42 | ($2,000) |
| 18 | 43 | ($2,000) |
| 19 | 44 | ($2,000) |
| 20 | 45 | ($2,000) |
| 21 | 46 | ($2,000) |
| 22 | 47 | ($2,000) |
| 23 | 48 | ($2,000) |
| 24 | 49 | ($2,000) |
| 25 | 50 | ($2,000) |
| 26 | 51 | ($2,000) |
| 27 | 52 | ($2,000) |
| 28 | 53 | ($2,000) |
| 29 | 54 | ($2,000) |
| 30 | 55 | ($2,000) |
| 31 | 56 | ($2,000) |
| 32 | 57 | ($2,000) |
| 33 | 58 | ($2,000) |
| 34 | 59 | ($2,000) |
| 35 | 60 | ($2,000) |
| 36 | 61 | ($2,000) |
| 37 | 62 | ($2,000) |
| 38 | 63 | ($2,000) |
| 39 | 64 | ($2,000) |
| 40 | 65 | ($2,000) |

$975,704

($975,704)

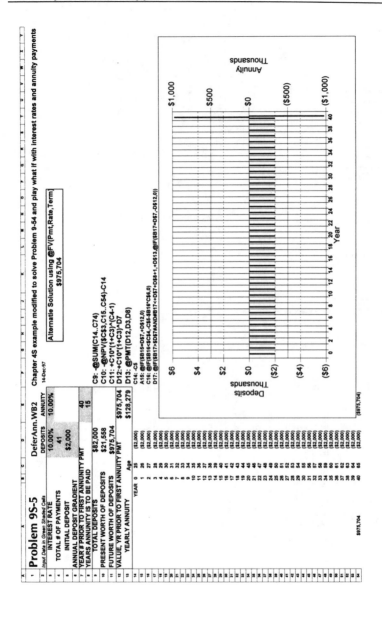

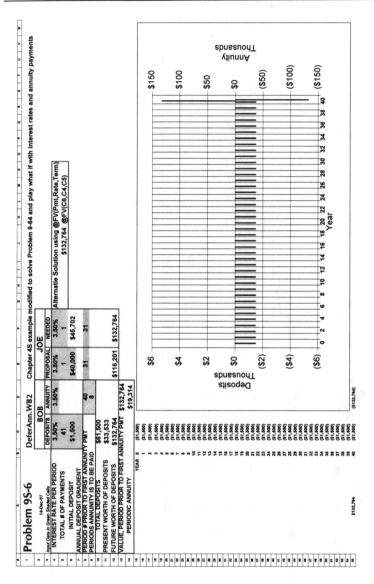

Problem 9S-6

DeferAnn.WB2   Chapter 4S example modified to solve Problem 9-S4 and play what if with interest rates and annuity payments

14-Dec-97

Input Data in Green Shaded Cells

| | BOB | | JOE | | |
|---|---|---|---|---|---|
| | DEPOSITS | ANNUITY | PROPOSAL | NEEDED | Alternative Solution using @FV(Pmt,Rate,Term) |
| INTEREST RATE PER PERIOD | 3.50% | 3.50% | 3.50% | 3.50% | $132,764  @FV(C6,C4,C5) |
| TOTAL # OF PAYMENTS | 41 | 1 | 1 | 1 | |
| INITIAL DEPOSIT | $1,500 | | $40,000 | $45,702 | |
| ANNUAL DEPOSIT GRADIENT | | | | | |
| PERIOD # PRIOR TO FIRST ANNUITY PMT | | 40 | 31 | 31 | |
| PERIODS ANNUITY IS TO BE PAID | | 8 | | | |
| TOTAL DEPOSITS | $61,500 | | | | |
| PRESENT WORTH OF DEPOSITS | $33,533 | | | | |
| FUTURE WORTH OF DEPOSITS | $132,764 | $132,764 | $116,201 | $132,764 | |
| VALUE, PERIOD PRIOR TO FIRST ANNUITY PMT | | $132,764 | | | |
| PERIODIC ANNUITY | | $19,314 | | | |

| YEAR | 0 | ($1,500) |
|---|---|---|
| | 1 | ($1,500) |
| | 2 | ($1,500) |
| | 3 | ($1,500) |
| | 4 | ($1,500) |
| | 5 | ($1,500) |
| | 6 | ($1,500) |
| | 7 | ($1,500) |
| | 8 | ($1,500) |
| | 9 | ($1,500) |
| | 10 | ($1,500) |
| | 11 | ($1,500) |
| | 12 | ($1,500) |
| | 13 | ($1,500) |
| | 14 | ($1,500) |
| | 15 | ($1,500) |
| | 16 | ($1,500) |
| | 17 | ($1,500) |
| | 18 | ($1,500) |
| | 19 | ($1,500) |
| | 20 | ($1,500) |
| | 21 | ($1,500) |
| | 22 | ($1,500) |
| | 23 | ($1,500) |
| | 24 | ($1,500) |
| | 25 | ($1,500) |
| | 26 | ($1,500) |
| | 27 | ($1,500) |
| | 28 | ($1,500) |
| | 29 | ($1,500) |
| | 30 | ($1,500) |
| | 31 | ($1,500) |
| | 32 | ($1,500) |
| | 33 | ($1,500) |
| | 34 | ($1,500) |
| | 35 | ($1,500) |
| | 36 | ($1,500) |
| | 37 | ($1,500) |
| | 38 | ($1,500) |
| | 39 | ($1,500) |
| | 40 | ($1,500) |

$132,764

06-Dec-97

# Problem 11S-1

| Analysis Life (<51 yr) | 5 |
|---|---|
| Total First Cost | $600,000 |
| Deprec. Amount | $600,000 |

| | |
|---|---|
| Revenue Factor | 1.00 |
| Reference Revenue | $200,000 |
| Annual Revenues | $200,000 |
| Change/yr | |
| Annual Fixed Costs | |
| Change/yr | |
| Marginal Tax Rate | 35.0% |

| BTNPW | BTIRR | BTEUAW |
|---|---|---|
| ($4,804) | 22.72% | ($1,716) |
| ATNPW | ATIRR | ATEUAW |
| $13,816 | 15.95% | $4,121 |
| AT B/C = | 1.02 | |

| Sum of Depreciation | $565,440 |
|---|---|
| Book Value | $34,560 |

## ATAXNL.WB1

| Salvage Value | $100,000 | |
|---|---|---|
| Sale Price | $100,000 | |
| ATMARR | 15.0% | |
| BTMARR | 23.1% | |
| IRR Guess | 10.83% | |
| | | |
| MACRS Life, Years | 5.0 | |
| Deprec. Life for SL and SYD | 5.0 | |
| Sub-period placed in Serv. | 2.5 | Use 2.5 for |
| Sub-Periods per year | 4 | half-year |
| Rounding decimal places | 4 | convention |
| Declining Balance Factor | 200% | |
| | | |
| Use Depreciation Method: | 1 | |
| 1 | MACRS | |
| 2 | Straight Line | |
| 3 | Sum of Years Digits | |

| Sum of taxes | $175,000 |
|---|---|
| Sum of After Tax Cash Flows | $325,000 |

| Year | BTCF | Depreciation | Taxable Inc. | Income Tax | ATCF | PWATCF | CUM. CASH FLOW | MACRS DEPR. % |
|---|---|---|---|---|---|---|---|---|
| 0 | (600,000) | — | — | | (600,000) | (600,000) | (600,000) | |
| 1 | 200,000 | 120,000 | 80,000 | (28,000) | 172,000 | 149,565 | (428,000) | 20.000% |
| 2 | 200,000 | 192,000 | 8,000 | (2,800) | 197,200 | 149,112 | (230,800) | 32.000% |
| 3 | 200,000 | 115,200 | 84,800 | (29,680) | 170,320 | 111,988 | (60,480) | 19.200% |
| 4 | 200,000 | 69,120 | 130,880 | (45,808) | 154,192 | 88,160 | 93,712 | 11.520% |
| 5 | 200,000 | 69,120 | 130,880 | (45,808) | 154,192 | 76,661 | 247,904 | 11.520% |
| 5 | 100,000 | | 65,440 | (22,904) | 77,096 | 38,330 | 325,000 | 5.760% |

## Problem 11S-2

ATAXNL.WB1                                                             06-Dec-97

| | |
|---|---|
| Analysis Life (<51 yr) | 6 |
| Total First Cost | $250,000 |
| Deprec. Amount | $200,000 |
| Revenue Factor | 1.00 |
| Reference Revenue | $50,000 |
| Annual Revenues | $50,000 |
| Change/yr | |
| Annual Fixed Costs | |
| Change/yr | |
| Marginal Tax Rate | 40.0% |

| | | | | | |
|---|---|---|---|---|---|
| BTNPW | $16,745 | BTIRR | 21.92% | BTEUAW | $5,035 |
| ATNPW | $18,269 | ATIRR | 13.75% | ATEUAW | $4,444 |
| AT B/C = | 1.07 | | | | |

Sum of Depreciation   $43,330
Book Value   $206,670

| | |
|---|---|
| Salvage Value | $300,000 |
| Sale Price | $300,000 |
| ATMARR | 12.0% |
| BTMARR | 20.0% |
| IRR Guess | 14.00% |

| | | |
|---|---|---|
| MACRS Life, Years | 27.5 | |
| Deprec. Life for SL and SYD | 27.5 | |
| Sub-period placed in Serv. | 1 | Use 2.5 for |
| Sub-Periods per year | 12 | half-year |
| Rounding decimal places | 5 | convention |
| Declining Balance Factor | 150% | |

| Use Depreciation Method: | 1 |
|---|---|
| 1 | MACRS |
| 2 | Straight Line |
| 3 | Sum of Years Digits |

Sum of taxes   $140,000
Sum of After Tax Cash Flows   $210,000

| Year | BTCF | Depreciation | Taxable Inc. | Income Tax | ATCF | PWATCF | CUM. CASH FLOW | MACRS DEPR. % |
|---|---|---|---|---|---|---|---|---|
| 0 | (250,000) | --- | | | (250,000) | (250,000) | (250,000) | |
| 1 | 50,000 | 6,970 | 43,030 | (17,212) | 32,788 | 29,275 | (217,212) | 3.485% |
| 2 | 50,000 | 7,272 | 42,728 | (17,091) | 32,909 | 26,235 | (184,303) | 3.636% |
| 3 | 50,000 | 7,272 | 42,728 | (17,091) | 32,909 | 23,424 | (151,394) | 3.636% |
| 4 | 50,000 | 7,272 | 42,728 | (17,091) | 32,909 | 20,914 | (118,486) | 3.636% |
| 5 | 50,000 | 7,272 | 42,728 | (17,091) | 32,909 | 18,673 | (85,577) | 3.636% |
| 6 | 50,000 | 7,272 | 42,728 | (17,091) | 32,909 | 16,673 | (52,668) | 3.636% |
| 6 | 300,000 | | 93,330 | (37,332) | 262,668 | 133,076 | 210,000 | 3.636% |

## Problem 11S-3

| | |
|---|---|
| Analysis Life (<51 yr) | 5 |
| Total First Cost | $250,000 |
| Deprec. Amount | $250,000 |
| | |
| Revenue Factor | 1.00 |
| Reference Revenue | $45,000 |
| Annual Revenues | $45,000 |
| Change/yr | |
| Annual Fixed Costs | $5,000 |
| Change/yr | |
| Marginal Tax Rate | 35.0% |

| BTNPW | BTIRR | BTEUAW |
|---|---|---|
| ($47,563) | 8.07% | ($14,318) |
| ATNPW | ATIRR | ATEUAW |
| ($31,627) | 5.49% | ($8,343) |
| AT B/C = | 0.87 | |

| Sum of Depreciation | $194,225 |
|---|---|
| Book Value | $55,775 |

### ATAXNL.WB1

06-Dec-97

| | |
|---|---|
| Salvage Value | $50,000 |
| Sale Price | $50,000 |
| ATMARR | 10.0% |
| BTMARR | 15.4% |
| IRR Guess | 3.90% |

| | | |
|---|---|---|
| MACRS Life, Years | 7.0 | |
| Deprec. Life for SL and SYD | 7.0 | |
| Sub-period placed in Serv. | 2.5 | Use 2.5 for |
| Sub-Periods per year | 4 | half-year |
| Rounding decimal places | 4 | convention |
| Declining Balance Factor | 200% | |

| Use Depreciation Method: | 1 |
|---|---|
| 1 | MACRS |
| 2 | Straight Line |
| 3 | Sum of Years Digits |

| Sum of taxes | $26,250 |
|---|---|
| Sum of After Tax Cash Flows | $48,750 |

| Year | BTCF | Depreciation | Taxable Inc. | Income Tax | ATCF | PWATCF | CUM. CASH FLOW | MACRS DEPR. % |
|---|---|---|---|---|---|---|---|---|
| 0 | (250,000) | --- | --- | | (250,000) | (250,000) | (250,000) | |
| 1 | 45,000 | 35,725 | 9,275 | (3,246) | 41,754 | 37,958 | (208,246) | 14.290% |
| 2 | 50,000 | 61,225 | (11,225) | 3,929 | 53,929 | 44,569 | (154,318) | 24.490% |
| 3 | 55,000 | 43,725 | 11,275 | (3,946) | 51,054 | 38,357 | (103,264) | 17.490% |
| 4 | 60,000 | 31,225 | 28,775 | (10,071) | 49,929 | 34,102 | (53,335) | 12.490% |
| 5 | 65,000 | 22,325 | 42,675 | (14,936) | 50,064 | 31,086 | (3,271) | 8.930% |
| 5 | 50,000 | | (5,775) | 2,021 | 52,021 | 32,301 | 48,750 | 8.920% |

06-Dec-97

## Problem 11S-4    ATAXNL.WB1

| | |
|---|---|
| Analysis Life (<51 yr) | 6 |
| Total First Cost | $55,000 |
| Deprec. Amount | $55,000 |
| Revenue Factor | 1.15 |
| Reference Revenue | $10,000 |
| Annual Revenues | $11,493 |
| Change/yr | |
| Annual Fixed Costs | |
| Change/yr | |
| Marginal Tax Rate | 34.0% |

| BTNPW | ($2,141) | BTIRR | 16.94% | BTEUAW | ($615) |
|---|---|---|---|---|---|
| ATNPW | ($0) | ATIRR | 12.00% | ATEUAW | ($0) |
| AT B/C = | 1.00 | | | | |

| | |
|---|---|
| Sum of Depreciation | $38,781 |
| Book Value | $16,220 |

## Problem 11-30, Breakeven Lease Fee

| | |
|---|---|
| Salvage Value | $35,000 |
| Sale Price | $35,000 |
| ATMARR | 12.0% |
| BTMARR | 18.2% |
| IRR Guess | 9.79% |

| | | |
|---|---|---|
| MACRS Life, Years | 10.0 | |
| Deprec. Life for SL and SYD | 10.0 | |
| Sub-period placed in Serv. | 2.5 | Use 2.5 for |
| Sub-Periods per year | 4 | half-year |
| Rounding decimal places | 4 | convention |
| Declining Balance Factor | 200% | |

| Use Depreciation Method: | 1 |
|---|---|
| 1 | MACRS |
| 2 | Straight Line |
| 3 | Sum of Years Digits |

| | |
|---|---|
| Sum of taxes | $16,647 |
| Sum of After Tax Cash Flows | $32,314 |

| Year | BTCF | Depreciation | Taxable Inc. | Income Tax | ATCF | PWATCF | CUM. CASH FLOW | MACRS DEPR. % |
|---|---|---|---|---|---|---|---|---|
| 0 | (55,000) | — | — | | (55,000) | (55,000) | (55,000) | 10.000% |
| 1 | 11,493 | 5,500 | 5,993 | (2,038) | 9,456 | 8,443 | (45,544) | 18.000% |
| 2 | 11,493 | 9,900 | 1,593 | (542) | 10,952 | 8,731 | (34,593) | 14.400% |
| 3 | 11,493 | 7,920 | 3,573 | (1,215) | 10,278 | 7,316 | (24,314) | 11.520% |
| 4 | 11,493 | 6,336 | 5,157 | (1,754) | 9,740 | 6,190 | (14,574) | 11.520% |
| 5 | 11,493 | 5,071 | 6,422 | (2,184) | 9,310 | 5,283 | (5,265) | 9.220% |
| 6 | 11,493 | 4,053 | 7,440 | (2,530) | 8,964 | 4,541 | 3,699 | 7.370% |
| 6 | 35,000 | | 18,781 | (6,385) | 28,615 | 14,497 | 32,314 | |

06-Dec-97

## Problem 11S-5 — ATAXNL.WB1

| Analysis Life (<51 yr) | 5 |
|---|---|
| Total First Cost | $300,000 |
| Deprec. Amount | $300,000 |
| Revenue Factor | 0.62 |
| Reference Revenue | $150,000 |
| Annual Revenues | $93,628 |
| Change/yr | |
| Annual Fixed Costs | |
| Change/yr | |
| Marginal Tax Rate | 39.0% |

| BTNPW | BTIRR | BTEUAW |
|---|---|---|
| ($17,963) | 16.93% | ($5,963) |
| ATNPW | ATIRR | ATEUAW |
| | 12.00% | |

AT B/C = 1.00

| Sum of Depreciation | $300,000 |
|---|---|
| Book Value | |

| Year | BTCF | Depreciation | Taxable Inc. |
|---|---|---|---|
| 0 | (300,000) | — | |
| 1 | 93,628 | 99,990 | (6,362) |
| 2 | 93,628 | 133,350 | (39,722) |
| 3 | 93,628 | 44,430 | 49,198 |
| 4 | 93,628 | 22,230 | 71,398 |
| 5 | 93,628 | | 93,628 |
| 5 | | | |

## Problem 11-41, Breakeven Savings

| Salvage Value | |
|---|---|
| Sale Price | |
| ATMARR | 12.0% |
| BTMARR | 19.7% |
| IRR Guess | 6.84% |

| MACRS Life, Years | 3.0 | |
|---|---|---|
| Deprec. Life for SL and SYD | 3.0 | |
| Sub-period placed in Serv. | 2.5 | Use 2.5 for |
| Sub-Periods per year | 4 | half-year |
| Rounding decimal places | 4 | convention |
| Declining Balance Factor | 200% | |

| Use Depreciation Method: | 1 |
|---|---|
| 1 | MACRS |
| 2 | Straight Line |
| 3 | Sum of Years Digits |

| Sum of taxes | $65,574 |
|---|---|
| Sum of After Tax Cash Flows | $102,565 |

| Income Tax | ATCF | PWATCF | CUM. CASH FLOW | MACRS DEPR. % |
|---|---|---|---|---|
| — | (300,000) | (300,000) | (300,000) | |
| 2,481 | 96,109 | 85,812 | (203,891) | 33.330% |
| 15,492 | 109,119 | 86,989 | (94,771) | 44.450% |
| (19,187) | 74,441 | 52,985 | (20,331) | 14.810% |
| (27,845) | 65,783 | 41,806 | 45,452 | 7.410% |
| (36,515) | 57,113 | 32,407 | 102,565 | |
| | | | 102,565 | |

# 12S-1          BEFORE TAX EUAC ANALYSIS          Problem 12S-1

EUAC: %INC

| Initial Cost | $250,000 | | SOYD LIFE | 10 |
|---|---|---|---|---|
| Discount Rate | 15.00% | | Initial Salvage Value: | $210,000 |
| Initial Maint. Cost | $20,000 | | Salvage Gradient: | ($40,000) |
| Mainten. % Inc./yr | 20.00% | | Minimum Salvage Value | $0 |
| Mainten. Gradient: | $5,000 | (For Arithmetic Gradient on Pages 2&4) | | |

| Year | Mainten. Cost | NPW Maint. | EUAC Maint. | Salvage Value | EUAC Cap. Rec. | EUAC Total | Marginal Cost |
|---|---|---|---|---|---|---|---|
| 0 | | | | $250,000 | | | |
| 1 | $20,000 | $17,391 | $20,000 | $210,000 | $77,500 | $97,500 | $97,500 |
| 2 | $24,000 | $35,539 | $21,860 | $170,000 | $74,709 | $96,570 | $95,500 |
| 3 | $28,800 | $54,475 | $23,859 | $130,000 | $72,057 | $95,916 | $94,300 |
| 4 | $34,560 | $74,235 | $26,002 | $90,000 | $69,542 | $95,544 | $94,060 |
| 5 | $41,472 | $94,854 | $28,296 | $50,000 | $67,163 | $95,460 | $94,972 |
| 6 | $49,766 | $116,369 | $30,749 | $10,000 | $64,917 | $95,666 | $94,972 |
| 7 | $59,720 | $138,820 | $33,367 | $0 | $60,090 | $93,457 | $71,220 |
| 8 | $71,664 | $162,247 | $36,157 | $0 | $55,713 | $91,869 | $71,664 |
| 9 | $85,996 | $186,693 | $39,126 | $0 | $52,394 | $91,519 | $85,996 |
| 10 | $103,196 | $212,201 | $42,281 | $0 | $49,813 | $92,095 | $103,196 |

| MARR | 8.00% | 10.00% | 12.00% | 14.00% | 16.00% | 18.00% | 20.00% |
|---|---|---|---|---|---|---|---|
| | EUAC Total | EUAC Total | EUAC Total | EUAC Total | EUAC Total | EUAC Total | EUAC Total |
| 1 | $80,000 | $85,000 | $90,000 | $95,000 | $100,000 | $105,000 | $110,000 |
| 2 | $80,385 | $85,000 | $89,623 | $94,252 | $98,889 | $103,532 | $108,182 |
| 3 | $81,005 | $85,242 | $89,497 | $93,772 | $98,065 | $102,375 | $106,703 |
| 4 | $81,883 | $85,741 | $89,636 | $93,566 | $97,531 | $101,529 | $105,559 |
| 5 | $83,040 | $86,516 | $90,051 | $93,643 | $97,290 | $100,990 | $104,741 |
| 6 | $84,502 | $87,585 | $90,755 | $94,009 | $97,343 | $100,754 | $104,240 |
| 7 | $82,935 | $85,808 | $88,789 | $91,876 | $95,063 | $98,346 | $101,722 |
| 8 | $81,876 | $84,571 | $87,397 | $90,348 | $93,420 | $96,606 | $99,900 |
| 9 | $82,206 | $84,676 | $87,302 | $90,078 | $92,996 | $96,050 | $99,232 |
| 10 | $83,655 | $85,838 | $88,208 | $90,756 | $93,474 | $96,353 | $99,384 |

| Salvage Gradient @MARR 15.00% | ($20,000) | ($25,000) | ($30,000) | ($35,000) | ($40,000) | ($45,000) | ($50,000) |
|---|---|---|---|---|---|---|---|
| | EUAC Total | EUAC Total | EUAC Total | EUAC Total | EUAC Total | EUAC Total | EUAC Total |
| 1 | $77,500 | $82,500 | $87,500 | $92,500 | $97,500 | $102,500 | $107,500 |
| 2 | $77,965 | $82,616 | $87,267 | $91,919 | $96,570 | $101,221 | $105,872 |
| 3 | $78,638 | $82,957 | $87,277 | $91,596 | $95,916 | $100,236 | $104,555 |
| 4 | $79,523 | $83,528 | $87,534 | $91,539 | $95,544 | $99,550 | $103,555 |
| 5 | $80,628 | $84,336 | $88,044 | $91,752 | $95,460 | $99,167 | $102,875 |
| 6 | $81,957 | $85,385 | $88,812 | $92,239 | $95,666 | $96,808 | $96,808 |
| 7 | $83,517 | $86,680 | $89,843 | $93,005 | $93,457 | $93,457 | $93,457 |
| 8 | $85,313 | $88,227 | $91,141 | $91,869 | $91,869 | $91,869 | $91,869 |
| 9 | $87,349 | $90,030 | $91,519 | $91,519 | $91,519 | $91,519 | $91,519 |
| 10 | $89,632 | $92,095 | $92,095 | $92,095 | $92,095 | $92,095 | $92,095 |

Done using copy EUACTotal solutions and past values only

## 12S-2   BEFORE TAX EUAC ANALYSIS   Problem 12S-2

EUAC: %INC

| Initial Cost | $200,000 | | SOYD LIFE | 10 |
|---|---|---|---|---|
| Discount Rate | 15.00% | | Initial Salvage Value: | $175,000 |
| Initial Maint. Cost | $20,000 | | Salvage Gradient: | ($15,000) |
| Mainten. % Inc./yr | 15.00% | | Minimum Salvage Value | $0 |
| Mainten. Gradient: | $5,000 | (For Arithmetic Gradient on Pages 2&4) | | |

| Year | Mainten. Cost | NPW Maint. | EUAC Maint. | Salvage Value | EUAC Cap. Rec. | EUAC Total | Marginal Cost |
|---|---|---|---|---|---|---|---|
| 0 | | | | $200,000 | | | |
| 1 | $20,000 | $17,391 | $20,000 | $175,000 | $55,000 | $75,000 | $75,000 |
| 2 | $23,000 | $34,783 | $21,395 | $160,000 | $48,605 | $70,000 | $64,250 |
| 3 | $26,450 | $52,174 | $22,851 | $145,000 | $45,839 | $68,690 | $65,450 |
| 4 | $30,417 | $69,565 | $24,366 | $130,000 | $44,019 | $68,385 | $67,168 |
| 5 | $34,980 | $86,957 | $25,940 | $115,000 | $42,607 | $68,547 | $69,480 |
| 6 | $40,227 | $104,348 | $27,573 | $100,000 | $41,424 | $68,996 | $72,477 |
| 7 | $46,261 | $121,739 | $29,261 | $85,000 | $40,391 | $69,653 | $76,261 |
| 8 | $53,200 | $139,130 | $31,005 | $70,000 | $39,471 | $70,476 | $80,950 |
| 9 | $61,180 | $156,522 | $32,803 | $55,000 | $38,638 | $71,441 | $86,680 |
| 10 | $70,358 | $173,913 | $34,653 | $40,000 | $37,880 | $72,533 | $93,608 |

a. The Economic Useful Life appears to be 4 years, but the 5th year is also well below the total lease cost of $75,000.
b. Replace the defender (the lease) immediately and keep the new machine 4 to 5 years, evaluating the marginal cost ever year.

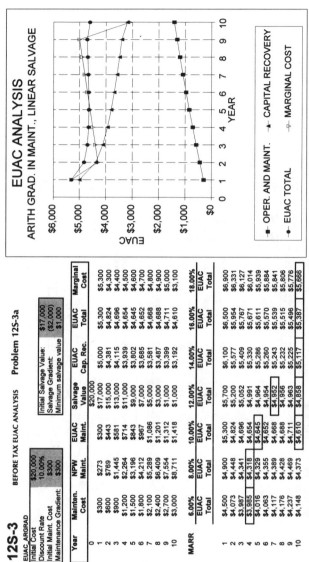

EUAC ANALYSIS
ARITH GRAD. IN MAINT., LINEAR SALVAGE

## 12S-3

BEFORE TAX EUAC ANALYSIS   Problem 12S-3a

| EUAC_ARGRAD | |
|---|---|
| Initial Cost | $20,000 |
| Discount Rate | 10.00% |
| Initial Maint. Cost | $300 |
| Maintenance Gradient: | $300 |

| Initial Salvage Value: | $17,000 |
|---|---|
| Salvage Gradient: | ($2,000) |
| Minimum salvage value | $1,000 |

| Year | Mainten. Cost | NPW Maint. | EUAC Maint. | Salvage Value | EUAC Cap. Rec. | EUAC Total | Marginal Cost |
|---|---|---|---|---|---|---|---|
| 0 | | | | $20,000 | | | |
| 1 | $300 | $273 | $300 | $17,000 | $5,000 | $5,300 | $5,300 |
| 2 | $600 | $769 | $443 | $15,000 | $4,381 | $4,824 | $4,300 |
| 3 | $900 | $1,445 | $581 | $13,000 | $4,115 | $4,696 | $4,400 |
| 4 | $1,200 | $2,264 | $714 | $11,000 | $3,939 | $4,654 | $4,500 |
| 5 | $1,500 | $3,196 | $843 | $9,000 | $3,802 | $4,645 | $4,600 |
| 6 | $1,800 | $4,212 | $967 | $7,000 | $3,685 | $4,652 | $4,700 |
| 7 | $2,100 | $5,289 | $1,086 | $5,000 | $3,581 | $4,668 | $4,800 |
| 8 | $2,400 | $6,409 | $1,201 | $3,000 | $3,487 | $4,688 | $4,900 |
| 9 | $2,700 | $7,554 | $1,312 | $1,000 | $3,399 | $4,711 | $5,000 |
| 10 | $3,000 | $8,711 | $1,418 | $1,000 | $3,192 | $4,610 | $3,100 |

| MARR | 6.00% | 8.00% | 10.00% | 12.00% | 14.00% | 16.00% | 18.00% |
|---|---|---|---|---|---|---|---|
| | EUAC Total | EUAC Total | EUAC Total | EUAC Total | EUAC Total | EUAC Total | EUAC Total |
| 1 | $4,500 | $4,900 | $5,300 | $5,700 | $6,100 | $6,500 | $6,900 |
| 2 | $4,073 | $4,448 | $4,824 | $5,200 | $5,577 | $5,954 | $6,331 |
| 3 | $3,987 | $4,341 | $4,696 | $5,052 | $5,409 | $5,767 | $6,127 |
| 4 | $3,985 | $4,318 | $4,654 | $4,991 | $5,330 | $5,671 | $6,014 |
| 5 | $4,016 | $4,329 | $4,645 | $4,964 | $5,286 | $5,611 | $5,939 |
| 6 | $4,063 | $4,355 | $4,652 | $4,954 | $5,260 | $5,570 | $5,884 |
| 7 | $4,117 | $4,389 | $4,668 | $4,952 | $5,243 | $5,539 | $5,841 |
| 8 | $4,176 | $4,428 | $4,688 | $4,956 | $5,232 | $5,515 | $5,806 |
| 9 | $4,237 | $4,469 | $4,711 | $4,963 | $5,225 | $5,496 | $5,776 |
| 10 | $4,148 | $4,373 | $4,610 | $4,858 | $5,117 | $5,387 | $5,666 |

Done using copy EUACTotal solutions and past values only
For MARR > 12%, the analysis should be carried beyond 10 years

# 12S-3   BEFORE TAX EUAC ANALYSIS   Problem 12S-3b

Developed by Prof. B. Johnson, USNA
johnson@nadn.navy.mil

EUAC: %INC

| | | | |
|---|---|---|---|
| Initial Cost | $20,000 | SOYD LIFE | 10 |
| Discount Rate | 10.00% | Initial Salvage Value: | $17,000 |
| Initial Maint. Cost | $300 | Salvage Gradient: | ($2,000) |
| Mainten. % Inc./yr | 30.00% | Minimum Salvage Value | $1,000 |
| Mainten. Gradient: | $300 | (For Arithmetic Gradient on Pages 2&4) | |

| Year | Mainten. Cost | NPW Maint. | EUAC Maint. | Salvage Value | EUAC Cap. Rec. | EUAC Total | Marginal Cost |
|---|---|---|---|---|---|---|---|
| 0 | $300 | | | $20,000 | | | |
| 1 | $390 | $273 | $300 | $17,000 | $5,000 | $5,300 | $5,300 |
| 2 | $507 | $595 | $343 | $15,000 | $4,381 | $4,724 | $4,090 |
| 3 | $659 | $976 | $392 | $13,000 | $4,115 | $4,507 | $4,007 |
| 4 | $857 | $1,426 | $450 | $11,000 | $3,939 | $4,389 | $3,959 |
| 5 | $1,114 | $1,958 | $517 | $9,000 | $3,802 | $4,318 | $3,957 |
| 6 | $1,448 | $2,587 | $594 | $7,000 | $3,685 | $4,279 | $4,014 |
| 7 | $1,882 | $3,330 | $684 | $5,000 | $3,581 | $4,265 | $4,148 |
| 8 | $2,447 | $4,208 | $789 | $3,000 | $3,487 | $4,275 | $4,382 |
| 9 | $3,181 | $5,246 | $911 | $1,000 | $3,399 | $4,310 | $4,747 |
| 10 | | $6,473 | $1,053 | $1,000 | $3,192 | $4,246 | $3,281 |

| MARR | 6.00% | 8.00% | 10.00% | 12.00% | 14.00% | 16.00% | 18.00% |
|---|---|---|---|---|---|---|---|
| Year | EUAC Total | EUAC Total | EUAC Total | EUAC Total | EUAC Total | EUAC Total | EUAC Total |
| 1 | $4,500 | $4,900 | $5,300 | $5,700 | $6,100 | $6,500 | $6,900 |
| 2 | $3,971 | $4,347 | $4,724 | $5,101 | $5,479 | $5,856 | $6,235 |
| 3 | $3,794 | $4,150 | $4,507 | $4,866 | $5,225 | $5,586 | $5,947 |
| 4 | $3,713 | $4,050 | $4,389 | $4,730 | $5,074 | $5,419 | $5,765 |
| 5 | $3,678 | $3,997 | $4,318 | $4,643 | $4,971 | $5,302 | $5,636 |
| 6 | $3,674 | $3,974 | $4,279 | $4,588 | $4,901 | $5,219 | $5,540 |
| 7 | $3,698 | $4,007 | $4,265 | $4,558 | $4,857 | $5,162 | $5,472 |
| 8 | $3,747 | $4,061 | $4,275 | $4,552 | $4,836 | $5,128 | $5,427 |
| 9 | $3,823 | $4,006 | $4,310 | $4,569 | $4,838 | $5,117 | $5,404 |
| 10 | $3,779 | | $4,246 | $4,497 | $4,760 | $5,033 | $5,317 |

Done using copy EUACTotal solutions and past values only
For MARR > 12%, the analysis should be carried beyond 10 years

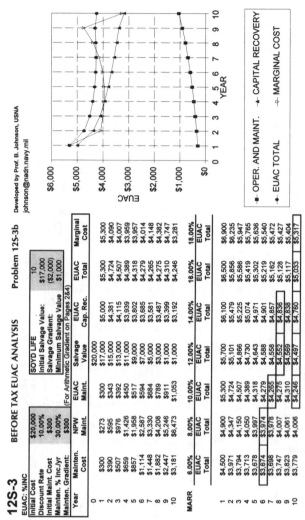

Legend: ■ OPER. AND MAINT.   ⊕ CAPITAL RECOVERY   ◆ EUAC TOTAL   ☐ MARGINAL COST

(Chart: EUAC ($0–$6,000) vs. YEAR (0–10))

# 20-1

| Analysis | A | B | C | D | E | F | G |
|---|---|---|---|---|---|---|---|
| 1 | **Problem** | | COMPARISON OF ALTERNATIVES WITH EQUAL LIVES | | | | |
| 2 | | | | | | | |
| 3 | 5ALTEL | | MARR | | 18.00% | IRR GUES | 25% |
| 4 | | | ANALYSIS LIFE (<21yr) | | 6 | YEARS | |
| 5 | | | | | | | |
| 6 | ALTERNATIVE | | A | B | C | D | E |
| 7 | INITIAL COST | | $150,000 | $200,000 | $300,000 | $350,000 | $400,000 |
| 8 | ANNUAL COSTS | | $30,000 | $50,000 | $80,000 | $70,000 | $60,000 |
| 9 | ANNUAL COST GRADIEN | | | | | ($1,000) | ($5,000) |
| 10 | ANNUAL REVENUE | | $70,000 | $100,000 | $150,000 | $150,000 | $150,000 |
| 11 | SALVAGE VALUE | | $80,000 | $110,000 | $155,000 | $170,000 | $180,000 |
| 12 | | | | | | | |
| 13 | | | Salvage value as a reduced cost | | | | |
| 14 | EUAB | | $70,000 | $100,000 | $150,000 | $150,000 | $150,000 |
| 15 | EUAC(CR) + EUAC(0&M) | | $64,414 | $95,532 | $149,357 | $150,039 | $145,174 |
| 16 | EUAW | | $5,586 | $4,468 | $643 | ($39) | $4,826 |
| 17 | | | | | | | |
| 18 | | | Salvage value as a benefit | | | | |
| 19 | EUAB | | $78,473 | $111,650 | $166,416 | $168,005 | $169,064 |
| 20 | EUAC | | $72,887 | $107,182 | $165,773 | $168,043 | $164,238 |
| 21 | EUAW | | $5,586 | $4,468 | $643 | ($39) | $4,826 |
| 22 | | | | | | | |
| 23 | | | Salvage value as a benefit | | | | |
| 24 | PW BENEFITS | | $274,467 | $390,508 | $582,057 | $587,614 | $591,318 |
| 25 | PW COSTS | | $254,928 | $374,880 | $579,808 | $587,749 | $574,439 |
| 26 | NPW FROM CASH FLOW | | $19,539 | $15,628 | $2,249 | ($135) | $16,879 |
| 27 | | | | | | | |
| 28 | | | Net Annual Cash Flow (NACF) Method | | | | |
| 29 | PWB | | $169,539 | $215,628 | $302,249 | $349,865 | $416,879 |
| 30 | PWC | | $150,000 | $200,000 | $300,000 | $350,000 | $400,000 |
| 31 | NPW=PWB-PWC | | $19,539 | $15,628 | $2,249 | ($135) | $16,879 |
| 32 | | | | | | | |
| 33 | | | Net Annual Cash Flow (NACF) Method | | | | |
| 34 | B/C = PWB/PWC | | 1.130 | 1.078 | 1.007 | 1.000 | 1.042 |
| 35 | DELTA B/C [B-A, C-B, D-C, E-D] | | | 0.92 | 0.87 | 0.95 | 1.34 |
| 36 | DELTA B/C [    C-A, D-B, E-C] | | | | 0.88 | 0.89 | 1.15 |
| 37 | DELTA B/C [        D-A, E-B] | | | | | 0.90 | 1.01 |
| 38 | DELTA B/C [            E-A] | | | | | | 0.99 |
| 39 | | | | | | | |
| 40 | | | Net Annual Cash Flow (NACF) Method | | | | |
| 41 | IRR | | 22.22% | 20.53% | 18.25% | 17.99% | 19.36% |
| 42 | DELTA IRR [B-A, C-B, D-C, E-D] | | | 15.49% | 13.47% | 16.41% | 27.85% |
| 43 | DELTA IRR [    C-A, D-B, E-C] | | | | 14.17% | 14.46% | 22.52% |
| 44 | DELTA IRR [        D-A, E-B] | | | | | 14.73% | 18.20% |
| 45 | DELTA IRR [            E-A] | | | | | | 17.66% |
| 46 | | | | | | | |
| 47 | | | NET ANNUAL CASH FLOWS | | | | |
| 48 | | | A | B | C | D | E |
| 49 | | YEAR 0 | ($150,000) | ($200,000) | ($300,000) | ($350,000) | ($400,000) |
| 50 | | 1 | $40,000 | $50,000 | $70,000 | $80,000 | $90,000 |
| 51 | | 2 | $40,000 | $50,000 | $70,000 | $81,000 | $95,000 |
| 52 | | 3 | $40,000 | $50,000 | $70,000 | $82,000 | $100,000 |
| 53 | | 4 | $40,000 | $50,000 | $70,000 | $83,000 | $105,000 |
| 54 | | 5 | $40,000 | $50,000 | $70,000 | $84,000 | $110,000 |
| 55 | | 6 | $120,000 | $160,000 | $225,000 | $255,000 | $295,000 |
| 56 | | | | | | | |
| 57 | | | Note that Alternative A is always preferred when | | | | |
| 58 | | | 17.67% is less than the MARR which is less than 22.23% | | | | |

# 20-2

| Analysis | A | B | C | D | E | F | G |
|---|---|---|---|---|---|---|---|
| 1 | **Problem** | | COMPARISON OF ALTERNATIVES WITH EQUAL LIVES | | | | |
| 2 | | | | | | | |
| 3 | 5ALTEL | | MARR | | 15.00% | IRR GUES | 25% |
| 4 | | | ANALYSIS LIFE (<21yr) | | 6 | YEARS | |
| 5 | | | | | | | |
| 6 | ALTERNATIVE | | A | B | C | D | E |
| 7 | INITIAL COST | | $150,000 | $200,000 | $300,000 | $350,000 | $400,000 |
| 8 | ANNUAL COSTS | | $30,000 | $50,000 | $80,000 | $70,000 | $60,000 |
| 9 | ANNUAL COST GRADIEN | | | | | ($1,000) | ($5,000) |
| 10 | ANNUAL REVENUE | | $60,497 | $90,281 | $141,564 | $140,965 | $134,646 |
| 11 | SALVAGE VALUE | | $80,000 | $110,000 | $155,000 | $170,000 | $180,000 |
| 12 | | | | | | | |
| 13 | | | Salvage value as a reduced cost | | | | |
| 14 | EUAB | | $60,497 | $90,281 | $141,564 | $140,965 | $134,646 |
| 15 | EUAC(CR) + EUAC(0&M) | | $60,497 | $90,281 | $141,564 | $140,965 | $134,646 |
| 16 | EUAW | | $0 | $0 | ($0) | ($0) | $0 |
| 17 | | | | | | | |
| 18 | | | Salvage value as a benefit | | | | |
| 19 | EUAB | | $69,636 | $102,847 | $159,271 | $160,386 | $155,209 |
| 20 | EUAC | | $69,636 | $102,847 | $159,271 | $160,386 | $155,209 |
| 21 | EUAW | | $0 | $0 | ($0) | ($0) | $0 |
| 22 | | | | | | | |
| 23 | | | Salvage value as a benefit | | | | |
| 24 | PW BENEFITS | | $263,535 | $389,224 | $602,759 | $606,977 | $587,385 |
| 25 | PW COSTS | | $263,534 | $389,224 | $602,759 | $606,977 | $587,385 |
| 26 | NPW FROM CASH FLOW | | $0 | $0 | ($0) | ($0) | $0 |
| 27 | | | | | | | |
| 28 | | | Net Annual Cash Flow (NACF) Method | | | | |
| 29 | PWB | | $150,000 | $200,000 | $300,000 | $350,000 | $400,000 |
| 30 | PWC | | $150,000 | $200,000 | $300,000 | $350,000 | $400,000 |
| 31 | NPW=PWB-PWC | | $0 | $0 | ($0) | ($0) | $0 |
| 32 | | | | | | | |
| 33 | | | Net Annual Cash Flow (NACF) Method | | | | |
| 34 | B/C = PWB/PWC | | 1.000 | 1.000 | 1.000 | 1.000 | 1.000 |
| 35 | DELTA B/C [B-A, C-B, D-C, E-D] | | | 1.00 | 1.00 | 1.00 | 1.00 |
| 36 | DELTA B/C [      C-A, D-B, E-C] | | | | 1.00 | 1.00 | 1.00 |
| 37 | DELTA B/C [          D-A, E-B] | | | | | 1.00 | 1.00 |
| 38 | DELTA B/C [          E-A] | | | | | | 1.00 |
| 39 | | | | | | | |
| 40 | | | Net Annual Cash Flow (NACF) Method | | | | |
| 41 | IRR | | 15.00% | 15.00% | 15.00% | 15.00% | 15.00% |
| 42 | DELTA IRR [B-A, C-B, D-C, E-D] | | | 15.00% | 15.00% | 15.00% | 15.00% |
| 43 | DELTA IRR [      C-A, D-B, E-C] | | | | 15.00% | 15.00% | 15.00% |
| 44 | DELTA IRR [          D-A, E-B] | | | | | 15.00% | 15.00% |
| 45 | DELTA IRR [          E-A] | | | | | | 15.00% |
| 46 | | | | | | | |
| 47 | | | NET ANNUAL CASH FLOWS | | | | |
| 48 | | | A | B | C | D | E |
| 49 | | YEAR 0 | ($150,000) | ($200,000) | ($300,000) | ($350,000) | ($400,000) |
| 50 | | 1 | $30,497 | $40,281 | $61,564 | $70,965 | $74,646 |
| 51 | | 2 | $30,497 | $40,281 | $61,564 | $71,965 | $79,646 |
| 52 | | 3 | $30,497 | $40,281 | $61,564 | $72,965 | $84,646 |
| 53 | | 4 | $30,497 | $40,281 | $61,564 | $73,965 | $89,646 |
| 54 | | 5 | $30,497 | $40,281 | $61,564 | $74,965 | $94,646 |
| 55 | | 6 | $110,497 | $150,281 | $216,564 | $245,965 | $279,646 |
| 56 | | 7 | | | | | |
| 57 | | 8 | | | | | |
| 58 | | 9 | | | | | |
| 59 | | 10 | | | | | |

# 20-3

| Analysis | A | B | C | D | E | F | G |
|---|---|---|---|---|---|---|---|
| 1 | **Problem** | | COMPARISON OF ALTERNATIVES WITH EQUAL LIVES | | | | |
| 2 | | | | | | | |
| 3 | **5ALTEL** | | MARR | | 6.00% | IRR GUES | 25% |
| 4 | | | ANALYSIS LIFE (<21yr) | | 20 | YEARS | |
| 5 | | | | | | | |
| 6 | ALTERNATIVE | | A (D) | B (B) | C (A) | D (C) | E (E) |
| 7 | INITIAL COST | | $1,000 | $2,000 | $4,000 | $6,000 | $9,000 |
| 8 | ANNUAL COSTS | | | | | | |
| 9 | ANNUAL COST GRADIENT | | | | | | |
| 10 | ANNUAL REVENUE | | $117 | $410 | $639 | $761 | $785 |
| 11 | SALVAGE VALUE | | | | | | |
| 12 | | | | | | | |
| 13 | | | Salvage value as a reduced cost | | | | |
| 14 | EUAB | | $117 | $410 | $639 | $761 | $785 |
| 15 | EUAC(CR) + EUAC(0&M) | | $87 | $174 | $349 | $523 | $785 |
| 16 | EUAW | | $30 | $236 | $290 | $238 | $0 |
| 17 | | | | | | | |
| 18 | | | Salvage value as a benefit | | | | |
| 19 | EUAB | | $117 | $410 | $639 | $761 | $785 |
| 20 | EUAC | | $87 | $174 | $349 | $523 | $785 |
| 21 | EUAW | | $30 | $236 | $290 | $238 | $0 |
| 22 | | | | | | | |
| 23 | | | Salvage value as a benefit | | | | |
| 24 | PW BENEFITS | | $1,342 | $4,703 | $7,329 | $8,729 | $9,004 |
| 25 | PW COSTS | | $1,000 | $2,000 | $4,000 | $6,000 | $9,000 |
| 26 | NPW FROM CASH FLOW | | $342 | $2,703 | $3,329 | $2,729 | $4 |
| 27 | | | | | | | |
| 28 | | | Net Annual Cash Flow (NACF) Method | | | | |
| 29 | PWB | | $1,342 | $4,703 | $7,329 | $8,729 | $9,004 |
| 30 | PWC | | $1,000 | $2,000 | $4,000 | $6,000 | $9,000 |
| 31 | NPW=PWB-PWC | | $342 | $2,703 | $3,329 | $2,729 | $4 |
| 32 | | | | | | | |
| 33 | | | Net Annual Cash Flow (NACF) Method | | | | |
| 34 | B/C = PWB/PWC | | 1.342 | 2.351 | 1.832 | 1.455 | 1.000 |
| 35 | DELTA B/C [B-A, C-B, D-C, E-D] | | | 3.36 | 1.31 | 0.70 | 0.09 |
| 36 | DELTA B/C [     C-A, D-B, E-C] | | | | 2.00 | 1.01 | 0.33 |
| 37 | DELTA B/C [         D-A, E-B] | | | | | 1.48 | 0.61 |
| 38 | DELTA B/C [         E-A] | | | | | | 0.96 |
| 39 | | | | | | | |
| 40 | | | Net Annual Cash Flow (NACF) Method | | | | |
| 41 | IRR | | 9.94% | 19.96% | 15.00% | 11.15% | 6.01% |
| 42 | DELTA IRR [B-A, C-B, D-C, E-D] | | | 29.12% | 9.63% | 1.97% | -13.39% |
| 43 | DELTA IRR [     C-A, D-B, E-C] | | | | 16.59% | 6.08% | -4.65% |
| 44 | DELTA IRR [         D-A, E-B] | | | | | 11.39% | 0.67% |
| 45 | DELTA IRR [         E-A] | | | | | | 5.47% |
| 46 | | | | | | | |
| 47 | | | NET ANNUAL CASH FLOWS | | | | |
| 48 | | | A | B | C | D | E |
| 49 | | YEAR 0 | ($1,000) | ($2,000) | ($4,000) | ($6,000) | ($9,000) |
| 50 | | 1 | $117 | $410 | $639 | $761 | $785 |
| 51 | | 2 | $117 | $410 | $639 | $761 | $785 |
| 52 | | 3 | $117 | $410 | $639 | $761 | $785 |
| 53 | | 4 | $117 | $410 | $639 | $761 | $785 |
| 54 | | 5 | $117 | $410 | $639 | $761 | $785 |
| 55 | | 6 | $117 | $410 | $639 | $761 | $785 |
| 56 | | 7 | $117 | $410 | $639 | $761 | $785 |
| 57 | | 8 | $117 | $410 | $639 | $761 | $785 |
| 58 | | 9 | $117 | $410 | $639 | $761 | $785 |
| 59 | | 10 | $117 | $410 | $639 | $761 | $785 |

# 20-4

**Problem**    COMPARISON OF ALTERNATIVES WITH EQUAL LIVES

**5ALTEL**

| MARR | | 8.00% | IRR GUES | 50% |
|---|---|---|---|---|
| ANALYSIS LIFE (<21yr) | | 10 | YEARS | |

| ALTERNATIVE | A (A) | B (B) | C (C) | D (D) |
|---|---|---|---|---|
| INITIAL COST | $1,300 | $1,300 | $1,300 | $1,300 |
| ANNUAL COSTS | | | | |
| ANNUAL COST GRADIEN | ($30) | ($50) | | $50 |
| ANNUAL REVENUE | $100 | $10 | $260 | $450 |
| SALVAGE VALUE | | | | |

| | Salvage value as a reduced cost | | | |
|---|---|---|---|---|
| EUAB | $100 | $10 | $260 | $450 |
| EUAC(CR) + EUAC(0&M) | $78 | $0 | $194 | $387 |
| EUAW | $22 | $10 | $66 | $63 |

This relatively simple problem poses some interpretation problems for the incremental rate of return method.

| | Salvage value as a benefit | | | |
|---|---|---|---|---|
| EUAB | $100 | $10 | $260 | $450 |
| EUAC | $78 | $0 | $194 | $387 |
| EUAW | $22 | $10 | $66 | $63 |

If the incremental cash flows are analayzed using 3ALTUL (next page) with original alternative B discarded, one can see the cause of the problem.

| | Salvage value as a benefit | | | |
|---|---|---|---|---|
| PW BENEFITS | $671 | $67 | $1,745 | $3,020 |
| PW COSTS | $521 | $1 | $1,300 | $2,599 |
| NPW FROM CASH FLOW | $150 | $66 | $445 | $421 |

The incremental situations involve being a borrower of money as discussed on page 169. However, the cumulative cash flow for B(C) -A indicates it will have no positive rate of return. The increment C(D)- B(C) has an

| | Net Annual Cash Flow (NACF) Method | | | |
|---|---|---|---|---|
| PWB | $1,450 | $1,366 | $1,745 | $1,721 |
| PWC | $1,300 | $1,300 | $1,300 | $1,300 |
| NPW=PWB-PWC | $150 | $66 | $445 | $421 |

IRR greater than the MARR, but in a borrowing situation so B(C) is still selected in 3ALTUL. and the equivalent C(C) is selected in 5ALTEL.

| | Net Annual Cash Flow (NACF) Method | | | |
|---|---|---|---|---|
| B/C = PWB/PWC | 1.116 | 1.051 | 1.342 | 1.324 |
| DELTA B/C [B-A, C-B, D-C, E-D] | | 0.60 | 2.51 | 0.94 |
| DELTA B/C [    C-A, D-B, E-C] | | | 3.27 | 1.53 |
| DELTA B/C [    D-A, E-B] | | | | 1.50 |
| DELTA B/C [    E-A] | | | | |

All other measures of C(D) - B(C) make B(C) the winner in both spreadsheets. Therefore the @IRR function does not always give an easily understood result for the incremental cash flows such as alternative C(D) - B(C).

| | Net Annual Cash Flow (NACF) Method | | | |
|---|---|---|---|---|
| IRR | 10.02% | 8.79% | 15.10% | 18.15% |
| DELTA IRR [B-A, C-B, D-C, E-D] | | 0.00% | -5.92% | 8.97% |
| DELTA IRR [    C-A, D-B, E-C] | | | -9.77% | 1.22% |
| DELTA IRR [    D-A, E-B] | | | | 1.53% |
| DELTA IRR [    E-A] | | | | |

| | NET ANNUAL CASH FLOWS | | | |
|---|---|---|---|---|
| | A | B | C | D |
| YEAR 0 | ($1,300) | ($1,300) | ($1,300) | ($1,300) |
| 1 | $100 | $10 | $260 | $450 |
| 2 | $130 | $60 | $260 | $400 |
| 3 | $160 | $110 | $260 | $350 |
| 4 | $190 | $160 | $260 | $300 |
| 5 | $220 | $210 | $260 | $250 |
| 6 | $250 | $260 | $260 | $200 |
| 7 | $280 | $310 | $260 | $150 |
| 8 | $310 | $360 | $260 | $100 |
| 9 | $340 | $410 | $260 | $50 |
| 10 | $370 | $460 | $260 | |

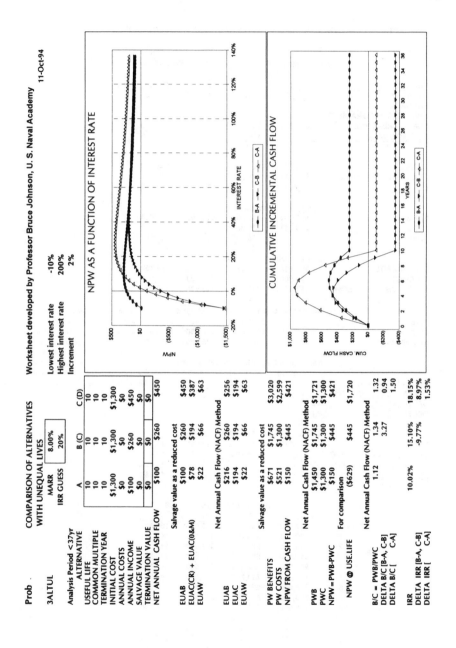

Prob .

**3ALTUL**

COMPARISON OF ALTERNATIVES
WITH UNEQUAL LIVES

Worksheet developed by Professor Bruce Johnson, U. S. Naval Academy

11-Oct-94

| | MARR | 8.00% |
| | IRR GUESS | 20% |

| | Lowest interest rate | -10% |
| | Highest interest rate | 200% |
| | Increment | 2% |

| ALTERNATIVE | A | B (C) | C (D) |
|---|---|---|---|
| Analysis Period <37yr | | | |
| USEFUL LIFE | 10 | 10 | 10 |
| COMMON MULTIPLE | 10 | 10 | 10 |
| TERMINATION YEAR | 10 | 10 | 10 |
| INITIAL COST | $1,300 | $1,300 | $1,300 |
| ANNUAL COSTS | $0 | $0 | $0 |
| ANNUAL INCOME | $100 | $260 | $450 |
| SALVAGE VALUE | $0 | $0 | $0 |
| TERMINATION VALUE | $0 | $0 | $0 |
| NET ANNUAL CASH FLOW | $100 | $260 | $450 |

Salvage value as a reduced cost

| | A | B (C) | C (D) |
|---|---|---|---|
| EUAB | $100 | $260 | $450 |
| EUAC(CR) + EUAC(O&M) | $78 | $194 | $387 |
| EUAW | $22 | $66 | $63 |

Net Annual Cash Flow (NACF) Method

| | A | B (C) | C (D) |
|---|---|---|---|
| EUAB | $216 | $260 | $256 |
| EUAC | $194 | $194 | $194 |
| EUAW | $22 | $66 | $63 |

Salvage value as a reduced cost

| | A | B (C) | C (D) |
|---|---|---|---|
| PW BENEFITS | $671 | $1,745 | $3,020 |
| PW COSTS | $521 | $1,300 | $2,599 |
| NPW FROM CASH FLOW | $150 | $445 | $421 |

Net Annual Cash Flow (NACF) Method

| | A | B (C) | C (D) |
|---|---|---|---|
| PWB | $1,450 | $1,745 | $1,721 |
| PWC | $1,300 | $1,300 | $1,300 |
| NPW = PWB-PWC | $150 | $445 | $421 |

For comparison

| | A | B (C) | C (D) |
|---|---|---|---|
| NPW @ USE.LIFE | ($629) | $445 | $1,720 |

Net Annual Cash Flow (NACF) Method

| | A | B (C) | C (D) |
|---|---|---|---|
| B/C = PWB/PWC | 1.12 | 1.34 | 1.32 |
| DELTA B/C [B-A, C-B] | | 3.27 | 0.94 |
| DELTA B/C [ C-A] | | | 1.50 |
| IRR | 10.02% | 15.10% | 18.15% |
| DELTA IRR [B-A, C-B] | | -9.77% | 8.97% |
| DELTA IRR [ C-A] | | | 1.53% |

# 20-5

**Problem** COMPARISON OF ALTERNATIVES WITH EQUAL LIVES

| 5ALTEL | MARR | | 10.00% | IRR GUES | 50% |
|--------|------|--|--------|----------|-----|
| | ANALYSIS LIFE (<21yr) | | 15 | YEARS | |

| ALTERNATIVE | A (C) | B (A) | C (D) | D (B) |
|-------------|-------|-------|-------|-------|
| INITIAL COST | $100,000 | $145,000 | $200,000 | $300,000 |
| ANNUAL COSTS | | | | |
| ANNUAL COST GRADIENT | | | | |
| ANNUAL REVENUE | $10,000 | $23,300 | $27,500 | $44,300 |
| SALVAGE VALUE | $70,000 | $70,000 | $70,000 | $70,000 |

| | Salvage value as a reduced cost | | | |
|--|--|--|--|--|
| EUAB | $10,000 | $23,300 | $27,500 | $44,300 |
| EUAC(CR) + EUAC(0&M) | $10,944 | $16,861 | $24,092 | $37,239 |
| EUAW | ($944) | $6,439 | $3,408 | $7,061 |

| | Salvage value as a benefit | | | |
|--|--|--|--|--|
| EUAB | $12,203 | $25,503 | $29,703 | $46,503 |
| EUAC | $13,147 | $19,064 | $26,295 | $39,442 |
| EUAW | ($944) | $6,439 | $3,408 | $7,061 |

| | Salvage value as a benefit | | | |
|--|--|--|--|--|
| PW BENEFITS | $92,818 | $193,979 | $225,925 | $353,707 |
| PW COSTS | $100,000 | $145,000 | $200,000 | $300,000 |
| NPW FROM CASH FLOW | ($7,182) | $48,979 | $25,925 | $53,707 |

| | Net Annual Cash Flow (NACF) Method | | | |
|--|--|--|--|--|
| PWB | $92,818 | $193,979 | $225,925 | $353,707 |
| PWC | $100,000 | $145,000 | $200,000 | $300,000 |
| NPW=PWB-PWC | ($7,182) | $48,979 | $25,925 | $53,707 |

Although the automatic car wash facility, D(B), wins at a MARR of 10%, the higher IRR of the conventional gas station, B(A) makes nearly as much profit with half the investment. A MARR of 11% or a $700 reduction in D(B)'s revenue would make B(A) the winner.

| | Net Annual Cash Flow (NACF) Method | | | |
|--|--|--|--|--|
| B/C = PWB/PWC | 0.928 | 1.338 | 1.130 | 1.179 |
| DELTA B/C [B-A, C-B, D-C, E-D] | | 2.25 | 0.58 | 1.28 |
| DELTA B/C [ C-A, D-B, E-C] | | | 1.33 | 1.03 |
| DELTA B/C [ D-A, E-B] | | | | 1.30 |
| DELTA B/C [ E-A] | | | | |

| | Net Annual Cash Flow (NACF) Method | | | |
|--|--|--|--|--|
| IRR | 8.98% | 14.98% | 12.01% | 12.85% |
| DELTA IRR [B-A, C-B, D-C, E-D] | | 28.90% | 1.75% | 14.63% |
| DELTA IRR [ C-A, D-B, E-C] | | | 15.48% | 10.53% |
| DELTA IRR [ D-A, E-B] | | | | 15.06% |
| DELTA IRR [ E-A] | | | | |

| | NET ANNUAL CASH FLOWS | | | |
|--|--|--|--|--|
| | A | B | C | D |
| YEAR 0 | ($100,000) | ($145,000) | ($200,000) | ($300,000) |
| 1 | $10,000 | $23,300 | $27,500 | $44,300 |
| 2 | $10,000 | $23,300 | $27,500 | $44,300 |
| 3 | $10,000 | $23,300 | $27,500 | $44,300 |
| 4 | $10,000 | $23,300 | $27,500 | $44,300 |
| 5 | $10,000 | $23,300 | $27,500 | $44,300 |
| 6 | $10,000 | $23,300 | $27,500 | $44,300 |
| 7 | $10,000 | $23,300 | $27,500 | $44,300 |
| 8 | $10,000 | $23,300 | $27,500 | $44,300 |
| 9 | $10,000 | $23,300 | $27,500 | $44,300 |
| 10 | $10,000 | $23,300 | $27,500 | $44,300 |
| 11 | $10,000 | $23,300 | $27,500 | $44,300 |
| 12 | $10,000 | $23,300 | $27,500 | $44,300 |
| 13 | $10,000 | $23,300 | $27,500 | $44,300 |
| 14 | $10,000 | $23,300 | $27,500 | $44,300 |
| 15 | $80,000 | $93,300 | $97,500 | $114,300 |

# 20-6

**Problem**    COMPARISON OF ALTERNATIVES WITH EQUAL LIVES

**5ALTEL**

| | MARR | 8.00% | IRR GUESS | 50% |
|---|---|---|---|---|
| | ANALYSIS LIFE (<21yr) | 20 | YEARS | |

| ALTERNATIVE | 2 Stories | 5 Stories | 10 Stories |
|---|---|---|---|
| INITIAL COST | $500,000 | $900,000 | $2,200,000 |
| ANNUAL COSTS | | | |
| ANNUAL COST GRADIENT | | | |
| ANNUAL REVENUE | $70,000 | $105,000 | $256,000 |
| SALVAGE VALUE | $200,000 | $300,000 | $400,000 |

Salvage value as a reduced cost

| | | | |
|---|---|---|---|
| EUAB | $70,000 | $105,000 | $256,000 |
| EUAC(CR) + EUAC(0&M) | $46,556 | $85,111 | $215,334 |
| EUAW | $23,444 | $19,889 | $40,666 |

Salvage value as a benefit

| | | | |
|---|---|---|---|
| EUAB | $74,370 | $111,556 | $264,741 |
| EUAC | $50,926 | $91,667 | $224,075 |
| EUAW | $23,444 | $19,889 | $40,666 |

Salvage value as a benefit

| | | | |
|---|---|---|---|
| PW BENEFITS | $730,180 | $1,095,270 | $2,599,265 |
| PW COSTS | $500,000 | $900,000 | $2,200,000 |
| NPW FROM CASH FLOW | $230,180 | $195,270 | $399,265 |

Net Annual Cash Flow (NACF) Method

| | | | | |
|---|---|---|---|---|
| PWB | $730,180 | $1,095,270 | $2,599,265 | Another case where a change |
| PWC | $500,000 | $900,000 | $2,200,000 | in MARR to greater than 9.27% or a |
| NPW=PWB-PWC | $230,180 | $195,270 | $399,265 | $18,000 per year reduction |

in revenues for the 10-story
building would make the

Net Annual Cash Flow (NACF) Method

| | | | | |
|---|---|---|---|---|
| B/C = PWB/PWC | 1.460 | 1.217 | 1.181 | the 2-story building, the |
| DELTA B/C [B-A, C-B, D-C, E-D] | | 0.91 | 1.16 | more conservative investment, |
| DELTA B/C [    C-A, D-B, E-C] | | | 1.10 | a better choice. |
| DELTA B/C [        D-A, E-B] | | | | In an independent investment allocation, |
| DELTA B/C [            E-A] | | | | the 2-story building would be the clear |

choice.

Net Annual Cash Flow (NACF) Method

| | | | |
|---|---|---|---|
| IRR | 13.28% | 10.58% | 10.25% |
| DELTA IRR [B-A, C-B, D-C, E-D] | | 6.90% | 10.00% |
| DELTA IRR [    C-A, D-B, E-C] | | | 9.27% |
| DELTA IRR [        D-A, E-B] | | | |
| DELTA IRR [            E-A] | | | |

|  | NET ANNUAL CASH FLOWS | | |
|---|---|---|---|
| | A | B | C |
| YEAR 0 | ($500,000) | ($900,000) | ($2,200,000) |
| 1 | $70,000 | $105,000 | $256,000 |
| 2 | $70,000 | $105,000 | $256,000 |
| 3 | $70,000 | $105,000 | $256,000 |
| 4 | $70,000 | $105,000 | $256,000 |
| 5 | $70,000 | $105,000 | $256,000 |
| 6 | $70,000 | $105,000 | $256,000 |
| 7 | $70,000 | $105,000 | $256,000 |
| 8 | $70,000 | $105,000 | $256,000 |
| 9 | $70,000 | $105,000 | $256,000 |
| 10 | $70,000 | $105,000 | $256,000 |
| 11 | $70,000 | $105,000 | $256,000 |
| 12 | $70,000 | $105,000 | $256,000 |
| 13 | $70,000 | $105,000 | $256,000 |
| 14 | $70,000 | $105,000 | $256,000 |
| 15 | $70,000 | $105,000 | $256,000 |
| 16 | $70,000 | $105,000 | $256,000 |
| 17 | $70,000 | $105,000 | $256,000 |
| 18 | $70,000 | $105,000 | $256,000 |
| 19 | $70,000 | $105,000 | $256,000 |
| 20 | $270,000 | $405,000 | $656,000 |

# 20-7

**Problem**
Prob 9-24
**5ALTEL**

COMPARISON OF ALTERNATIVES WITH EQUAL LIVES

| MARR | 8.00% | |
|---|---|---|
| ANALYSIS PERIOD | 8 | YEARS |

| ALTERNATIVE | A (D) | B (C) | C (B) | D (A) |
|---|---|---|---|---|
| INITIAL COST | $50,000 | $60,000 | $80,000 | $100,000 |
| ANNUAL COSTS | | | | |
| ANNUAL COST GRADIENT | | | | |
| ANNUAL REVENUE | $12,200 | $9,700 | $12,000 | $12,200 |
| SALVAGE VALUE | | $50,000 | $50,000 | $75,000 |

Salvage value as a reduced cost

| | A (D) | B (C) | C (B) | D (A) |
|---|---|---|---|---|
| EUAB | $12,200 | $9,700 | $12,000 | $12,200 |
| EUAC(CR) + EUAC(O&M) | $8,701 | $5,740 | $9,220 | $10,350 |
| EUAW | $3,499 | $3,960 | $2,780 | $1,850 |

Salvage value as a benefit

| | A (D) | B (C) | C (B) | D (A) |
|---|---|---|---|---|
| EUAB | $12,200 | $14,401 | $16,701 | $19,251 |
| EUAC | $8,701 | $10,441 | $13,921 | $17,401 |
| EUAW | $3,499 | $3,960 | $2,780 | $1,850 |

Salvage value as a benefit

| | A (D) | B (C) | C (B) | D (A) |
|---|---|---|---|---|
| PW BENEFITS | $70,109 | $82,756 | $95,973 | $110,629 |
| PW COSTS | $50,000 | $60,000 | $80,000 | $100,000 |
| NPW FROM CASH FLOW | $20,109 | $22,756 | $15,973 | $10,629 |

Net Annual Cash Flow (NACF) Method

| | A (D) | B (C) | C (B) | D (A) |
|---|---|---|---|---|
| PWB | $70,109 | $82,756 | $95,973 | $110,629 |
| PWC | $50,000 | $60,000 | $80,000 | $100,000 |
| NPW=PWB-PWC | $20,109 | $22,756 | $15,973 | $10,629 |

Net Annual Cash Flow (NACF) Method

| | A (D) | B (C) | C (B) | D (A) |
|---|---|---|---|---|
| B/C = PWB/PWC | 1.402 | 1.379 | 1.200 | 1.106 |
| DELTA B/C [B-A, C-B, D-C, E-D] | | 1.12 | 0.66 | 0.73 |
| DELTA B/C [     C-A, D-B, E-C] | | | 0.87 | 0.70 |
| DELTA B/C [          D-A, E-B] | | | | 0.81 |
| DELTA B/C [               E-A] | | | | |

The NACF method gives different ratios when a salvage value is present, but the decision tree results remain the same. Choose Alt C (shown as B (C)) using 5ALTEL.
Alternative A(D) would be chosen in a mutually independent alternative situation.

Net Annual Cash Flow (NACF) Method

| | A (D) | B (C) | C (B) | D (A) |
|---|---|---|---|---|
| IRR | 17.84% | 14.95% | 11.95% | 10.02% |
| DELTA IRR [B-A, C-B, D-C, E-D] | | 9.99% | -1.82% | 3.74% |
| DELTA IRR [     C-A, D-B, E-C] | | | 6.06% | 1.86% |
| DELTA IRR [          D-A, E-B] | | | | 5.20% |
| DELTA IRR [               E-A] | | | | |

NET ANNUAL CASH FLOWS

| | A | B | C | D |
|---|---|---|---|---|
| YEAR 0 | ($50,000) | ($60,000) | ($80,000) | ($100,000) |
| 1 | $12,200 | $9,700 | $12,000 | $12,200 |
| 2 | $12,200 | $9,700 | $12,000 | $12,200 |
| 3 | $12,200 | $9,700 | $12,000 | $12,200 |
| 4 | $12,200 | $9,700 | $12,000 | $12,200 |
| 5 | $12,200 | $9,700 | $12,000 | $12,200 |
| 6 | $12,200 | $9,700 | $12,000 | $12,200 |
| 7 | $12,200 | $9,700 | $12,000 | $12,200 |
| 8 | $12,200 | $59,700 | $62,000 | $87,200 |

# 20-8

| Problem | DAILY REQUIRED FREIGHT RATE | | | (EQUAL LIVES) | |
|---|---|---|---|---|---|

| DRFREL | BTMARR | | 20.00% | IRR GUESS | 20% |
|---|---|---|---|---|---|
| | ANALYSIS LIFI (<21 Yr) | | 10 | DDB Life, Yr. | 20 |

| ALTERNATIVE | A | B | C | D | E |
|---|---|---|---|---|---|
| INITIAL COST ($000s) | $100,000 | $150,000 | $200,000 | $300,000 | $320,000 |
| VARIABLE DAILY COST/PASS. | $12 | $30 | $13 | $13 | $30 |
| FIXED DAILY COST/PASS CAP. | $42 | $42 | $42 | $42 | $42 |
| ANNUAL COST GRAD. | $0 | $0 | $0 | $0 | $0 |
| SALVAGE VALUE ($000s) | ($13,024) | $65,271 | $197,534 | $337,419 | $131,021 |
| PASSENGER CAPACITY | 1,200 | 1,600 | 2,000 | 2,600 | 2,000 |
| VOYAGE DAYS/YEAR | 330 | 330 | 330 | 330 | 330 |
| AVERAGE DAILY FARE | $150 | $170 | $150 | $160 | $230 |
| PROJ. LOAD FACTOR | 0.75 | 0.75 | 0.75 | 0.75 | 0.75 |

| | | | | | |
|---|---|---|---|---|---|
| Ref. Var. Net Revenue @ L.F. = 1.0 | $54,648 | $73,920 | $90,420 | $126,126 | $132,000 |
| PROJ. ANNUAL REVENUE ($000s) | $44,550 | $67,320 | $74,250 | $102,960 | $113,850 |
| PROJ. EUAC (Var. O&M) ($000s) | $3,564 | $11,880 | $6,435 | $8,366 | $14,850 |
| PROJ. EUAC (Fixed O&M) ($000s) | $16,632 | $22,176 | $27,720 | $36,036 | $27,720 |
| PROJ. EUAC (CAP. REC.) ($000s) | $24,354 | $33,264 | $40,095 | $58,558 | $71,280 |

| | | | | | |
|---|---|---|---|---|---|
| RFR/DAY @ PROJ. L. F. | $150 | $170 | $150 | $160 | $230 |
| BREAKEVEN LF | 0.750 | 0.750 | 0.750 | 0.750 | 0.750 |

| All Values in $000s | Salvage value as a reduced cost | | | | |
|---|---|---|---|---|---|
| EUAB | $44,550 | $67,320 | $74,250 | $102,960 | $113,850 |
| EUAC(CR) + EUAC(0&M) | $44,550 | $67,320 | $74,250 | $102,960 | $113,850 |
| EUAW | ($0) | ($0) | ($0) | $0 | ($0) |

| | Net Annual Cash Flow (NACF) Method | | | | |
|---|---|---|---|---|---|
| EUAB | $23,852 | $35,778 | $47,705 | $71,557 | $76,327 |
| EUAC | $23,852 | $35,778 | $47,705 | $71,557 | $76,327 |
| EUAW | ($0) | ($0) | ($0) | $0 | ($0) |

| | Salvage value as a reduced cost | | | | |
|---|---|---|---|---|---|
| PW BENEFITS | $186,775 | $282,237 | $311,291 | $431,657 | $477,313 |
| PW COSTS | $186,775 | $282,237 | $311,291 | $431,657 | $477,313 |
| NPW FROM CASH FLOW | ($0) | ($0) | ($0) | $0 | ($0) |

| | Net Annual Cash Flow (NACF) Method | | | | |
|---|---|---|---|---|---|
| PWB | $100,000 | $150,000 | $200,000 | $300,000 | $320,000 |
| PWC | $100,000 | $150,000 | $200,000 | $300,000 | $320,000 |
| NPW=PWB-PWC | ($0) | ($0) | ($0) | $0 | ($0) |

| | Net Annual Cash Flow (NACF) Method | | | | |
|---|---|---|---|---|---|
| B/C = PWB/PWC | 1.000 | 1.000 | 1.000 | 1.000 | 1.000 |
| DELTA B/C [B-A, C-B, D-C, E-D] | | 1.00 | 1.00 | 1.00 | 1.00 |
| DELTA B/C [    C-A, D-B, E-C] | | | 1.00 | 1.00 | 1.00 |
| DELTA B/C [        D-A, E-B] | | | | 1.00 | 1.00 |
| DELTA B/C [            E-A] | | | | | 1.00 |

| | Net Annual Cash Flow (NACF) Method | | | | |
|---|---|---|---|---|---|
| IRR | 20.00% | 20.00% | 20.00% | 20.00% | 20.00% |
| DELTA IRR [B-A, C-B, D-C, E-D] | | 20.00% | 20.00% | 20.00% | 20.00% |
| DELTA IRR [    C-A, D-B, E-C] | | | 20.00% | 20.00% | 20.00% |
| DELTA IRR [        D-A, E-B] | | | | 20.00% | 20.00% |
| DELTA IRR [            E-A] | | | | | 20.00% |

Discussion: This problem illustrates another aspect of breakeven and sensitivity analysis in choosing between alternatives. Only Alternative A has a breakeven salvalge value less than that assumed in the original problem statement. Breakeven analysis nearly always favors the alternative with the highest B/C or IRR since this alternative has the largest "cushion" relative to the assumptions made in the problem statement. Thus the incremental analysis of mutually exclusive alternatives can lead to the choice of an alternative which may have higher risk than expected. Decisions should never be based on a single set of assumptions without some risk analysis on a spreadsheet.

# 20-9

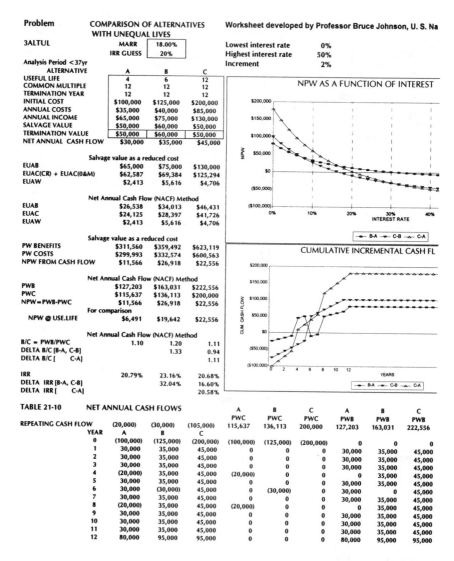

| Problem | COMPARISON OF ALTERNATIVES WITH UNEQUAL LIVES | | | Worksheet developed by Professor Bruce Johnson, U. S. Na |
|---|---|---|---|---|
| 3ALTUL | MARR | 18.00% | | Lowest interest rate 0% |
| | IRR GUESS | 20% | | Highest interest rate 50% |
| Analysis Period <37yr | | | | Increment 2% |

| ALTERNATIVE | A | B | C |
|---|---|---|---|
| USEFUL LIFE | 4 | 6 | 12 |
| COMMON MULTIPLE | 12 | 12 | 12 |
| TERMINATION YEAR | 12 | 12 | 12 |
| INITIAL COST | $100,000 | $125,000 | $200,000 |
| ANNUAL COSTS | $35,000 | $40,000 | $85,000 |
| ANNUAL INCOME | $65,000 | $75,000 | $130,000 |
| SALVAGE VALUE | $50,000 | $60,000 | $50,000 |
| TERMINATION VALUE | $50,000 | $60,000 | $50,000 |
| NET ANNUAL CASH FLOW | $30,000 | $35,000 | $45,000 |

Salvage value as a reduced cost

| | | | |
|---|---|---|---|
| EUAB | $65,000 | $75,000 | $130,000 |
| EUAC(CR) + EUAC(0&M) | $62,587 | $69,384 | $125,294 |
| EUAW | $2,413 | $5,616 | $4,706 |

Net Annual Cash Flow (NACF) Method

| | | | |
|---|---|---|---|
| EUAB | $26,538 | $34,013 | $46,431 |
| EUAC | $24,125 | $28,397 | $41,726 |
| EUAW | $2,413 | $5,616 | $4,706 |

Salvage value as a reduced cost

| | | | |
|---|---|---|---|
| PW BENEFITS | $311,560 | $359,492 | $623,119 |
| PW COSTS | $299,993 | $332,574 | $600,563 |
| NPW FROM CASH FLOW | $11,566 | $26,918 | $22,556 |

Net Annual Cash Flow (NACF) Method

| | | | |
|---|---|---|---|
| PWB | $127,203 | $163,031 | $222,556 |
| PWC | $115,637 | $136,113 | $200,000 |
| NPW = PWB-PWC | $11,566 | $26,918 | $22,556 |
| For comparison | | | |
| NPW @ USE.LIFE | $6,491 | $19,642 | $22,556 |

Net Annual Cash Flow (NACF) Method

| | | | |
|---|---|---|---|
| B/C = PWB/PWC | 1.10 | 1.20 | 1.11 |
| DELTA B/C [B-A, C-B] | | 1.33 | 0.94 |
| DELTA B/C [ C-A] | | | 1.11 |

| | | | |
|---|---|---|---|
| IRR | 20.79% | 23.16% | 20.68% |
| DELTA IRR [B-A, C-B] | | 32.04% | 16.60% |
| DELTA IRR [ C-A] | | | 20.58% |

**TABLE 21-10** NET ANNUAL CASH FLOWS

| | | | | A PWC 115,637 | B PWC 136,113 | C PWC 200,000 | A PWB 127,203 | B PWB 163,031 | C PWB 222,556 |
|---|---|---|---|---|---|---|---|---|---|
| REPEATING CASH FLOW | (20,000) | (30,000) | (105,000) | | | | | | |
| YEAR | A | B | C | | | | | | |
| 0 | (100,000) | (125,000) | (200,000) | (100,000) | (125,000) | (200,000) | 0 | 0 | 0 |
| 1 | 30,000 | 35,000 | 45,000 | 0 | 0 | 0 | 30,000 | 35,000 | 45,000 |
| 2 | 30,000 | 35,000 | 45,000 | 0 | 0 | 0 | 30,000 | 35,000 | 45,000 |
| 3 | 30,000 | 35,000 | 45,000 | 0 | 0 | 0 | 30,000 | 35,000 | 45,000 |
| 4 | (20,000) | 35,000 | 45,000 | (20,000) | 0 | 0 | 0 | 35,000 | 45,000 |
| 5 | 30,000 | 35,000 | 45,000 | 0 | 0 | 0 | 30,000 | 35,000 | 45,000 |
| 6 | 30,000 | (30,000) | 45,000 | 0 | (30,000) | 0 | 30,000 | 0 | 45,000 |
| 7 | 30,000 | 35,000 | 45,000 | 0 | 0 | 0 | 30,000 | 35,000 | 45,000 |
| 8 | (20,000) | 35,000 | 45,000 | (20,000) | 0 | 0 | 0 | 35,000 | 45,000 |
| 9 | 30,000 | 35,000 | 45,000 | 0 | 0 | 0 | 30,000 | 35,000 | 45,000 |
| 10 | 30,000 | 35,000 | 45,000 | 0 | 0 | 0 | 30,000 | 35,000 | 45,000 |
| 11 | 30,000 | 35,000 | 45,000 | 0 | 0 | 0 | 30,000 | 35,000 | 45,000 |
| 12 | 80,000 | 95,000 | 95,000 | 0 | 0 | 0 | 80,000 | 95,000 | 95,000 |

This problem represents another example of multiple sign changes in the cash flows and cumulative cash flows which do not result in multiple rates of return. Alternative B is the best alternative by all methods of analysis.

**20-10**

Problem          ATAXFIN:ATAXSI

| | |
|---|---|
| Analysis Life | 5 |
| Total First Cost | $250,000 |
| Deprec. Amount | $250,000 |
| | |
| Revenue Factor | 1.0000 |
| Reference Revenue | $45,000 |
| Annual Revenues | $45,000 |
| Change/yr | $5,000 |
| Annual Costs | $0 |
| Change/yr | $0 |
| Marginal Tax Rate | 35.00% |

| | | | |
|---|---|---|---|
| BTNPW | ($20,732) | BTIRR | 0.00% | BTEUAW | ($6,241) |
| ATNPW | ($11,725) | ATIRR | -0.00% | ATEUAW | ($3,093) |
| B/C = | 0.91 | | |

| | |
|---|---|
| Sum of Depreciation | $194,225 |
| Book Value | $55,775 |

| | |
|---|---|
| Salvage Value | $50,000 |
| Sale Price | $50,000 |
| ATMARR | 10.00% |
| BTMARR | 15.38% |
| IRR GUESS | 50% |
| Percent Equity Financing | 40% |
| Equity Financing | $100,000 |
| Loan or Bond Value | $150,000 |
| Loan Interest Rate | 10.00% |
| Loan Term, Years | 10 |
| | |
| MACRS Life, Years | 7 |
| Deprec. Life for SL and SYD | 7 |
| Sub-period placed in Serv. | 2.5 |
| Sub-Periods per year | 4 |
| Rounding decimal places | 4 |
| Declining Balance Factor | 200% |
| | |
| Sum of Interest Paid | $75,000 |
| Sum of taxes | $0 |
| Sum of After Tax Cash Flows | $0 |

| Use Depreciation Method: | 1 |
|---|---|
| 1 | MACRS |
| 2 | Straight Line |
| 3 | Sum of Years Digits |

| Year | BTCF | Depreciation | Tax. Income | INCOME TAX | ATCF | INTEREST | PRINCIPAL | BALANCE | CUMULATIVE CASH FLOW |
|---|---|---|---|---|---|---|---|---|---|
| 0 | (100,000) | -- | -- | -- | (100,000) | | | 150,000 | (100,000) |
| 1 | 30,000 | 35,725 | (5,725) | 2,004 | 32,004 | 15,000 | 0 | 150,000 | (67,996) |
| 2 | 35,000 | 61,225 | (26,225) | 9,179 | 44,179 | 15,000 | 0 | 150,000 | (23,818) |
| 3 | 40,000 | 43,725 | (3,725) | 1,304 | 41,304 | 15,000 | 0 | 150,000 | 17,486 |
| 4 | 45,000 | 31,225 | 13,775 | (4,821) | 40,179 | 15,000 | 0 | 150,000 | 57,665 |
| 5 | 50,000 | 22,325 | 27,675 | (9,686) | 40,314 | 15,000 | 0 | 150,000 | 0 |
| 5 | (100,000) | 0 | (5,775) | 2,021 | (97,979) | 0 | 150,000 | 0 | 0 |

# 20-11

## Problem — SUMMARY OF ATAXFIN ANALYSIS

| | | | |
|---|---|---|---|
| Analysis Life (< 31 yr) | 7 | Salvage Value | $10,000 |
| Total First Cost | $100,000 | Sale Price | $10,000 |
| Deprec. Amount | $100,000 | ATMARR | 10.00% |
| | | BTMARR | 16.67% |
| Revenue Factor | 0.5357 | IRR GUESS | 50.00% |
| Reference Revenue | $24,000 | Percent Equity Financing | 20.00% |
| Annual Revenues | $12,857 | Equity Financing | $20,000 |
| Change/yr | | Loan or Bond Value | $80,000 |
| Annual Costs | | Loan Interest Rate | 10.00% |
| Change/yr | | Loan Term, Years | 10 |
| Marginal Tax Rate | 40.00% | | |

## MUTUALLY EXCLUSIVE ALTERNATIVES

| | | |
|---|---|---|
| MACRS Life, Years | 7.0 | |
| Deprec. Life for SL and SYD | 7.0 | |
| Sub-period placed in Serv. | 2.5 | Use 2.5 for |
| Sub-Periods per year | 4 | half-year |
| Rounding decimal places | 4 | convention |
| Declining Balance Factor | 200% | |
| Use Depreciation Method: | 1 | |
| 1 | MACRS | |
| 2 | Straight Line | |
| 3 | Sum of Years Digits | |

## NET ANNUAL CASH FLOW (NACF) METHODS

| | ATAXBL | ATAXM | ATAXSI | ATAXNL |
|---|---|---|---|---|
| B/C = PWB/PWC | 0.31 | 0.45 | 0.72 | 0.70 |
| DELTA B/C [M-BL, SI-M, NL-SI] | | 1.20 | 1.14 | 0.81 |
| DELTA B/C [  SI-BL, NL-M] | | | 1.16 | 0.84 |
| DELTA B/C [    NL-BL] | | | | 0.86 |
| ATIRR | ***** | ***** | ***** | 0.00% |
| DELTA IRR [M-BL, SI-M, NL-SI] | 6.00% | 6.00% | 6.00% | 6.00% |
| DELTA IRR [  SI-BL, NL-M] | | 6.00% | 6.00% | 6.00% |
| DELTA IRR [    NL-BL] | | | | 6.00% |

| | ATAXBL | ATAXM | ATAXSI | ATAXNL |
|---|---|---|---|---|
| ATNPV | (18,929) | (17,847) | (14,844) | (30,423) |
| PWC | (27,620) | (32,663) | (53,730) | (100,000) |
| PWB | 8,692 | 14,816 | 38,885 | 69,577 |
| **ATCF** | | | | |
| YEAR 0 | (20,000) | (20,000) | (20,000) | (100,000) |
| 1 | 630 | 3,611 | 8,630 | 13,430 |
| 2 | 5,190 | 7,490 | 12,710 | 17,510 |
| 3 | 2,870 | 4,469 | 9,910 | 14,710 |
| 4 | 1,350 | 2,226 | 7,910 | 12,710 |
| 5 | 406 | 535 | 6,486 | 11,286 |
| 6 | 882 | 237 | 6,482 | 11,282 |
| 7 | (14,850) | (24,676) | (65,730) | 19,070 |

## SUMMING WITHOUT TIME VALUE OF MONEY EFFECTS

| Life of Project Totals | ATAXBL | ATAXM | ATAXSI | ATAXNL |
|---|---|---|---|---|
| Sum of Taxes Paid | ($15,680) | ($17,406) | ($22,400) | $0 |
| Sum of Interest Paid | $39,200 | $43,515 | $56,000 | $0 |
| Total Taxes + Interest | $23,520 | $26,109 | $33,600 | $0 |
| Cumulative ATCF | ($23,520) | ($26,109) | ($33,600) | $0 |
| Sum of last two rows | $0 | $0 | $0 | $0 |

| | ATAXBL | ATAXM | ATAXSI | ATAXNL |
|---|---|---|---|---|
| BTNPW | ($29,617) | ($28,250) | ($24,557) | ($45,680) |
| ATNPV | ($18,929) | ($17,847) | ($14,844) | ($30,423) |
| ATEUAW | ($3,888) | ($3,666) | ($3,049) | ($6,249) |

A "what if" revenue factor analysis shows that ATAXSI remains the most attractive alternative using the traditional criteria as Figure 2-5 previously illustrated.
Note however that all the borrowed money situations do not have the cumulative cash flow to pay off the loan.
The owner would probably have to refinance some portion of the loan balance from other assets, with the SI alternative requiring the largest refinancing.
The choice of financing alternatives by only comparing projected discounted cash flows at the original MARR can lead to financial difficulties in reduced revenue situations.

| | **Part 3c** | | **Percent Equity Financing** | | 20.00% | |
| --- | --- | --- | --- | --- | --- | --- |
| INCREMENTAL CASH FLOWS | | | **Revenue Factor** | | 0.5357 | |
| | M-BL | SI-M | SI-BL | NL-SI | NL-M | NL-BL |
| DELTA ROR | 6.00% | 6.00% | 6.00% | 6.00% | 6.00% | 6.00% |
| YEAR          0 | | | | ($80,000) | ($80,000) | ($80,000) |
| 1 | $2,980 | $5,020 | $8,000 | $4,800 | $9,820 | $12,800 |
| 2 | $2,300 | $5,220 | $7,520 | $4,800 | $10,020 | $12,320 |
| 3 | $1,599 | $5,441 | $7,040 | $4,800 | $10,241 | $11,840 |
| 4 | $876 | $5,684 | $6,560 | $4,800 | $10,484 | $11,360 |
| 5 | $129 | $5,951 | $6,080 | $4,800 | $10,751 | $10,880 |
| 6 | ($645) | $6,245 | $5,600 | $4,800 | $11,045 | $10,400 |
| 7 | ($9,827) | ($41,053) | ($50,880) | $84,800 | $43,747 | $33,920 |
| 8 | | | | | | |
| 9 | | | | | | |
| 10 | | | | | | |

The constant value of the incremental IRRs for all financing alternatives is related to borrowing
at the after-tax cost of money for the first three incremental cash flows. Since 6% is less than the ATMARR,
the first three increments are desirable and ATAXSI wins the tournament. However, the no loan (NL)
alternative involves investing an increment of $80,000 at a 6% incremental rate of return, which is
undesirable. So long as revenues cover the loan payments, leveraging is the desirable alternative.
Both the incremental IRRs and the incremental benefits and costs, discounted at the ATMARR, are
independent of the revenues; compare this page to part 1c.

INCREMENTAL BENEFITS

| | M-BL | SI-M | SI-BL | NL-SI | NL-M | NL-BL |
| --- | --- | --- | --- | --- | --- | --- |
| | PWB | PWB | PWB | PWB | PWB | PWB |
| | $6,489 | $24,069 | $30,194 | $64,421 | $67,423 | $68,505 |
| YEAR          0 | | | | | | |
| 1 | $2,980 | $5,020 | $8,000 | $4,800 | $9,820 | $12,800 |
| 2 | $2,300 | $5,220 | $7,520 | $4,800 | $10,020 | $12,320 |
| 3 | $1,599 | $5,441 | $7,040 | $4,800 | $10,241 | $11,840 |
| 4 | $876 | $5,684 | $6,560 | $4,800 | $10,484 | $11,360 |
| 5 | $129 | $5,951 | $6,080 | $4,800 | $10,751 | $10,880 |
| 6 | | $6,245 | $5,600 | $4,800 | $11,045 | $10,400 |
| 7 | | | | $84,800 | $43,747 | $33,920 |
| 8 | | | | | | |
| 9 | | | | | | |
| 10 | | | | | | |

INCREMENTAL COSTS

| | M-BL | SI-M | SI-BL | NL-SI | NL-M | NL-BL |
| --- | --- | --- | --- | --- | --- | --- |
| | PWC | PWC | PWC | PWC | PWC | PWC |
| | $5,407 | $21,067 | $26,109 | $80,000 | $80,000 | $80,000 |
| YEAR          0 | | | | ($80,000) | ($80,000) | ($80,000) |
| 1 | | | | | | |
| 2 | | | | | | |
| 3 | | | | | | |
| 4 | | | | | | |
| 5 | | | | | | |
| 6 | ($645) | | | | | |
| 7 | ($9,827) | ($41,053) | ($50,880) | | | |

EXAMPLE   3c

**ATAXFIN:ATAXSI**

| | |
|---|---|
| Analysis Life | 7 |
| Total First Cost | $100,000 |
| Deprec. Amount | $100,000 |
| | |
| Revenue Factor | 0.5357 |
| Reference Revenue | $24,000 |
| Annual Revenues | $12,857 |
| Change/yr | $0 |
| Annual Costs | $0 |
| Change/yr | $0 |
| Marginal Tax Rate | 40.00% |

| BTNPW | ($24,557) | BTIRR | *************** | BTEUAW | ($6,201) |
|---|---|---|---|---|---|
| ATNPW | ($14,844) | ATIRR | *************** | ATEUAW | ($3,049) |
| B/C = | 0.72 | | | | |

| | |
|---|---|
| Sum of Depreciation | $95,540 |
| Book Value | $4,460 |

**ATAXFIN:ATAXSI**

| | |
|---|---|
| Salvage Value | $10,000 |
| Sale Price | $10,000 |
| ATMARR | 10.00% |
| BTMARR | 16.67% |
| IRR GUESS | 50% |
| Percent Equity Financing | 20% |
| Equity Financing | $20,000 |
| Loan or Bond Value | $80,000 |
| Loan Interest Rate | 10.00% |
| Loan Term, Years | 10 |
| MACRS Life, Years | 7 |
| Deprec. Life for SL and SYD | 7 |
| Sub-period placed in Serv. | 2.5 |
| Sub-Periods per year | 4 |
| Rounding decimal places | 4 |
| Declining Balance Factor | 200% |
| Sum of Interest Paid | $56,000 |
| Sum of taxes | ($22,400) |
| Sum of After Tax Cash Flows | ($33,600) |

| Use Depreciation Method: | 1 |
|---|---|
| 1 | MACRS |
| 2 | Straight Line |
| 3 | Sum of Years Digits |

| Year | BTCF | Depreciation | Tax. Income | INCOME TAX | INTEREST | PRINCIPAL | BALANCE | ATCF | CUMULATIVE CASH FLOW |
|---|---|---|---|---|---|---|---|---|---|
| 0 | (20,000) | --- | --- | --- | | | 80,000 | (20,000) | (20,000) |
| 1 | 4,857 | 14,290 | (9,433) | 3,773 | 8,000 | 0 | 80,000 | 8,630 | (11,370) |
| 2 | 4,857 | 24,490 | (19,633) | 7,853 | 8,000 | 0 | 80,000 | 12,710 | 1,341 |
| 3 | 4,857 | 17,490 | (12,633) | 5,053 | 8,000 | 0 | 80,000 | 9,910 | 11,251 |
| 4 | 4,857 | 12,490 | (7,633) | 3,053 | 8,000 | 0 | 80,000 | 7,910 | 19,161 |
| 5 | 4,857 | 8,930 | (4,073) | 1,629 | 8,000 | 0 | 80,000 | 6,486 | 25,647 |
| 6 | 4,857 | 8,920 | (4,063) | 1,625 | 8,000 | 0 | 80,000 | 6,482 | 32,130 |
| 7 | 4,857 | 8,930 | (4,073) | 1,629 | 8,000 | 0 | 80,000 | 6,486 | (33,600) |
| 7 | (70,000) | 0 | 5,540 | (2,216) | 0 | 80,000 | 0 | (72,216) | (33,600) |

Note that the depreciation deductions are always greater than the before tax cash flows for this highly leveraged situation when revenues are well below initial projections. This type of tax sheltering was common before the change in the 1986 tax code which eliminated passive losses. There is insufficient cash flow to pay back the principal so the loan would be in default unless other assets are used to pay down the balance.

Part 3c

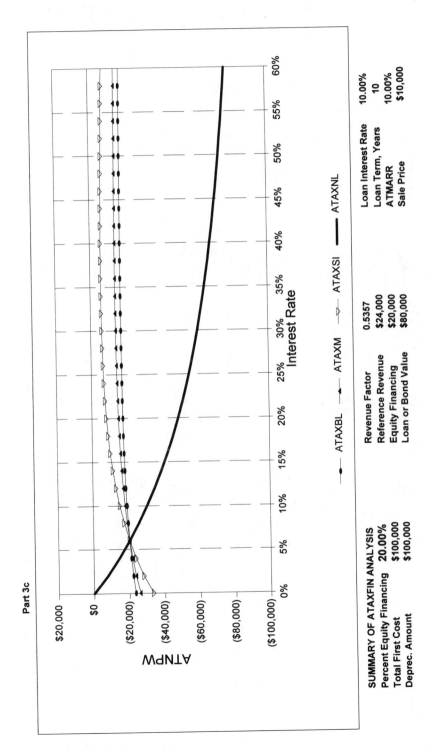

| SUMMARY OF ATAXFIN ANALYSIS | | |
|---|---|---|
| Percent Equity Financing | 20.00% | |
| Total First Cost | $100,000 | |
| Deprec. Amount | $100,000 | |

| | | |
|---|---|---|
| Revenue Factor | 0.5357 | |
| Reference Revenue | $24,000 | |
| Equity Financing | $20,000 | |
| Loan or Bond Value | $80,000 | |

| | | |
|---|---|---|
| Loan Interest Rate | 10.00% |
| Loan Term, Years | 10 |
| ATMARR | 10.00% |
| Sale Price | $10,000 |

# 20-12a

## SUMMARY OF ATAX4ALT ANALYSIS

| ALTERNATIVE | A | B | C | D |
|---|---|---|---|---|
| Total First Cost (thousands) | $100,000 | $150,000 | $200,000 | $300,000 |
| Deprec. Amount | $100,000 | $150,000 | $200,000 | $300,000 |
| Percent Equity Financing | 100.00% | 100.00% | 100.00% | 100.00% |
| Equity Financing | $100,000 | $150,000 | $200,000 | $300,000 |
| Loan or Bond Value | | | | |
| Loan Interest Rate | 10.00% | 10.00% | 10.00% | 10.00% |
| Loan Term, Years | 10 | 10 | 10 | 10 |
| Bank Loan (1) or Mortgage Loan (2) | 1 | 1 | 1 | 1 |
| Salvage Value | $34,868 | $52,302 | $69,736 | $104,604 |
| Sale Price | $34,868 | $52,302 | $69,736 | $104,604 |
| Revenue Factor | 0.7568 | 0.7568 | 0.7568 | 0.7568 |
| Reference Revenue | $54,648 | $73,920 | $90,420 | $126,126 |
| Annual Revenues | $41,355 | $55,940 | $68,426 | $95,447 |
| Change/yr | | | | |
| Annual Fixed Costs | $16,632 | $22,176 | $27,720 | $38,036 |
| Change/yr | | | | |
| Deprec. Life | 15 | 15 | 15 | 15 |
| MACRS Life | 15 | 15 | 15 | 15 |
| Use Depreciation Method: | 1 | 1 | 1 | 1 |
| Month Placed in Service | 1 | 1 | 1 | 1 |

| ALTERNATIVE | A | B | C | D |
|---|---|---|---|---|
| AT B/C = PWB/PWC | 1.10 | 1.03 | 0.96 | 0.94 |
| INCREMENTAL B/C [Adjacent Alt.] | | 0.88 | 0.74 | 0.90 |
| INCREMENTAL B/C [Two Alt. Apart] | | | 0.81 | 0.85 |
| INCREMENTAL B/C [Three Alt. Apart] | | | | 0.85 |
| ATIRR | 14.24% | 12.63% | 11.04% | 10.63% |
| INCREMENTAL IRR [Adjacent Alt.] | | 9.33% | 6.08% | 9.80% |
| INCREMENTAL IRR [Two Alt. Apart] | | | 7.72% | 8.58% |
| INCREMENTAL IRR [Three Alt. Apart] | | | | 8.76% |

| | A | | | B | | | C | | | D | | |
|---|---|---|---|---|---|---|---|---|---|---|---|---|
| | ATNPV | PWC | PWB | ATNPV | PWC | PWB | ATNPV | PWC | PWB | ATNPV | PWC | PWB |
| | 10,410 | (100,000) | 110,410 | 4,354 | (150,000) | 154,354 | (8,812) | (200,000) | 191,188 | (18,806) | (300,000) | 281,194 |
| YEAR 0 | | (100,000) | | | (150,000) | | | (200,000) | | | (300,000) | |
| 1 | | 16,834 | | | 23,258 | | | 28,424 | | | 41,647 | |
| 2 | | 18,634 | | | 25,958 | | | 32,024 | | | 47,047 | |
| 3 | | 18,254 | | | 25,388 | | | 31,264 | | | 45,907 | |
| 4 | | 17,914 | | | 24,878 | | | 30,584 | | | 44,887 | |
| 5 | | 17,606 | | | 24,416 | | | 29,968 | | | 43,963 | |
| 6 | | 17,326 | | | 23,996 | | | 29,408 | | | 43,123 | |
| 7 | | 17,194 | | | 23,798 | | | 29,144 | | | 42,727 | |
| 8 | | 17,194 | | | 23,798 | | | 29,144 | | | 42,727 | |
| 9 | | 17,198 | | | 23,804 | | | 29,152 | | | 42,739 | |
| 10 | | 51,107 | | | 74,667 | | | 96,969 | | | 144,465 | |

## COMMON INPUT DATA

| | |
|---|---|
| Analysis Life (< 21 yr) | 10 |
| Marginal Tax Rate | 40.00% |
| DDB life for Salvage Value | 20 |
| ATMARR | 12.00% |
| BTMARR | 20.00% |
| IRR GUESS | 20.00% |

Lookup Table Depreciation Schedules available from ALT_C
1 MACRS 3,5,7,10,15,20, Half-year convention
2 MACRS 27.5 YRS, Residential
3 MACRS 39 YRS, Commercial
4 STRAIGHT LINE
5 STRAIGHT LINE, Half-year Conventio (Student Exerc

Analysis of NPW as a function of Interest Rate
| Minimum Interest Rate: | 100.00% |
|---|---|
| Maximum Interest Rate: | 2.00% |
| Increment: | |

| ALTERNATIVE | A | B | C | D |
|---|---|---|---|---|
| BTNPW | $9,283 | ($30) | ($18,078) | ($34,027) |
| ATNPW | $10,410 | $4,354 | ($8,812) | ($18,806) |
| ATEUAW | $1,842 | $771 | ($1,560) | ($3,328) |

SUMMING WITHOUT TIME VALUE OF MONEY EFFECTS
| | A | B | C | D |
|---|---|---|---|---|
| Life of Project Totals | | | | |
| Sum of Taxes Paid | $72,841 | $95,975 | $110,719 | $159,485 |
| Sum of Interest Paid | | | | |
| Total Taxes + Interest | $72,841 | $95,975 | $110,719 | $159,485 |
| Cumulative ATCF | $109,261 | $143,963 | $166,078 | $239,228 |
| Sum of last two rows | $182,101 | $239,938 | $276,797 | $398,713 |

## SUMMARY OF ATAX4ALT ANALYSIS

| ALTERNATIVE | A | B | C | D |
|---|---|---|---|---|
| Total First Cost (thousands) | $100,000 | $150,000 | $200,000 | $300,000 |
| Deprec. Amount | $100,000 | $150,000 | $200,000 | $300,000 |
| Percent Equity Financing | 40.00% | 40.00% | 40.00% | 40.00% |
| Equity Financing | $40,000 | $60,000 | $80,000 | $120,000 |
| Loan or Bond Value | $60,000 | $90,000 | $120,000 | $180,000 |
| Loan Interest Rate | 10.00% | 10.00% | 10.00% | 10.00% |
| Loan Term, Years | 10 | 10 | 10 | 10 |
| Bank Loan (1) or Mortgage Loan (2) | 1 | 1 | 1 | 1 |
| Salvage Value | $34,868 | $52,302 | $69,736 | $104,604 |
| Sale Price | $34,868 | $52,302 | $69,736 | $104,604 |
| Revenue Factor | 0.7568 | 0.7568 | 0.7568 | 0.7568 |
| Reference Revenue | $54,648 | $73,920 | $90,420 | $126,126 |
| Annual Revenues | $41,355 | $55,940 | $68,426 | $95,447 |
| Change/yr | | | | |
| Annual Fixed Costs | $16,632 | $22,176 | $27,720 | $36,036 |
| Change/yr | | | | |
| Deprec. Life | 15 | 15 | 15 | 15 |
| MACRS Life | 15 | 15 | 15 | 15 |
| Use Depreciation Method: | 1 | 1 | 1 | 1 |
| Month Placed in Service | 1 | 1 | 1 | 1 |

**COMMON INPUT DATA**

| | |
|---|---|
| Analysis Life (< 21 yr) | 10 |
| Marginal Tax Rate | 40.00% |
| DDB life for Salvage Value | 20 |
| ATMARR | 12.00% |
| BTMARR | 20.00% |
| IRR GUESS | 20.00% |

Lookup Table Depreciation Schedules available from ALT_C
1  MACRS 3,5,7,10,15,20, Half-year convention
2  MACRS 27.5 YRS, Residential
3  MACRS 39 YRS, Commercial
4  STRAIGHT LINE
5  STRAIGHT LINE, Half-year Conventio (Student Exerc

Analysis of NPW as a function of Interest Rate
| | |
|---|---|
| Minimum Interest Rate: | |
| Maximum Interest Rate: | 100.00% |
| Increment: | 2.00% |

| ALTERNATIVE | A | B | C | D |
|---|---|---|---|---|
| AT B/C = PWB/PWC | 1.59 | 1.40 | 1.22 | 1.17 |
| INCREMENTAL B/C [Adjacent Alt.] | | 1.02 | 0.67 | 1.08 |
| INCREMENTAL B/C [Two Alt. Apart] | | | 0.85 | 0.94 |
| INCREMENTAL B/C [Three Alt. Apart] | | | | 0.96 |
| ATIRR | 22.24% | 18.98% | 15.79% | 14.97% |
| INCREMENTAL IRR [Adjacent Alt.] | | 12.41% | 6.15% | 13.34% |
| INCREMENTAL IRR [Two Alt. Apart] | | | 9.29% | 10.95% |
| INCREMENTAL IRR [Three Alt. Apart] | | | | 11.32% |

| ALTERNATIVE | A | B | C | D |
|---|---|---|---|---|
| BTNPW | $26,706 | $26,134 | $16,767 | $18,241 |
| ATNPW | $23,459 | $23,928 | $17,286 | $20,342 |
| ATEUAW | $4,152 | $4,235 | $3,059 | $3,600 |

**SUMMING WITHOUT TIME VALUE OF MONEY EFFECTS**

| | A | B | C | D |
|---|---|---|---|---|
| Life of Project Totals | | | | |
| Sum of Taxes Paid | $59,641 | $76,175 | $84,319 | $119,885 |
| Sum of Interest Paid | $33,000 | $49,500 | $66,000 | $99,000 |
| Total Taxes + Interest | $92,641 | $125,675 | $150,319 | $218,885 |
| Cumulative ATCF | $89,461 | $114,263 | $126,478 | $179,828 |
| Sum of last two rows | $182,101 | $239,938 | $276,797 | $398,713 |

**A**

| | ATNPV | PWC | PWB |
|---|---|---|---|
| | 23,459 | (40,000) | 63,459 |
| YEAR 0 | | (40,000) | (40,000) |
| 1 | | | 7,234 |
| 2 | | | 9,394 |
| 3 | | | 9,374 |
| 4 | | | 9,394 |
| 5 | | | 9,446 |
| 6 | | | 9,526 |
| 7 | | | 9,754 |
| 8 | | | 10,114 |
| 9 | | | 10,478 |
| 10 | | | 44,747 |

**B**

| | ATNPV | PWC | PWB |
|---|---|---|---|
| | 23,928 | (60,000) | 83,928 |
| YEAR 0 | | (60,000) | (60,000) |
| 1 | | | 8,858 |
| 2 | | | 12,098 |
| 3 | | | 12,068 |
| 4 | | | 12,098 |
| 5 | | | 12,176 |
| 6 | | | 12,296 |
| 7 | | | 12,638 |
| 8 | | | 13,178 |
| 9 | | | 13,724 |
| 10 | | | 65,127 |

**C**

| | ATNPV | PWC | PWB |
|---|---|---|---|
| | 17,286 | (80,000) | 97,286 |
| YEAR 0 | | (80,000) | (80,000) |
| 1 | | | 9,224 |
| 2 | | | 13,544 |
| 3 | | | 13,504 |
| 4 | | | 13,544 |
| 5 | | | 13,648 |
| 6 | | | 13,808 |
| 7 | | | 14,264 |
| 8 | | | 14,984 |
| 9 | | | 15,712 |
| 10 | | | 84,249 |

**D**

| | ATNPV | PWC | PWB |
|---|---|---|---|
| | 20,342 | (120,000) | 140,342 |
| YEAR 0 | | (120,000) | (120,000) |
| 1 | | | 12,847 |
| 2 | | | 19,327 |
| 3 | | | 19,267 |
| 4 | | | 19,327 |
| 5 | | | 19,483 |
| 6 | | | 19,723 |
| 7 | | | 20,407 |
| 8 | | | 21,487 |
| 9 | | | 22,579 |
| 10 | | | 125,385 |

# 20-12b

## SUMMARY OF ATAX4ALT ANALYSIS

| ALTERNATIVE | A | B | C | D |
|---|---|---|---|---|
| Total First Cost (thousands) | $100,000 | $150,000 | $200,000 | $300,000 |
| Deprec. Amount | $100,000 | $150,000 | $200,000 | $300,000 |
| Percent Equity Financing | 100.00% | 100.00% | 100.00% | 100.00% |
| Equity Financing | $100,000 | $150,000 | $200,000 | $300,000 |
| Loan or Bond Value | | | | |
| Loan Interest Rate | 10.00% | 10.00% | 10.00% | 10.00% |
| Loan Term, Years | 10 | 10 | 10 | 10 |
| Bank Loan (1) or Mortgage Loan (2) | | | | |
| Salvage Value | $34,868 | $52,302 | $69,736 | $104,604 |
| Sale Price | $34,868 | $52,302 | $69,736 | $104,604 |
| Revenue Factor | 0.7006 | 0.7394 | 0.7855 | 0.8007 |
| Reference Revenue | $54,648 | $73,920 | $90,420 | $126,126 |
| Annual Revenues | $38,285 | $54,655 | $71,026 | $100,994 |
| Change/yr | | | | |
| Annual Fixed Costs | $16,632 | $22,176 | $27,720 | $36,036 |
| Change/yr | | | | |
| Deprec. Life | 15 | 15 | 15 | 15 |
| MACRS Life | 15 | 15 | 15 | 15 |
| Use Depreciation Method | 1 | 1 | 1 | 1 |
| Month Placed in Service | 1 | 1 | 1 | 1 |

## COMMON INPUT DATA

| | |
|---|---|
| Analysis Life (< 21 yr) | 10 |
| Marginal Tax Rate | 40.00% |
| DDB life for Salvage Value | 20 |
| ATMARR | 12.00% |
| BTMARR | 20.00% |
| IRR GUESS | 20.00% |

Lookup Table Depreciation Schedules available from ALT_C

| | |
|---|---|
| 1 | MACRS 3,5,7,10,15,20, Half-year convention |
| 2 | MACRS 27.5 YRS, Residential |
| 3 | MACRS 39 YRS, Commercial |
| 4 | STRAIGHT LINE |
| 5 | STRAIGHT LINE, Half-year Conventio (Student Exerc |

Analysis of NPW as a function of Interest Rate

| | |
|---|---|
| Minimum Interest Rate: | |
| Maximum Interest Rate: | 100.00% |
| Increment: | 2.00% |

## B/C Analysis

| ALTERNATIVE | A | B | C | D |
|---|---|---|---|---|
| AT B/C = PWB/PWC | 1.00 | 1.00 | 1.00 | 1.00 |
| INCREMENTAL B/C [Adjacent Alt.] | | 1.00 | 1.00 | 1.00 |
| INCREMENTAL B/C [Two Alt. Apart] | | | 1.00 | 1.00 |
| INCREMENTAL B/C [Three Alt. Apart] | | | | 1.00 |

| ATIRR | A | B | C | D |
|---|---|---|---|---|
| ATIRR | 12.00% | 12.00% | 12.00% | 12.00% |
| INCREMENTAL IRR [Adjacent Alt.] | | 12.00% | 12.00% | 12.00% |
| INCREMENTAL IRR [Two Alt. Apart] | | | 12.00% | 12.00% |
| INCREMENTAL IRR [Three Alt. Apart] | | | | 12.00% |

## NPW / Summing

| ALTERNATIVE | A | B | C | D |
|---|---|---|---|---|
| BTNPW | ($3,590) | ($5,385) | ($7,180) | ($10,770) |
| ATNPW | $0 | $0 | $0 | $0 |
| ATEUAW | $0 | $0 | $0 | $0 |

SUMMING WITHOUT TIME VALUE OF MONEY EFFECTS

| | A | B | C | D |
|---|---|---|---|---|
| Life of Project Totals | | | | |
| Sum of Taxes Paid | $60,558 | $90,837 | $121,116 | $181,675 |
| Sum of Interest Paid | | | | |
| Total Taxes + Interest | $60,558 | $90,837 | $121,116 | $181,675 |
| Cumulative ATCF | $90,837 | $136,256 | $181,675 | $272,512 |
| Sum of last two rows | $151,396 | $227,093 | $302,791 | $454,187 |

## Year-by-Year Cash Flows

| | A ATNPV | A PWC | A PWB | B ATNPV | B PWC | B PWB | C ATNPV | C PWC | C PWB | D ATNPV | D PWC | D PWB |
|---|---|---|---|---|---|---|---|---|---|---|---|---|
| (i) | 0 | (100,000) | 100,000 | 0 | (150,000) | 150,000 | 0 | (200,000) | 200,000 | 0 | (300,000) | 300,000 |
| YEAR 0 | (100,000) | (100,000) | | (150,000) | (150,000) | | (200,000) | (200,000) | | (300,000) | (300,000) | |
| 1 | 14,992 | | 14,992 | 22,487 | | 22,487 | 29,983 | | 29,983 | 44,975 | | 44,975 |
| 2 | 16,792 | | 16,792 | 25,187 | | 25,187 | 33,583 | | 33,583 | 50,375 | | 50,375 |
| 3 | 16,412 | | 16,412 | 24,617 | | 24,617 | 32,823 | | 32,823 | 49,235 | | 49,235 |
| 4 | 16,072 | | 16,072 | 24,107 | | 24,107 | 32,143 | | 32,143 | 48,215 | | 48,215 |
| 5 | 15,764 | | 15,764 | 23,645 | | 23,645 | 31,527 | | 31,527 | 47,291 | | 47,291 |
| 6 | 15,484 | | 15,484 | 23,225 | | 23,225 | 30,967 | | 30,967 | 46,451 | | 46,451 |
| 7 | 15,352 | | 15,352 | 23,027 | | 23,027 | 30,703 | | 30,703 | 46,055 | | 46,055 |
| 8 | 15,352 | | 15,352 | 23,027 | | 23,027 | 30,703 | | 30,703 | 46,055 | | 46,055 |
| 9 | 15,356 | | 15,356 | 23,033 | | 23,033 | 30,711 | | 30,711 | 46,067 | | 46,067 |
| 10 | 49,264 | | 49,264 | 73,897 | | 73,897 | 98,529 | | 98,529 | 147,793 | | 147,793 |

## SUMMARY OF ATAX4ALT ANALYSIS

### ALTERNATIVE

| | A | B | C | D |
|---|---|---|---|---|
| Total First Cost (thousands) | $100,000 | $150,000 | $200,000 | $300,000 |
| Deprec. Amount | $100,000 | $150,000 | $200,000 | $300,000 |
| Percent Equity Financing | 40.00% | 40.00% | 40.00% | 40.00% |
| Equity Financing | $40,000 | $60,000 | $80,000 | $120,000 |
| Loan or Bond Value | $60,000 | $90,000 | $120,000 | $180,000 |
| Loan Interest Rate | 10.00% | 10.00% | 10.00% | 10.00% |
| Loan Term, Years | 10 | 10 | 10 | 10 |
| Bank Loan (1) or Mortgage Loan (2) | 1 | 1 | 1 | 1 |
| Salvage Value | $34,868 | $52,302 | $69,736 | $104,604 |
| Sale Price | $34,868 | $52,302 | $69,736 | $104,604 |
| Revenue Factor | 0.6301 | 0.6613 | 0.7004 | 0.7092 |
| Reference Revenue | $54,648 | $73,920 | $90,420 | $126,126 |
| Annual Revenues | $34,436 | $48,881 | $63,327 | $89,447 |
| Change/yr | | | | |
| Annual Fixed Costs | $16,632 | $22,176 | $27,720 | $36,036 |
| Change/yr | | | | |
| Deprec. Life | 15 | 15 | 15 | 15 |
| MACRS Life | 15 | 15 | 15 | 15 |
| Use Depreciation Method: | 1 | 1 | 1 | 1 |
| Month Placed in Service | 1 | 1 | 1 | 1 |

### COMMON INPUT DATA

| | |
|---|---|
| Analysis Life (< 21 yr) | 10 |
| Marginal Tax Rate | 40.00% |
| DDB life for Salvage Value | 20 |
| ATMARR | 12.00% |
| BTMARR | 20.00% |
| IRR GUESS | 20.00% |

Lookup Table Depreciation Schedules available from ALT_C
1  MACRS 3,5,7,10,15,20, Half-year convention
2  MACRS 27.5 YRS, Residential
3  MACRS 39 YRS, Commercial
4  STRAIGHT LINE
5  STRAIGHT LINE, Half-year Conventio (Student Exerc

Analysis of NPW as a function of Interest Rate
| | |
|---|---|
| Minimum Interest Rate: | |
| Maximum Interest Rate: | 100.00% |
| Increment: | 2.00% |

### ALTERNATIVE

| | A | B | C | D |
|---|---|---|---|---|
| BTNPW | ($2,305) | ($3,458) | ($4,610) | ($6,915) |
| ATNPW | ($0) | ($0) | ($0) | ($0) |
| ATEUAW | ($0) | ($0) | ($0) | ($0) |

SUMMING WITHOUT TIME VALUE OF MONEY EFFECTS

| Life of Project Totals | A | B | C | D |
|---|---|---|---|---|
| Sum of Taxes Paid | $31,961 | $47,942 | $63,923 | $95,884 |
| Sum of Interest Paid | $33,000 | $49,500 | $66,000 | $99,000 |
| Total Taxes + Interest | $64,961 | $97,442 | $129,923 | $194,884 |
| Cumulative ATCF | $47,942 | $71,913 | $95,884 | $143,826 |
| Sum of last two rows | $112,904 | $169,355 | $225,807 | $338,711 |

### ALTERNATIVE

| | A | B | C | D |
|---|---|---|---|---|
| AT B/C = PWB/PWC | 1.00 | 1.00 | 1.00 | 1.00 |
| INCREMENTAL B/C [Adjacent Alt.] | | 1.00 | 1.00 | 1.00 |
| INCREMENTAL B/C [Two Alt. Apart] | | | 1.00 | 1.00 |
| INCREMENTAL B/C [Three Alt. Apart] | | | | 1.00 |
| **ATIRR** | 12.00% | 12.00% | 12.00% | 12.00% |
| INCREMENTAL IRR [Adjacent Alt.] | | 12.00% | 12.00% | 12.00% |
| INCREMENTAL IRR [Two Alt. Apart] | | | 12.00% | 12.00% |
| INCREMENTAL IRR [Three Alt. Apart] | | | | 12.00% |

|  | A | | | B | | | C | | | D | | |
|---|---|---|---|---|---|---|---|---|---|---|---|---|
|  | ATNPV | PWC | PWB | ATNPV | PWC | PWB | ATNPV | PWC | PWB | ATNPV | PWC | PWB |
|  | (0) | (40,000) | 40,000 | (0) | (60,000) | 60,000 | (0) | (80,000) | 80,000 | (0) | (120,000) | 120,000 |
| YEAR 0 | (40,000) | (40,000) | 40,000 | (60,000) | (60,000) | 60,000 | (80,000) | (80,000) | 80,000 | (120,000) | (120,000) | 120,000 |
| 1 | 3,082 | | 3,082 | 4,623 | | 4,623 | 6,164 | | 6,164 | 9,246 | | 9,246 |
| 2 | 5,242 | | 5,242 | 7,863 | | 7,863 | 10,484 | | 10,484 | 15,726 | | 15,726 |
| 3 | 5,222 | | 5,222 | 7,833 | | 7,833 | 10,444 | | 10,444 | 15,666 | | 15,666 |
| 4 | 5,242 | | 5,242 | 7,863 | | 7,863 | 10,484 | | 10,484 | 15,726 | | 15,726 |
| 5 | 5,294 | | 5,294 | 7,941 | | 7,941 | 10,588 | | 10,588 | 15,882 | | 15,882 |
| 6 | 5,374 | | 5,374 | 8,061 | | 8,061 | 10,748 | | 10,748 | 16,122 | | 16,122 |
| 7 | 5,602 | | 5,602 | 8,403 | | 8,403 | 11,204 | | 11,204 | 16,806 | | 16,806 |
| 8 | 5,962 | | 5,962 | 8,943 | | 8,943 | 11,924 | | 11,924 | 17,886 | | 17,886 |
| 9 | 6,326 | | 6,326 | 9,489 | | 9,489 | 12,652 | | 12,652 | 18,978 | | 18,978 |
| 10 | 40,595 | | 40,595 | 60,892 | | 60,892 | 81,190 | | 81,190 | 121,785 | | 121,785 |

## 20-13a

Chart — Breakeven Load Factor (vertical axis) vs. % Equity Financing (horizontal axis)

Vertical axis labels: 0.72, 0.7, 0.68, 0.66, 0.64, 0.62

Horizontal axis labels: 40%, 60%, 80%, 100%

### SUMMARY OF ATAX4ALT ANALYSIS

| ALTERNATIVE | A | B | C | D |
|---|---|---|---|---|
| Total First Cost (thousands) | $100,000 | $100,000 | $100,000 | $100,000 |
| Deprec. Amount | $100,000 | $100,000 | $100,000 | $100,000 |
| Percent Equity Financing | 40.00% | 60.00% | 80.00% | 100.00% |
| Equity Financing | $40,000 | $60,000 | $80,000 | $100,000 |
| Loan or Bond Value | $60,000 | $40,000 | $20,000 | |
| Loan Interest Rate | 10.00% | 10.00% | 10.00% | 10.00% |
| Loan Term, Years | 10 | 10 | 10 | 10 |
| Bank Loan (1) or Mortgage Loan (2) | 1 | 1 | 1 | 1 |
| Salvage Value | $34,868 | $34,868 | $34,868 | $34,868 |
| Sale Price | $34,868 | $34,868 | $34,868 | $34,868 |
| Revenue Factor | 0.6301 | 0.6536 | 0.6771 | 0.7006 |
| Reference Revenue | $54,648 | $54,648 | $54,648 | $54,648 |
| Annual Revenues | $34,436 | $35,719 | $37,002 | $38,285 |
| Change/yr | | | | |
| Annual Fixed Costs | $16,632 | $16,632 | $16,632 | $16,632 |
| Change/yr | | | | |
| Deprec. Life | 15 | 15 | 15 | 15 |
| MACRS Life | 15 | 15 | 15 | 15 |
| Use Depreciation Method: | 1 | 1 | 1 | 1 |
| Month Placed in Service | 1 | 1 | 1 | 1 |

| ALTERNATIVE | A | B | C | D |
|---|---|---|---|---|
| AT B/C = PWB/PWC | 1.00 | 1.00 | 1.00 | 1.00 |
| INCREMENTAL B/C [Adjacent Alt.] | | 1.00 | 1.00 | 1.00 |
| INCREMENTAL B/C [Two Alt. Apart] | | | 1.00 | 1.00 |
| INCREMENTAL B/C [Three Alt. Apart] | | | | 1.00 |
| **ATIRR** | | | | |
| INCREMENTAL IRR [Adjacent Alt.] | 12.00% | 12.00% | 12.00% | 12.00% |
| INCREMENTAL IRR [Adjacent Alt.] | | 12.00% | 12.00% | 12.00% |
| INCREMENTAL IRR [Two Alt. Apart] | | | 12.00% | 12.00% |
| INCREMENTAL IRR [Three Alt. Apart] | | | | 12.00% |

| ALTERNATIVE | A | | | B | | |
|---|---|---|---|---|---|---|
| | ATNPV | PWC | PWB | ATNPV | PWC | PWB |
| | (0) | (40,000) | 40,000 | (0) | (60,000) | 60,000 |
| YEAR 0 | (40,000) | | | (60,000) | | |
| 1 | 3,082 | | | 7,052 | | |
| 2 | 5,242 | | | 9,092 | | |
| 3 | 5,222 | | | 8,952 | | |
| 4 | 5,242 | | | 8,852 | | |
| 5 | 5,294 | | | 8,784 | | |
| 6 | 5,374 | | | 8,744 | | |
| 7 | 5,602 | | | 8,852 | | |
| 8 | 5,962 | | | 9,092 | | |
| 9 | 6,326 | | | 9,336 | | |
| 10 | 40,595 | | | 43,485 | | |

| ALTERNATIVE | A | | | B | | |
|---|---|---|---|---|---|---|
| | BTNPW | ATNPW | ATEUAW | BTNPW | | |
| | ($2,305) | ($0) | ($0) | ($2,734) | ($0) | ($0) |

| | C | | | D | | |
|---|---|---|---|---|---|---|
| | ($3,162) | ($0) | ($0) | ($3,590) | ($0) | ($0) |

**SUMMING WITHOUT TIME VALUE OF MONEY EFFECTS**

| | A | B | C | D |
|---|---|---|---|---|
| Life of Project Totals | | | | |
| Sum of Taxes Paid | $31,961 | $41,494 | $51,026 | $60,558 |
| Sum of Interest Paid | $33,000 | $22,000 | $11,000 | $0 |
| Total Taxes + Interest | $64,961 | $63,494 | $62,026 | $60,558 |
| Cumulative ATCF | $47,942 | $62,240 | $76,539 | $90,837 |
| Sum of last two rows | $112,903 | $125,734 | $138,565 | $151,396 |

| | C | | | D | | |
|---|---|---|---|---|---|---|
| | ATNPV | PWC | PWB | ATNPV | PWC | PWB |
| | (0) | (80,000) | 80,000 | (0) | (100,000) | 100,000 |
| YEAR 0 | (80,000) | | | (100,000) | | |
| 1 | 11,022 | | | 14,992 | | |
| 2 | 12,942 | | | 16,792 | | |
| 3 | 12,682 | | | 16,412 | | |
| 4 | 12,462 | | | 16,072 | | |
| 5 | 12,274 | | | 15,764 | | |
| 6 | 12,114 | | | 15,484 | | |
| 7 | 12,102 | | | 15,352 | | |
| 8 | 12,222 | | | 15,352 | | |
| 9 | 12,346 | | | 15,356 | | |
| 10 | 46,375 | | | 49,264 | | |

**20-13b**

Chart — ATIRR vs. % Equity Financing

Y-axis (ATIRR): 11.5%, 11.0%, 10.5%, 10.0%, 9.5%, 9.0%, 8.5%, 8.0%, 7.5%

X-axis (% Equity Financing): 20%, 40%, 60%, 80%, 100%

## SUMMARY OF ATAX4ALT ANALYSIS

| ALTERNATIVE | A | B | C | D |
|---|---|---|---|---|
| Total First Cost (thousands) | $100,000 | $100,000 | $100,000 | $100,000 |
| Deprec. Amount | $100,000 | $100,000 | $100,000 | $100,000 |
| Percent Equity Financing | 20.00% | 40.00% | 70.00% | 100.00% |
| Equity Financing | $20,000 | $40,000 | $70,000 | $100,000 |
| Loan or Bond Value | $80,000 | $60,000 | $30,000 | |
| Loan Interest Rate | 10.00% | 10.00% | 10.00% | 10.00% |
| Loan Term, Years | 10 | 10 | 10 | 10 |
| Bank Loan (1) or Mortgage Loan (2) | 1 | 1 | 1 | 1 |
| Salvage Value | $34,868 | $34,868 | $34,868 | $34,868 |
| Sale Price | $34,868 | $34,868 | $34,868 | $34,868 |
| Revenue Factor | 0.6000 | 0.6000 | 0.6000 | 0.6000 |
| Reference Revenue | $54,648 | $54,648 | $54,648 | $54,648 |
| Annual Revenues | $32,789 | $32,789 | $32,789 | $32,789 |
| Change/yr | | | | |
| Annual Fixed Costs | $16,632 | $16,632 | $16,632 | $16,632 |
| Change/yr | | | | |
| Deprec. Life | 15 | 15 | 15 | 15 |
| MACRS Life | 15 | 15 | 15 | 15 |
| Use Depreciation Method: | 1 | 1 | 1 | 1 |
| Month Placed in Service: | 1 | 1 | 1 | 1 |

| ALTERNATIVE | A | B | C | D |
|---|---|---|---|---|
| AT B/C = PWB/PWC | 0.94 | 0.86 | 0.83 | 0.81 |
| INCREMENTAL B/C [Adjacent Alt.] | | 0.78 | 0.78 | 0.78 |
| INCREMENTAL B/C [Two Alt. Apart] | | | 0.78 | 0.78 |
| INCREMENTAL B/C [Three Alt. Apart] | | | | 0.78 |

**ATIRR**

| | A | B | C | D |
|---|---|---|---|---|
| AT IRR | 11.18% | 9.55% | 8.43% | 7.85% |
| INCREMENTAL IRR [Adjacent Alt.] | | 6.00% | 6.00% | 6.00% |
| INCREMENTAL IRR [Two Alt. Apart] | | | 6.00% | 6.00% |
| INCREMENTAL IRR [Three Alt. Apart] | | | | 6.00% |

| ALTERNATIVE | A | B | C | D |
|---|---|---|---|---|
| BTNPW | ($3,402) | ($9,209) | ($17,920) | ($26,632) |
| ATNPW | ($1,233) | ($5,583) | ($12,107) | ($18,632) |
| ATEUAW | ($218) | ($988) | ($2,143) | ($3,298) |

**SUMMING WITHOUT TIME VALUE OF MONEY EFFECTS**

| | A | B | C | D |
|---|---|---|---|---|
| Life of Project Totals | | | | |
| Sum of Taxes Paid | $20,974 | $25,374 | $31,974 | $38,574 |
| Sum of Interest Paid | $44,000 | $33,000 | $16,500 | |
| Total Taxes + Interest | $64,974 | $58,374 | $48,474 | $38,574 |
| Cumulative ATCF | $31,462 | $38,062 | $47,962 | $57,862 |
| Sum of last two rows | $96,436 | $96,436 | $96,436 | $96,436 |

**Alternative A**

| | ATNPV | PWC | PWB |
|---|---|---|---|
| | (1,233) | (20,987) | 19,754 |
| YEAR 0 | (20,000) | (20,000) | |
| 1 | (1,106) | (1,106) | 1,174 |
| 2 | 1,174 | | 1,274 |
| 3 | 1,274 | | 1,414 |
| 4 | 1,414 | | 1,586 |
| 5 | 1,586 | | 1,786 |
| 6 | 1,786 | | 2,134 |
| 7 | 2,134 | | 2,614 |
| 8 | 2,614 | | 3,098 |
| 9 | 3,098 | | 37,487 |
| 10 | 37,487 | | |

**Alternative B**

| | ATNPV | PWC | PWB |
|---|---|---|---|
| | (5,583) | (40,000) | 34,417 |
| YEAR 0 | (40,000) | (40,000) | |
| 1 | 2,094 | | 2,094 |
| 2 | 4,254 | | 4,254 |
| 3 | 4,254 | | 4,254 |
| 4 | 4,254 | | 4,306 |
| 5 | 4,306 | | 4,386 |
| 6 | 4,386 | | 4,614 |
| 7 | 4,614 | | 4,974 |
| 8 | 4,974 | | 5,338 |
| 9 | 5,338 | | 39,607 |
| 10 | 39,607 | | |

**Alternative C**

| | ATNPV | PWC | PWB |
|---|---|---|---|
| | (12,107) | (70,000) | |
| YEAR 0 | (70,000) | (70,000) | |
| 1 | 6,894 | | 6,894 |
| 2 | 8,874 | | 8,874 |
| 3 | 8,674 | | 8,674 |
| 4 | 8,514 | | 8,514 |
| 5 | 8,386 | | 8,386 |
| 6 | 8,286 | | 8,334 |
| 7 | 8,334 | | 8,514 |
| 8 | 8,514 | | 8,698 |
| 9 | 8,698 | | 42,787 |
| 10 | 42,787 | | |

**Alternative D**

| | ATNPV | PWC | PWB |
|---|---|---|---|
| | (18,632) | (100,000) | 81,368 |
| YEAR 0 | (100,000) | (100,000) | |
| 1 | 11,694 | | 11,694 |
| 2 | 13,494 | | 13,494 |
| 3 | 13,114 | | 13,114 |
| 4 | 12,774 | | 12,774 |
| 5 | 12,466 | | 12,466 |
| 6 | 12,186 | | 12,054 |
| 7 | 12,054 | | 12,054 |
| 8 | 12,054 | | 12,054 |
| 9 | 12,054 | | 12,058 |
| 10 | 12,058 | | 45,967 |
| | 45,967 | | |

(Money-value detail: A PWB 57,893; D PWB 81,368)

## 20-13c

Chart — ATIRR vs % Equity Financing

ATIRR (y-axis): 4.0%, 3.0%, 2.0%, 1.0%, 0.0%, −1.0%
% Equity Financing (x-axis): 20%, 40%, 60%, 80%, 100%

### SUMMARY OF ATAX4ALT ANALYSIS

| ALTERNATIVE | A | B | C | D |
|---|---|---|---|---|
| Total First Cost (thousands) | $100,000 | $100,000 | $100,000 | $100,000 |
| Deprec. Amount | $100,000 | $100,000 | $100,000 | $100,000 |
| Percent Equity Financing | 20.00% | 40.00% | 70.00% | 100.00% |
| Equity Financing | $20,000 | $40,000 | $70,000 | $100,000 |
| Loan or Bond Value | $80,000 | $60,000 | $30,000 | |
| Loan Interest Rate | 10.00% | 10.00% | 10.00% | 10.00% |
| Loan Term, Years | 10 | 10 | 10 | 10 |
| Bank Loan (1) or Mortgage Loan (2) | 1 | 1 | 1 | 1 |
| Salvage Value | $34,868 | $34,868 | $34,868 | $34,868 |
| Sale Price | $34,868 | $34,868 | $34,868 | $34,868 |
| Revenue Factor | 0.5000 | 0.5000 | 0.5000 | 0.5000 |
| Reference Revenue | $54,648 | $54,648 | $54,648 | $54,648 |
| Annual Revenues | $27,324 | $27,324 | $27,324 | $27,324 |
| Change/yr | | | | |
| Annual Fixed Costs | $16,632 | $16,632 | $16,632 | $16,632 |
| Change/yr | | | | |
| Deprec. Life | 15 | 15 | 15 | 15 |
| MACRS Life | 15 | 15 | 15 | 15 |
| Use Depreciation Method: | 1 | 1 | 1 | 1 |
| Month Placed in Service | 1 | 1 | 1 | 1 |

| ALTERNATIVE | A | B | C | D |
|---|---|---|---|---|
| AT B/C = PWB/PWC | 0.36 | 0.41 | 0.56 | 0.63 |
| INCREMENTAL B/C [Adjacent Alt.] | | 0.78 | 0.78 | 0.78 |
| INCREMENTAL B/C [Two Alt. Apart] | | | 0.78 | 0.78 |
| INCREMENTAL B/C [Three Alt. Apart] | | | | 0.78 |
| ATIRR | −0.45% | 1.33% | 2.74% | 3.51% |
| INCREMENTAL IRR [Adjacent Alt.] | | 6.00% | 6.00% | 6.00% |
| INCREMENTAL IRR [Two Alt. Apart] | | | 6.00% | 6.00% |
| INCREMENTAL IRR [Three Alt. Apart] | | | | 6.00% |

#### Alternative A

| | ATNPV | PWC | PWB |
|---|---|---|---|
| | (19,759) | (30,773) | 11,014 |
| YEAR 0 | (20,000) | (20,000) | |
| 1 | (4,385) | (4,385) | |
| 2 | (2,105) | (2,105) | |
| 3 | (2,005) | (2,005) | |
| 4 | (1,865) | (1,865) | |
| 5 | (1,693) | (1,693) | |
| 6 | (1,493) | (1,493) | |
| 7 | (1,145) | (1,145) | |
| 8 | (665) | (665) | |
| 9 | (181) | (181) | |
| 10 | 34,208 | | 34,208 |

#### Alternative B

| | ATNPV | PWC | PWB |
|---|---|---|---|
| | (24,109) | (41,058) | 16,949 |
| YEAR 0 | (40,000) | (40,000) | |
| 1 | (1,185) | (1,185) | |
| 2 | 975 | | 975 |
| 3 | 955 | | 955 |
| 4 | 975 | | 975 |
| 5 | 1,027 | | 1,027 |
| 6 | 1,107 | | 1,107 |
| 7 | 1,335 | | 1,335 |
| 8 | 1,695 | | 1,695 |
| 9 | 2,059 | | 2,059 |
| 10 | 36,328 | | 36,328 |

#### Alternative C

| | ATNPV | PWC | PWB |
|---|---|---|---|
| | (30,634) | (70,000) | 39,366 |
| YEAR 0 | (70,000) | (70,000) | |
| 1 | 3,615 | | 3,615 |
| 2 | 5,595 | | 5,595 |
| 3 | 5,395 | | 5,395 |
| 4 | 5,235 | | 5,235 |
| 5 | 5,107 | | 5,107 |
| 6 | 5,007 | | 5,007 |
| 7 | 5,055 | | 5,055 |
| 8 | 5,235 | | 5,235 |
| 9 | 5,419 | | 5,419 |
| 10 | 39,508 | | 39,508 |

#### Alternative D

| | ATNPV | PWC | PWB |
|---|---|---|---|
| | (37,158) | (100,000) | 62,842 |
| YEAR 0 | (100,000) | (100,000) | |
| 1 | 8,415 | | 8,415 |
| 2 | 10,215 | | 10,215 |
| 3 | 9,835 | | 9,835 |
| 4 | 9,495 | | 9,495 |
| 5 | 9,187 | | 9,187 |
| 6 | 8,907 | | 8,907 |
| 7 | 8,775 | | 8,775 |
| 8 | 8,775 | | 8,775 |
| 9 | 8,779 | | 8,779 |
| 10 | 42,688 | | 42,688 |

| ALTERNATIVE | A | B | C | D |
|---|---|---|---|---|
| BTNPW | ($26,313) | ($32,120) | ($40,831) | ($49,543) |
| ATNPW | ($19,759) | ($24,109) | ($30,634) | ($37,158) |
| ATEUAW | ($3,497) | ($4,267) | ($5,422) | ($6,576) |

#### SUMMING WITHOUT TIME VALUE OF MONEY EFFECTS

| Life of Project Totals | A | B | C | D |
|---|---|---|---|---|
| Sum of Taxes Paid | ($885) | $3,515 | $10,115 | $16,715 |
| Sum of Interest Paid | $44,000 | $33,000 | $16,500 | |
| Total Taxes + Interest | $43,115 | $36,515 | $26,615 | $16,715 |
| Cumulative ATCF | ($1,327) | $5,273 | $15,173 | $25,073 |
| Sum of last two rows | $41,788 | $41,788 | $41,788 | $41,788 |

| Summary | I | J | K | L | M | N |
|---|---|---|---|---|---|---|
| 61 | | | | | | |
| 62 | **ALTERNATIVE** | | **A** | **B** | **C** | **D** |
| 63 | Total First Cost | | $100,000 | $150,000 | $200,000 | $300,000 |
| 64 | % Equity Financing | | 20.00% | 26.67% | 35.00% | 33.33% |
| 65 | Equity Financing | | $20,000 | $40,000 | $70,000 | $100,000 |
| 66 | Revenue Factor | | 0.5 | 0.5 | 0.5 | 0.5 |
| 67 | ATIRR | | -0.45% | 1.33% | 2.74% | 3.51% |
| 68 | CUMATCF/PWC | | -0.04 | 0.13 | 0.22 | 0.25 |
| 69 | | | | | | |
| 70 | % Equity Financing | | ATIRR | | @Rev. Fact. 0.5 | |
| 71 | | 100.00% | 3.91% | 3.15% | 2.12% | 2.37% |
| 72 | | 90.00% | 3.71% | 2.88% | 1.75% | 2.02% |
| 73 | | 80.00% | 3.47% | 2.55% | 1.30% | 1.60% |
| 74 | | 70.00% | 3.17% | 2.14% | 0.74% | 1.08% |
| 75 | | 60.00% | 2.79% | 1.63% | 0.05% | 0.42% |
| 76 | | 50.00% | 2.31% | 0.96% | -0.85% | -0.42% |
| 77 | | 40.00% | 1.65% | 0.08% | -2.05% | -1.54% |
| 78 | | 30.00% | 0.74% | -1.15% | -3.68% | -3.07% |
| 79 | | 20.00% | -0.61% | -2.92% | -5.97% | -5.25% |
| 80 | | 10.00% | -2.73% | -5.59% | -9.23% | -8.38% |
| 81 | % Equity Financing | | ATIRR | | @Rev. Fact. 0.6 | |
| 82 | | 100.00% | 8.63% | 7.48% | 6.18% | 6.13% |
| 83 | | 90.00% | 8.87% | 7.61% | 6.19% | 6.14% |
| 84 | | 80.00% | 9.17% | 7.78% | 6.21% | 6.16% |
| 85 | | 70.00% | 9.54% | 7.99% | 6.24% | 6.18% |
| 86 | | 60.00% | 10.00% | 8.25% | 6.27% | 6.20% |
| 87 | | 50.00% | 10.62% | 8.59% | 6.31% | 6.23% |
| 88 | | 40.00% | 11.46% | 9.07% | 6.37% | 6.27% |
| 89 | | 30.00% | 12.70% | 9.75% | 6.45% | 6.33% |
| 90 | | 20.00% | 14.76% | 10.86% | 6.57% | 6.43% |
| 91 | | 10.00% | 19.01% | 13.01% | 6.80% | 6.59% |
| 92 | % Equity Financing | | CUMATCF/PWC | | @Rev. Fact. 0.5 | |
| 93 | | 100.00% | 0.25 | 0.20 | 0.13 | 0.15 |
| 94 | | 90.00% | 0.24 | 0.19 | 0.11 | 0.13 |
| 95 | | 80.00% | 0.23 | 0.17 | 0.08 | 0.10 |
| 96 | | 70.00% | 0.22 | 0.15 | 0.05 | 0.07 |
| 97 | | 60.00% | 0.20 | 0.11 | 0.00 | 0.03 |
| 98 | | 50.00% | 0.17 | 0.07 | -0.06 | -0.03 |
| 99 | | 40.00% | 0.13 | 0.01 | -0.16 | -0.12 |
| 100 | | 30.00% | 0.06 | -0.10 | -0.29 | -0.25 |
| 101 | | 20.00% | -0.06 | -0.25 | -0.45 | -0.41 |
| 102 | | 10.00% | -0.23 | -0.42 | -0.62 | -0.58 |
| 103 | Revenue Factor | | CUMATCF/PWC | | At Equal Invest. of $100 | |
| 104 | | 0.90 | 1.56 | 1.91 | 2.11 | 2.82 |
| 105 | | 0.85 | 1.40 | 1.69 | 1.84 | 2.44 |
| 106 | | 0.80 | 1.23 | 1.47 | 1.57 | 2.06 |
| 107 | | 0.75 | 1.07 | 1.24 | 1.29 | 1.68 |
| 108 | | 0.70 | 0.91 | 1.02 | 1.02 | 1.30 |
| 109 | | 0.65 | 0.74 | 0.80 | 0.75 | 0.92 |
| 110 | | 0.60 | 0.58 | 0.58 | 0.48 | 0.55 |
| 111 | | 0.55 | 0.41 | 0.36 | 0.21 | 0.17 |
| 112 | | 0.50 | 0.25 | 0.14 | -0.06 | -0.20 |
| 113 | | 0.45 | 0.09 | -0.09 | -0.33 | -0.50 |
| 114 | | 0.40 | -0.08 | -0.31 | -0.57 | -0.72 |

**Sensitivity Analysis**

# 20-14

(Page 1 of 3)

25-Nov.

Problem   Part a   SUMMARY OF ATAX4ALT ANALYSIS

| ALTERNATIVE | A | B | C | D |
|---|---|---|---|---|
| Total First Cost (thousands) | $500,000 | $500,000 | $2,500,000 | $2,500,000 |
| Deprec. Amount | $500,000 | $400,000 | $2,000,000 | $2,000,000 |
| Percent Equity Financing | 100.00% | 100.00% | 20.00% | 20.00% |
| Equity Financing | $500,000 | $500,000 | $500,000 | $500,000 |
| Loan or Bond Value | | | $2,000,000 | $2,000,000 |
| Loan Interest Rate | 10.00% | 10.00% | 10.00% | 9.00% |
| Loan Term, Years | 10 | 10 | 15 | 10 |
| Bank Loan (1) or Mortgage Loan (2) | 1 | 1 | 2 | 1 |
| Salvage Value | $150,000 | $600,000 | $3,000,000 | $3,000,000 |
| Sale Price | $150,000 | $600,000 | $3,000,000 | $3,000,000 |
| Revenue Factor | 1.0000 | 0.9000 | 0.9000 | 0.9000 |
| Reference Revenue | $150,000 | $100,000 | $500,000 | $500,000 |
| Annual Revenues | $150,000 | $90,000 | $450,000 | $450,000 |
| Change/yr | | | | |
| Annual Fixed Costs | $5,000 | | | |
| Change/yr | | | | |
| Deprec. Life | 5 | 39 | 39 | 39 |
| MACRS Life | 5 | 39 | 39 | 39 |
| Use Depreciation Method: | 1 | 3 | 3 | 3 |
| Month Placed in Service | 1 | 1 | 1 | 1 |

| COMMON INPUT DATA | |
|---|---|
| Analysis Life (< 21 yr) | 6 |
| Marginal Tax Rate | 35.00% |
| DDB life for Salvage Value | 20 |
| ATMARR | 15.00% |
| BTMARR | 23.08% |
| IRR GUESS | 50.00% |

Lookup Table Depreciation Schedules available from ALT_C
1   MACRS 3,5,7,10,15,20, Half-year convention
2   MACRS 27.5 YRS, Residential
3   MACRS 39 YRS, Commercial
4   STRAIGHT LINE
5   STRAIGHT LINE, Half-year Convention

Discussion: Alt C is the best alternative for the conditions analyzed. Inspection of its ATCFs show that the longer loan term makes for larger cash flows in the in the earlier years giving a larger time-value-of-money effect. The timing of the interest and principal payments is illustrated on the separate spreadsheet pages for Alternatives C & D makes a difference even though Alternative C pays more money in interest and taxes than Alternative D.

| ALTERNATIVE | A | B | C | D |
|---|---|---|---|---|
| BTNPW | $35,626 | ($49,583) | $504,792 | $455,118 |
| ATNPW | $57,712 | ($30,132) | $444,673 | $396,656 |
| ATEUAW | $15,250 | ($7,962) | $117,499 | $104,811 |

SUMMING WITHOUT TIME VALUE OF MONEY EFFECTS

| Life of Project Totals | A | B | C | D |
|---|---|---|---|---|
| Sum of Taxes Paid | $218,750 | $224,000 | $737,798 | $836,500 |
| Sum of Interest Paid | | | $1,092,007 | $810,000 |
| Total Taxes + Interest | $218,750 | $224,000 | $1,829,804 | $1,646,500 |
| Cumulative ATCF | $406,250 | $416,250 | $1,370,196 | $1,553,500 |
| Sum of last two rows | $625,000 | $640,000 | $3,200,000 | $3,200,000 |

| ALTERNATIVE | A | B | C | D |
|---|---|---|---|---|
| AT B/C = PWB/PWC | 1.12 | 0.94 | 1.89 | 1.78 |
| DELTA B/C [ B-A,C-B,D-C] | | 0.65 | 5.68 | 0.86 |
| DELTA B/C [ C-A, D-B] | | | | 3.62 |
| DELTA B/C [ D-A] | | | | 1.81 |
| ATIRR | 18.99% | 13.45% | 32.89% | 26.93% |
| DELTA IRR [ B-A,C-B,D-C] | | 0.83% | na | 10.04% |
| DELTA IRR [ C-A, D-B] | | | 85.07% | 58.88% |
| DELTA IRR [ D-A] | | | | 35.39% |

**A**

| | PWC | PWB |
|---|---|---|
| ATNPV | 57,712 | |
| | (500,000) | 557,712 |

| YEAR | PWC | PWB |
|---|---|---|
| 0 | (500,000) | (500,000) |
| 1 | | 132,500 |
| 2 | | 156,750 |
| 3 | | 137,600 |
| 4 | | 127,410 |
| 5 | | 130,660 |
| 6 | | 221,330 |

**B**

| | ATNPV | PWC | PWB |
|---|---|---|---|
| | (30,132) | (500,000) | 469,868 |

| YEAR | PWC | PWB |
|---|---|---|
| 0 | (500,000) | (500,000) |
| 1 | | 61,945 |
| 2 | | 62,090 |
| 3 | | 62,090 |
| 4 | | 62,090 |
| 5 | | 62,090 |
| 6 | | 605,696 |

**C**

| | PWC | PWB | ATNPV |
|---|---|---|---|
| | (500,000) | 944,673 | 444,673 |

| YEAR | PWC | PWB |
|---|---|---|
| 0 | (500,000) | (500,000) |
| 1 | | 116,779 |
| 2 | | 115,297 |
| 3 | | 112,874 |
| 4 | | 110,208 |
| 5 | | 107,276 |
| 6 | | 1,307,762 |

**D**

| | PWC | PWB | ATNPV |
|---|---|---|---|
| | (506,324) | 902,980 | 396,656 |

| YEAR | PWC | PWB |
|---|---|---|
| 0 | (500,000) | (500,000) |
| 1 | (7,273) | 5,148 |
| 2 | 5,148 | 16,848 |
| 3 | 16,848 | 28,548 |
| 4 | 28,548 | 40,248 |
| 5 | 40,248 | |
| 6 | | 1,969,981 |

## COMMON INPUT DATA

| | |
|---|---|
| Analysis Life (< 21 yr) | 6 |
| Marginal Tax Rate | 35.00% |
| DDB life for Salvage Value | 20 |
| ATMARR | 15.00% |
| BTMARR | 23.08% |
| IRR GUESS | 50.00% |

Lookup Table Depreciation Schedules available from ALT_C

| | |
|---|---|
| 1 | MACRS 3,5,7,10,15,20, Half-year convention |
| 2 | MACRS 27.5 YRS, Residential |
| 3 | MACRS 39 YRS, Commercial |
| 4 | STRAIGHT LINE |
| 5 | STRAIGHT LINE, Half-year Convention |

Discussion: Alt_C has the best cushion on selling price which one would expect from the original AT B/C ratio IRR analysis. The breakeven selling price on each of the leveraged alternatives shows a large capital loss in the last year of the analysis.

### ALTERNATIVE

| ALTERNATIVE | A | B | C | D |
|---|---|---|---|---|
| Total First Cost (thousands) | $500,000 | $500,000 | $2,500,000 | $2,500,000 |
| Deprec. Amount | $500,000 | $400,000 | $2,000,000 | $2,000,000 |
| Percent Equity Financing | 100.00% | 100.00% | 20.00% | 20.00% |
| Equity Financing | $500,000 | $500,000 | $500,000 | $500,000 |
| Loan or Bond Value | | | $2,000,000 | $2,000,000 |
| Loan Interest Rate | 10.00% | 10.00% | 10.00% | 9.00% |
| Loan Term, Years | 10 | 10 | 15 | 1 |
| Bank Loan (1) or Mortgage Loan (2) | 1 | 1 | 2 | 1 |
| Salvage Value | ($55,373) | $707,227 | $1,417,606 | $1,588,478 |
| Sale Price | ($55,373) | $707,227 | $1,417,606 | $1,588,478 |
| Revenue Factor | 1.0000 | 0.9000 | 0.9000 | 0.9000 |
| Reference Revenue | $150,000 | $100,000 | $500,000 | $500,000 |
| Annual Revenues | $5,000 | $90,000 | $450,000 | $450,000 |
| Change/yr | | | | |
| Annual Fixed Cost | | | | |
| Change/yr | | | | |
| Deprec. Life | 5 | 39 | 39 | 39 |
| MACRS Life | 5 | 39 | 39 | 39 |
| Use Depreciation Method: | 1 | 3 | 3 | 3 |
| Month Placed in Service | 1 | 1 | 1 | 1 |

| ALTERNATIVE | A | B | C | D |
|---|---|---|---|---|
| AT B/C = PWB/PWC | 1.00 | 1.00 | 1.00 | 1.00 |
| DELTA B/C [ B-A,C-B,D-C] | | 1.00 | 1.00 | 1.00 |
| DELTA B/C [ C-A, D-B] | | | 1.00 | 1.00 |
| DELTA B/C [ D-A] | | | | 1.00 |
| ATIRR | 15.00% | 15.00% | 15.00% | 15.00% |
| DELTA IRR [ B-A,C-B,D-C] | | 15.00% | 15.00% | 15.00% |
| DELTA IRR [ C-A, D-B] | | | 15.00% | 15.00% |
| DELTA IRR [ D-A] | | | | 15.00% |

| ALTERNATIVE | A | | | B | | | C | | | D | | |
|---|---|---|---|---|---|---|---|---|---|---|---|---|
| | ATNPV | PWC | PWB | ATNPV | PWC | PWB | ATNPV | PWC | PWB | ATNPV | PWC | PWB |
| | 0 | (500,000) | 500,000 | (0) | (500,000) | 500,000 | 0 | (500,000) | 500,000 | (0) | (506,324) | 506,324 |
| YEAR 0 | (500,000) | (500,000) | | (500,000) | (500,000) | | (500,000) | (500,000) | | (500,000) | (500,000) | |
| 1 | 132,500 | | 132,500 | 61,945 | | 61,945 | 116,779 | | 116,779 | (7,273) | (7,273) | |
| 2 | 156,750 | | 156,750 | 62,090 | | 62,090 | 115,297 | | 115,297 | 5,148 | | 5,148 |
| 3 | 137,600 | | 137,600 | 62,090 | | 62,090 | 112,874 | | 112,874 | 16,848 | | 16,848 |
| 4 | 127,410 | | 127,410 | 62,090 | | 62,090 | 110,208 | | 110,208 | 28,548 | | 28,548 |
| 5 | 130,660 | | 130,660 | 62,090 | | 62,090 | 107,276 | | 107,276 | 40,248 | | 40,248 |
| 6 | 87,838 | | 87,838 | 675,394 | | 675,394 | 279,206 | | 279,206 | 1,052,491 | | 1,052,491 |

### SUMMING WITHOUT TIME VALUE OF MONEY EFFECTS

| ALTERNATIVE | A | B | C | D |
|---|---|---|---|---|
| BTNPW | ($23,460) | ($18,734) | $49,537 | $49,023 |
| ATNPW | $0 | ($0) | $0 | ($0) |
| ATEUAW | $0 | ($0) | $0 | ($0) |

| | A | B | C | D |
|---|---|---|---|---|
| Life of Project Totals | | | | |
| Sum of Taxes Paid | $146,870 | $261,529 | $183,960 | $342,467 |
| Sum of Interest Paid | | | $1,092,007 | $810,000 |
| Total Taxes + Interest | $146,870 | $261,529 | $1,275,966 | $1,152,467 |
| Cumulative ATCF | $272,758 | $485,697 | $341,640 | $636,010 |
| Sum of last two rows | $419,627 | $747,227 | $1,617,606 | $1,788,478 |
| PWB | 500,000 | 500,000 | 500,000 | 506,324 |

25-Nov

Problem    Part c & d   SUMMARY OF ATAX4ALT ANALYSIS

| ALTERNATIVE | A | B | C | D |
|---|---|---|---|---|
| Total First Cost (thousands) | $500,000 | $500,000 | $2,500,000 | $2,500,000 |
| Deprec. Amount | $500,000 | $400,000 | $2,000,000 | $2,000,000 |
| Percent Equity Financing | 100.00% | 100.00% | 20.00% | 20.00% |
| Equity Financing | $500,000 | $500,000 | $500,000 | $500,000 |
| Loan or Bond Value | | | $2,000,000 | $2,000,000 |
| Loan Interest Rate | 10.00% | 10.00% | 10.00% | 9.00% |
| Loan Term, Years | 10 | 10 | 15 | 10 |
| Bank Loan (1) or Mortgage Loan (2) | 1 | 1 | 2 | 1 |
| Salvage Value | $150,000 | $600,000 | $3,000,000 | $3,000,000 |
| Sale Price | $150,000 | $600,000 | $3,000,000 | $3,000,000 |
| Revenue Factor | 0.8436 | 1.0225 | 0.5385 | 0.5775 |
| Reference Revenue | $150,000 | $100,000 | $500,000 | $500,000 |
| Annual Revenues | $126,539 | $102,249 | $269,232 | $288,752 |
| Change/yr | $5,000 | | | |
| Annual Fixed Costs | | | | |
| Change/yr | | | | |
| Deprec. Life | 5 | 39 | 39 | 39 |
| MACRS Life | 5 | 39 | 39 | 39 |
| Use Depreciation Method: | 1 | 3 | 3 | 3 |
| Month Placed in Service | 1 | 1 | 1 | 1 |

| COMMON INPUT DATA | |
|---|---|
| Analysis Life (< 21 yr) | 6 |
| Marginal Tax Rate | 35.00% |
| DDB life for Salvage Value | 20 |
| ATMARR | 15.00% |
| BTMARR | 23.08% |
| IRR GUESS | 50.00% |

Lookup Table Depreciation Schedules available from ALT_C

| | |
|---|---|
| 1 | MACRS 3,5,7,10,15,20, Half-year convention |
| 2 | MACRS 27.5 YRS, Residential |
| 3 | MACRS 39 YRS, Commercial |
| 4 | STRAIGHT LINE |
| 5 | STRAIGHT LINE, Half-year Convention |

Discussion: Alt_C has the best revenue factor cushion for the conditions analyzed.
Part d: Alt_C appears to have the least risk and is the preferred alternative.
However, the leveraged Alternatives C & D must have adequate cash reserves to
sustain the yearly negative ATCFs in the reduced revenue situation.
The profit is in the selling price for Alternatives C & D.
The unleveraged Alt_B is not desirable under any of the conditions analyzed.

| ALTERNATIVE | A | B | C | D |
|---|---|---|---|---|
| BTNPW | ($36,790) | ($11,774) | ($53,171) | ($42,595) |
| ATNPW | ($0) | $0 | $0 | $0 |
| ATEUAW | ($0) | $0 | $0 | $0 |

SUMMING WITHOUT TIME VALUE OF MONEY EFFECTS

| | A | B | C | D |
|---|---|---|---|---|
| Life of Project Totals | | | | |
| Sum of Taxes Paid | $169,482 | $249,724 | $358,185 | $497,879 |
| Sum of Interest Paid | | | $1,092,007 | $810,000 |
| Total Taxes + Interest | $169,482 | $249,724 | $1,450,192 | $1,307,879 |
| Cumulative ATCF | $314,752 | $463,772 | $665,201 | $924,633 |
| Sum of last two rows | $484,233 | $713,496 | $2,115,393 | $2,232,512 |

| ALTERNATIVE | A | B | C | D |
|---|---|---|---|---|
| AT B/C = PWB/PWC | 1.00 | 1.00 | 1.00 | 1.00 |
| DELTA B/C [ B-A,C-B,D-C] | | 1.00 | 1.00 | 1.00 |
| DELTA B/C [ C-A, D-B] | | | 1.00 | 1.00 |
| DELTA B/C [ D-A] | | | | 1.00 |
| ATIRR | 15.00% | 15.00% | 15.00% | 15.00% |
| DELTA IRR [ B-A,C-B,D-C] | | 15.00% | 15.00% | 15.00% |
| DELTA IRR [ C-A, D-B] | | | 15.00% | 15.00% |
| DELTA IRR [ D-A] | | | | 15.00% |

| | A | | | B | | | C | | | D | | |
|---|---|---|---|---|---|---|---|---|---|---|---|---|
| | ATNPV | PWC | PWB | ATNPV | PWC | PWB | ATNPV | PWC | PWB | ATNPV | PWC | PWB |
| | 0 | (500,000) | 500,000 | 0 | (500,000) | 500,000 | 0 | (514,583) | 514,583 | 0 | (806,364) | 806,364 |
| YEAR 0 | (500,000) | (500,000) | 500,000 | (500,000) | (500,000) | 500,000 | (500,000) | (500,000) | | (500,000) | (500,000) | |
| 1 | 117,250 | 117,250 | | 69,907 | | 69,907 | (720) | (720) | | (112,084) | (112,084) | |
| 2 | 141,500 | 141,500 | | 70,052 | | 70,052 | (2,202) | (2,202) | | (99,663) | (99,663) | |
| 3 | 122,350 | 122,350 | | 70,052 | | 70,052 | (4,625) | (4,625) | | (87,963) | (87,963) | |
| 4 | 112,160 | 112,160 | | 70,052 | | 70,052 | (7,291) | (7,291) | | (76,263) | (76,263) | |